CHARLES H. STODDARD is Regional Coordinator, Upper Mississippi–Western Great Lakes Area, in the United States Department of the Interior. He previously acted as Director of the Secretary's Resource Staff and Director of the Bureau of Land Management, and for thirty years has managed his own forest property in northern Wisconsin. A graduate of the University of Michigan, Mr. Stoddard has served with the United States Forest Service and as a private consultant. He has also served as Research Associate to Resources for the Future, Inc. In 1964 he was given a Distinguished Service Award by the National Association of Soil Conservation Districts.

ESSENTIALS

OF

FORESTRY PRACTICE

•

CHARLES H. STODDARD

Second Edition

THE RONALD PRESS COMPANY • NEW YORK

Library of Congress Catalog Card Number: 68–30894

PRINTED IN THE UNITED STATES OF AMERICA

To
My Children and Unborn Generations
that they will carry on
America's great conservation movement

Preface

The United States has entered an era of forest culture in which man must assist nature to produce the abundance of timber crops required to meet the demands of a mounting population. American forestry now has a solid foundation of research. Since the First Edition of this book, applied forestry has come to be practiced intensively on a majority of our forest lands, private and public. This achievement has required increasing amounts of technical manpower. Professional foresters are finding that their efforts are most effective when they are carried out with the assistance of well-trained forest technicians and forestry aides capable of assuming responsibility for on-the-ground technical work.

This book presents an expanded coverage of the basic and practical methods of forestry. The discussion of field practices and operations in timber growing, logging, protection, harvesting, and processing is designed to meet the needs both of those seeking an overview of the whole forestry field and of those needing a knowledge of principal forestry techniques used in woodland management. The results of recent research and future research problems are succinctly covered.

In recent years, a "knowledge explosion" has taken place in forestry as in nearly all other technical fields. The new developments run the gamut from measurements used in timber cruising, logging techniques, and methods for the control of forest fires and insect depredations to the impact of the use of forest lands for recreation. A wide variety of source material was reviewed, and the significant new developments were incorporated.

This book has proved to be well adapted to introductory college courses in forestry at the professional level as well as to the growing number of resource conservation courses requiring a comprehensive textbook in the forest resource sector. It has been widely used in forestry technician training programs and in vocational school courses. This textbook has also been used in farm forestry courses given in agricultural colleges and as a home study text for students and field employees unable to attend resident schools. It has proved suitable for in-service training classes such as those given by Federal and State resource management agencies and private companies for nonprofessional field employees. Also, individual forest owners who seek a better technical grasp of their own private forestry management problems have found the book useful.

The author acknowledges the assistance and help of the following friends and professional associates: M. W. Bryan, Dan Bulfer, the late S. R. Gevorkiantz, R. W. Harris, J. C. Kern, Elbert M. Little, Jr., Merle Lowden, C. W. Mattison, M. M. Nelson, William Parke, G. R. Salmond, Fred Simmons, Herbert Storey, and Lloyd Swift, all of the U. S. Forest Service. The assistance of C. W. Mattison has been extremely helpful at every stage. Source material from several Forest Service publications has been used with the permission of the Forest Service.

Also helpful have been George B. Amidon, Boise-Cascade Corporation; Kenneth B. Pomeroy, American Forestry Association; William E. Towell, Missouri Department of Conservation; Solon Barraclough; F. H. Eyre, The Society of American Foresters; Frank H. Fixmer, Mosinee Paper Mills Co.; James McClellan and John Witherspoon, American Forest Products Industries; Clarence Prout and Edward Lawson, Minnesota Department of Conservation; E. W. Littlefield, New York State Department of Conservation; and Charles G. Geltz, Professor Emeritus, University of Florida. Carl J. Holcomb, Virginia Polytechnic Institute, who was especially helpful in reviewing and commenting on the whole manuscript, made a number of valuable suggestions for improving the use of the text in teaching forestry students.

The author is also indebted to the following men, who have brought to his attention a large number of new techniques: Archie Craft, U. S. Department of the Interior, Bureau of Land Management; H. R. Josephson, U. S. Department of Agriculture, U. S. Forest Service; Arthur B. Meyer, Editor, *Journal of Forestry,*

Society of American Foresters; U. S. St. Arnold, U. S. Department of the Interior, Bureau of Sport Fisheries and Wildlife; Edwin Zaidlicz, U. S. Department of the Interior, Bureau of Land Management; and Donald H. Graves, Superintendent, and Robert L. Howard, Instructor, Department of Forestry, University of Kentucky.

Last but not least, the author records his indebtedness to Martha Ransopher for her careful work in executing many of the line drawings, and to Ruth Hodge and Isobel Douglas for their help in typing the manuscript.

CHARLES H. STODDARD

Washington, D. C.
    June, 1968

Contents

ESSENTIALS

OF

FORESTRY PRACTICE

1

Opportunities in Forestry

Forest lands and their products have contributed richly to the building of American civilization. Wood was of basic importance in the development of our farms, cities, and many of our industries. Food for explorers and pioneers, furs for the export trade, and all the fuel to heat the houses of our forefathers came out of the forested wilderness. A vast storehouse of timber stood ready for the taking—and at no cost!

During nearly three centuries of settlement on this continent little thought or care was given to forest lands until early in the present century. Although a beginning in forest conservation has been made since then, three hundred years of forest use and abuse cannot be reversed in a few decades. And once begun, good forest management must be continuously carried on.

Today, America's forests provide wood and other products for man's use, prevent erosion of the soil, regulate stream flow, supply water for municipal and other uses, provide game and fish, and give abundant opportunity for outdoor recreation.

The practice of forest management makes it possible to produce timber as a crop under scientific methods. Foresters have developed various techniques applicable to different forest types and regions, for timber growing and harvesting; protection from fire, disease, and insects; watershed protection; wildlife and recreation area management; and for producing livestock forage through range conservation practices.

The solution of one of this nation's major economic problems, that of putting to the best use for human welfare the 75 per cent of the land most suitable for forest purposes, can come about only if sufficient numbers of men are skilled in forestry practice. There

3

is widespread demand on the part of forest industries, tree farmers, and public employers for men with a knowledge of forestry methods. Thorough training is therefore fundamental to advancing intelligently applied forestry on land needing proper management.

Fig. 1–1. Foresters cruising (estimating volumes and mapping area) ponderosa pine timber. The man on the left is mapping forest cover type as well as tallying trees measured by the man on the right. (U. S. Forest Service)

WHAT IS FOREST CONSERVATION?

Conservation of all natural resources has come to mean wise use and management. Gifford Pinchot, pioneer American forester, described it as meaning "the greatest good for the greatest number over the longest time." On forest lands this means growing and managing timber crops so as to obtain the maximum yields of timber, wildlife, and watershed protection and other values without destruction of the forest or its soil. Because trees may take two decades or more to produce marketable timber products, forestry requires special knowledge of their growth habits, of the methods for their protection from fire, insects, and disease, measuring and mapping them, tree planting, and methods for harvesting the crop. In many ways forestry is similar to agriculture, but the long time element and the size of the final crop make for important differences. That is one of the reasons forestry as a career appeals to young men of vision and foresight.

Expanded forestry programs require trained men who have skills in the many-sided aspects of forestry. There are about 22,700 practicing professional foresters and a larger number of forestry technicians and forestry aides in the United States—only one forester per 30,000 acres! While more professional foresters will continue to be graduated from the forestry colleges in the country, there is a major shortage of skilled forestry technicians able to take over, with intelligence and responsibility, the many field jobs.

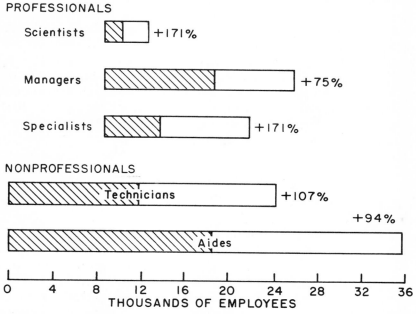

Fig. 1–2. Estimated 1961 (cross-hatched) and 1980 employment in forestry and related fields in the United States (timber, water, wildlife, range, and outdoor recreation resource management fields, but not wood and fiber science and technology). Based on the assumption that the intensity of forest resource management in 1980 will require one professional forester for every 20,000 acres of commercial forest, and one for every 40,000 acres of noncommercial forest, together with nonprofessional assistance in the ratio of 2 nonprofessionals to 1 professional.

In Germany, where intensive forestry has reached a high degree of development, one man trained in forestry techniques is responsible for the supervision of each 1,200 acres. One in six of these men is a graduate of a professional forestry college. The other five have technical or vocational school training. Federal, state, and private organizations in the United States are finding that their professionally trained foresters are devoting far too much time to the kinds of work that competent vocationally trained men could perform *if they were available.*

Many men will be needed to carry out reforestation programs for the millions of acres of forest land that lie idle and open. Other millions of acres of second growth require intensive stand improvement effort, thinning, and sanitation cuttings. Protection programs against fire, disease, and insects will be needed with increasing intensity as our young forests increase in acreage and size. For the young man willing to get the basic training needed, an excellent future is unfolding—in fact the opportunities are here today for those who are ready to seize them.

A study sponsored by the Society of American Foresters made an effort to assess and project the need for professional and technician forestry trained men in the United States. The chart shown above (Fig. 1–2) shows the tremendous increase expected during the decade of 1970.

EDUCATION IN FORESTRY

Training in forestry is available at several levels: professional schools of forestry located at universities and colleges offer a four-year college course leading to a degree in forestry, and an increasing number of technical, ranger, and vocational schools offer training in field techniques for the practical technician. Several of the latter schools give one- or two-year forestry courses while the others give courses of varying length and intensity. In addition, home study, in-service training, and special short courses are available through special schools of instruction for men on the job and for forest landowners and managers seeking a working knowledge of practical forestry. The Society of American Foresters in Washington, D. C., can furnish information on residence forestry and ranger schools, and the National Home Study Council, also in Washington, will supply the sources of home study, in-service training, and short courses.

The student who is seeking a professional forestry career will find this book a source of information concerning the major aspects of American forestry. It will serve as an introduction to the important specialized details with which a professional forester must be familiar and as a general survey of the forest situation in the United States. Each of the chapters treats one or more topics which are the subject of separate college courses and which are covered separately in special textbooks. The professional forester will be concerned in his career with over-all management, planning and supervision of forestry programs, forest research, or with the execution of policies. And, in addition, he must be intimately familiar with all technical details and be able to integrate them toward a unified management program. Unfortunately for the professional, more and more of his time is spent in the office making plans and less of his time in the field in actual practice! He still must continue to give field supervision to forestry technicians and coordinate field activities.

Another and completely different group of people interested in acquiring a working knowledge of forestry are the owners of forest land—more than four million in all. As farmers or nonresidents, they are occupied with other activities most of the time, but when a forestry problem comes up—such as when logging is to be done or replanting is to be carried out—they must turn to a reliable source for help. The advice of a professional forester is the first step, and the next step is to carry out his recommendations in practice. Many of the chapters of this book will be helpful in giving specific directions in the conduct of various forestry measures in the field. The book may also be used as a source of reference for many of the details of these practices.

In the newly developing field of training forestry technicians, teachers and students will find the material covered in a manner to give them a sound technical background in applied forestry. The more intensive technical and ranger schools will need to provide supplementary assignments from the professional-level material listed in the Bibliography. Because little information has been published on the forest-technician aspect of forestry careers, somewhat more detail is given in describing these opportunities than is devoted to the opportunities available to professional foresters. Professionally trained foresters often start their careers in forest-technician types of assignments. Forest landowners will find this information of specific interest as descriptive of different field operations.

Professional foresters, forestry technicians, and landowners, however, will find it easier to visualize many of the technical field practices after they obtain an understanding of the agencies and organization of forestry programs. A review of the job descriptions will be helpful in understanding how forestry work is conducted in the field and how responsibilities are divided.

PERSONAL REQUIREMENTS FOR A FORESTRY CAREER

A genuine preference for outdoor work and a feeling of being "at home in the woods" are essential characteristics of a career forester. But merely liking the outdoors is not enough. One must have spent some time in the open, have learned some of the trees, and acquired an interest in the plant and animal life of the forest. To be successful in forestry one must develop some of the qualities of a good woodsman: self-reliance and a sense of awareness of one's surroundings. Forestry does offer many inspiring experiences and challenges, but it is also hard work.

The qualities needed on most other responsible jobs are needed in forestry—only more so. These need not be listed here, but it should be pointed out that the forester or forest technician is on his own a good deal more than is the case with most jobs. The boss cannot always be looking over his shoulder. He will need to take responsibility willingly, use initiative, and go about his work in a business-like manner. He will find forestry work rewarding in many more ways than most routine desk jobs. And he will find that opportunities for advancement will open up as he develops with the job.

FIELDS OF WORK

Up to the close of the first decade of this century, the United States government was the principal employer of American foresters. Since then the states, municipalities, educational institutions, and private corporations have absorbed large numbers of forestry-trained men. However, even with the expansion of private industrial forestry activities in recent years, public agencies as a whole still remain the largest employers of trained foresters.

Federal Forestry Activities

Although a majority of foresters now employed by the federal government are in the Forest Service of the Department of Agriculture, numbers are employed in the management of forest lands on Indian reservations under the Bureau of Indian Affairs, by the National Park Service, the Bureau of Land Management, and by the Fish and Wildlife Service of the Department of Interior; by the Tennessee Valley Authority, and by the Soil Conservation Service of the Department of Agriculture.

In addition to its permanent force of professional foresters, the Forest Service also employs numbers of forestry technicians and aides, and clerical, administrative, custodial, protection, and construction forces. About two-thirds of this staff are employed on the national forests as supervisors, assistant supervisors, rangers, etc., and the remainder is engaged in administrative, scientific, and clerical work at the Washington and regional headquarters, the Forest Products Laboratory, and the forest and range experiment stations, or in state and private cooperation work in various parts of the country. In addition, about 13,000 lookouts, patrolmen, fire fighters, scalers, tree markers, and other forestry workers are employed seasonally on the national forests. Foresters

Fig. 1–3. This forest, located in the state of Washington, was named for this country's pioneer forester. It is one of 154 national forests managed by the U. S. Forest Service. (U. S. Forest Service)

also are assigned to wildlife management, recreation area supervision, livestock control, and a variety of other land-use supervisory responsibilities.

Some forestry activities are open to forestry-trained men in the Department of Interior's National Park Service, in the Bureau of Land Management, the Bureau of Indian Affairs, and in the Fish and Wildlife Service. The Civil Service Commission, which has long provided opportunities for college-trained foresters, is finding the demand for forestry technicians and aides by these agencies to be on the increase and is making an increasing number of openings available as federal forestry work expands.

The national forests, which are the responsibility of the Forest Service, and the national parks administered by the National Park Service, are shown on the map in Fig. 12–2. (See Chapter 12 for a discussion of federal forestry programs.) Industrial and state forests are not shown, but they include much of the area between and some within the public forests in the forested areas. Farm and other small forests are scattered over most forest regions but are located mainly in the eastern half of the country.

State Forestry Programs

Forestry work in the states has made notable progress in recent years, and nearly all states now employ foresters in various capacities. The state forester usually carries heavy responsibilities as directing head of a large organization and has under his control the annual disbursement of large appropriations. About 27 million acres of land in state and municipal forests are managed intensively, along lines similar to national forest management. Some state forests and parks are devoted primarily to public recreational use.

State activity in protecting forests from fire, with the cooperation and financial aid of the federal government, has opened a field for the employment of many foresters. Trained men are also used in the propagation and distribution of planting stock. In those states where an active state forestry program has been developed, a number of trained foresters are employed. The state forester's staff may include technical assistants in immediate charge of the various lines of activity carried on by the state organization. District foresters or state forest rangers may be assigned responsibility for the development and maintenance of the fire-control organization and other state forestry work in a designated part of the state. The work of the state district forester corresponds generally with that of a federal district ranger except that usually he deals cooperatively with private forest landowners in addition to supervising work on the state forests under his direct charge. Extension and intensification of cooperative technical assistance to landowners on a scale commensurate with the needs would call for employment of many additional foresters and forestry technicians in state forestry work.

Forest Products Industries

Although federal and state agencies, educational institutions, and semipublic associations will doubtless continue to lead in research and extension, an increasing important field for foresters and forestry technicians in the long run will be in private work. Three-fourths of the commercial forest land (367 million acres) is in private ownership. This fact alone clearly indicates a large and fruitful field in private work for the trained forester.

Private owners may be classified in a general way as industrial, including lumber, pulp, and paper manufacturing companies, and other large manufacturers of wood products; public service companies, such as railroads and water companies; recreation and hunting clubs; mining companies; owners of large private estates; and farmers and other small woodland owners. Many of these owners are included in the Tree Farm System and practice good forestry.

The man who enters the lumber, pulp, and paper, or other forest products industries may be assigned to estimating standing timber, appraisal of stumpage, determining the best methods of cutting, making growth studies, surveys for logging roads, and many types of duties on logging and milling operations. Many forestry-trained men find opportunities in this field, with possibilities of advancement to important managerial positions. Compensation in private forestry depends largely upon the earning capacity of the individual.

Other Private Forestry Work

A growing field for forestry is among public service corporations owning timberlands. Some railroads and public utilities own extensive tracts in need of management. Frequently mining companies hold considerable areas for mineral development which they are beginning to manage for timber, wildlife, and other uses.

Fig. 1—4. This well-managed private forest, located in California, is a part of the Tree Farm System sponsored by the American Forest Products Industries, Inc. (American Forest Products Industries, Inc.)

Another kind of private owner consists of clubs or individuals who have acquired forest property for hunting, fishing, and other recreational purposes. On such properties, work on the ground is usually supervised by a resident woods manager under the direction of a consulting forester who visits the tract at intervals and works closely with the land manager or owner himself. There are now about 400 private consulting foresters who also employ field assistants for field work on the tracts of forest owner-clients.

Forest Owner Management

One of the main purposes of this book is to supply owners of woodlands with the essential information needed in the handling of their properties. Although they may obtain the assistance of a consulting forester in making plans, the execution of his recommendations can be carried out more effectively with an understanding of technical details. The forest owner may select from the material presented here the information needed for his special situation.

DESCRIPTIONS OF FORESTRY POSITIONS

A young man trained in forestry generally starts at the forestry technician level, from which position new opportunities for advancement will develop. He may start at any one of a number of positions—compassman on a timber survey crew, fire guard, forest fire dispatcher, or he may work at insect and disease control, mark timber for sale, scale logs, or maintain forest roads and trails—to mention only a few positions. His training course will have prepared him to take on most such assignments, and they will give him the opportunity to show his supervisors that he does have sound technical training. One good way to get started is on a summer job with one of the forestry agencies or companies. This can then lead to a permanent assignment because good men are seldom passed up. They are too scarce!

Federal Agencies

The minimum of a high school education is usually required, but experience is counted heavily and forestry training is given credit in federal Civil Service examinations. Qualifying by starting in as a seasonal employee is often the route to permanent employment. Beginning employees are usually assigned to positions which include the principal titles and duties listed below.

Fire Control Aide. Under direction of the forester, the forest technician detects, locates, and reports fires; patrols fire lines; mans forest fire towers, assists in organizing and works with fire-fighting crews, and maintains and repairs fire-fighting equipment and tools; works on slash disposal, forest insect and disease control programs, and other work related to the above; and keeps records and makes reports.

Forestry Aide. A technician who has been made a forestry aide assists in timber cruising and mapping forest areas; marks timber for timber sales; directs forest planting crews; marks forest boundaries; scales (measures) logs on timber sales; does tree and log grading; assists in maintenance work on recreational areas; handles range improvement work and wildlife habitat improvement under the direction of the forester in charge; and assists in research investigations.

Forest Engineering Aide. Under the supervision of a forest engineer, the technician assists in surveying roads and trails; in the construction of roads, dams, and watershed improvements; and in the establishment and maintenance of recreational facilities.

State Forestry Agencies

Jobs in the state conservation departments are quite similar to those in the federal service but also include general forest fire prevention and control as well as technical aid services to private owners. Entrance requirements for many state forestry jobs emphasize field experience and offer many opportunities for rising within the organization to men with less formal education but with initiative and ability. The following list summarizes some of the titles and duties of forestry technicians employed in state forestry jobs:

Forest Ranger or District Forester	In charge of forest fire control activities in district, under supervision of the district forester.
District Fire Warden	In charge of fire control crews; issues burning permits.
Forest Fire Patrolman	Patrols forest fires after they have been brought under control.
Timber Scaler	Measures logs and pulpwood on state timber sales.
Timber Sales Marker	Marks timber prior to sale.
Fire Dispatcher	Handles central coordination of fire detection and control in the district forestry office.

Salaries in state forestry work compare well with other types of forestry employment. As a rule, they have retirement provisions, sick leave, and annual leave. Generally speaking, a state forestry technician will live in a town near the area where he works, but not necessarily in the forest. Occasionally, the state furnishes living quarters in state forests.

Private and Industrial Forestry

Working with one of the large paper companies or lumber companies with huge tracts of forest land offers one of the most challenging jobs in forestry. The technician will not specialize in one job or another but (usually) will shift from one job to another as the season progresses. In the spring he may have a planting crew reforesting idle land, but the planting crew will have to be ready for a fire call at any time. In the summer he may have a crew out thinning overcrowded young forests, marking timber for stand improvement, or controlling disease or insect outbreaks.

By fall he may shift over to marking timber for a winter logging job or help the forester in charge cruise a tract of land which the company is purchasing. When winter comes he will probably be checking loggers to see that they are cutting the right trees, scaling logs on the decks, and dispatching truckers to the mill with loads of logs.

Generally, the descriptions of industrial forest job duties are not given in the same detail as in the public agencies. This is partly due to the wide range of activities involved.

Types of Duties for Forestry-trained Men

The following responsibilities are frequently assigned to men skilled in forestry practice. In many cases a forest technician will find himself doing several of the jobs which may develop during the course of the year because of seasonal variation in work requirements: tree planting in the early spring, forest fire protection in the dry seasons, marking timber for cutting any time, etc. Some of the beginning jobs to which the newly trained man would be assigned when he arrives at his first assignment are these:

Timber Cruising Appraisal and Inventory. These highly skilled functions are usually undertaken by the professional forester with the assistance of forestry technicians or aides. They require considerable experience and additional training to handle well. All of these functions require knowledge of the several methods of estimating volumes of standing timber, and methods of financial evaluation.

General Engineering. The forestry aide or technician assists civil engineers in road location, surveying and topographic mapping in advance of logging, as well as supervision of road, bridge, and other heavy construction.

Compassman. The compassman on a timber survey party must be able to read and use his forester's compass to run the line for the estimator who determines the tree volume and sketches the map as the party progresses. He must also be able to run out boundaries, read maps, and pace distances.

Planting Crew Supervision. The reforestation crew foreman is assigned the task of training and supervising unskilled labor in tree planting—both machine and hand operation. He must call for seedlings at the nursery, know how to care for them until time for planting, show the crew how tree planting is properly done, and inspect their work as they proceed to make sure that the seedlings are properly set in the ground.

Marking Timber. The tree marker must be able to determine the proper trees to be marked for thinning, stand improvement cuttings, and harvesting, and to instruct unskilled markers in the methods of selection. He must be able to apply the knowledge gained from his studies and to defend his choices of marked trees to his superior.

Scaling Pulpwood and Logs. The log scaler measures the logs which are cut from logging operations and records them in a tally book. He must learn to use the log scale stick, learn the elements of volume tables, and know how to deduct for defective material in logs. He must also be able to identify the species. He should have a knowledge of pulpwood volumes, log grades, and other forest products. Much of this same work is done in sawmill and paper mill yards, at veneer mills, and at other industries where logs are bought from independent loggers.

Forest Fire Detection and Control. Forest fire dispatchers are usually assigned to the central ranger station, where they operate as the nerve center of the forest fire protection system. After the towerman calls in the bearings of a fire, the dispatcher must be able to use his knowledge of bearings and distance to locate fires on the map, then send the suppression crew out to the job. Accurate records of the time fires are reported, their location, the length of time needed to put them out, etc., must be recorded. Fire tower duty is assigned to a few men but not nearly as many as the public thinks!

Checking Timber Sales. Timber sale checkers are assigned to see that the requirements of a timber sale contract are lived up to— that the loggers cut low stumps, that they cut only marked trees, that good utilization is practiced, that slash is properly disposed of, and other requirements.

Controlling Insects and Diseases. Insect or disease control crew foremen are assigned to such work as supervision over white pine blister rust control, bark beetle eradication, etc. Some previous knowledge of these activities is essential, but a man with training and a little experience will have no difficulty in assuming such responsibility.

Inspecting Forest Practices. Many states have minimum forest practice cutting laws requiring forest owners to harvest their forests in such a way as to leave adequate growing stock for another crop of timber. In order to enforce such laws, these states have forest practice inspectors who are familiar with logging methods, principal species, and other aspects of this assignment.

Multiple Use Supervision. In addition to technical forestry functions, the forest land manager must give attention to recreational use and development; more often than not to the effect of logging and road building on watershed conservation, sometimes to livestock grazing and mineral development, and almost always to wildlife as an integral part of forest use. While specialists in these fields are available to help on more difficult problems, multiple use decisions often fall to the forest manager.

Public Relations. To convey the idea that forest land should be producing timber crops, much educational work is done by technical men at various times of year. Exhibits at fairs, talks before sportsmen's clubs, 4-H groups, scouts, and garden clubs often fall to the local forester because he is considered the authority on the subject in his locality. Supervision of group tree-planting programs, fire-prevention crusades, and similar activities will occasionally draw on the forester's time.

QUESTIONS

1. What has the term "conservation of resources" come to mean?
2. What must America's forests produce in the future, besides wood?
3. Name four important kinds of forestry work.
4. What are the two main classifications of forestry-trained men?
5. Give three major kinds of organizations employing professional foresters and forestry technicians.
6. Where do forestry men find more employment—in public agencies or private forestry programs?
7. Do you think that an interest in the outdoors is important in a forestry career? Why?
8. What value does a knowledge of forestry have for the forest owner?
9. Why does competence in forestry require both study and field work?
10. Why are more trained forestry technicians needed now (and in the future) than in the past?

EXERCISES

1. Find out what private and public forestry programs are being carried on in your locality.
2. Discuss different types of forestry jobs with one or more professional foresters or forestry technicians in your area and find out what qualifications are expected.

2

Forestry – Yesterday and Today

When the North American continent was first invaded by white men, a vast area of forests stretched from the Atlantic Coast to the Great Plains, broken only by Middle Western prairies (Fig. 2–1). Further west, forests covered much of the Rocky and other mountain ranges and the northern portion of the Pacific Coast region. The original forests of the continental United States, exclusive of Alaska, are estimated to have covered 820 million acres—more than 40 per cent of the total land area.

In contrast to Europe, which has less than a dozen commercial tree species, the new settlers found well over 100 conifers and broadleaved trees in the East alone. Western forests, which are mainly coniferous, contained additional species—many of greater size then elsewhere in the world. The outer limit of tree growth generally follows the 25-in. annual precipitation line.

Early settlers viewed the forests as a mixed blessing. A source of building material and fuelwood as well as game for food, the forests could be cleared for cultivation only with back-breaking labor. And too frequently they harbored unfriendly Indians. For nearly 200 years (1620–1800) white settlement was limited mainly to the coastal plain and piedmont between the Atlantic and the Appalachians. But timber—white pine lumber and oak for shipbuilding—made an important contribution to the Colonial trade because it was abundant and easily obtainable.

The greatest onslaught on our forests took place during the

18

Fig. 2–1. This stand of old-growth northern hardwood in Wisconsin is a remnant of the vast virgin forest that once extended from the Eastern seaboard to the prairies. (U. S. Forest Service)

century following the Revolutionary War. Lands were cleared for farms throughout the South, Middle West, and mountainous portions of the East; many of these lands proved to be too poor for agriculture. Commercial lumbering, which was begun in New England by the colonists, was extended into New York and Pennsylvania prior to the Civil War. The pineries of the Lake States were the main source of supplies for the lumber market for the remainder of the nineteenth century. Beginning about 1900 and continuing for nearly forty years, the Southern pine forests were the major source of forest products for the nation. In recent years the Douglas fir forests of the Pacific Northwest have become the nation's chief source of timber supplies.

In the process of supplying a growing nation with lumber, vast areas of timber were cut over with little thought of regrowth. Forestry as a method of growing a timber crop was unknown. It was believed by all but a few doubters that all the cleared land would be needed for farms, and what was a cheaper way of doing it than by logging and uncontrolled forest fires? The main difficulty was that the lands with the most marketable timber were frequently too sandy or rocky for profitable agriculture. Too often new communities sprang up around sawmills and lumber camps, flourished for a time, and then became stranded ghost towns in a sea of stumps. Long before there was serious danger of our national timber supplies becoming exhausted, thoughtful men became concerned with the manner in which the forests were being exploited. As might be expected, there was resistance to many of the conservation proposals, but public opinion ultimately demanded that action be taken.

The earliest laws passed by Congress regarding the nation's forests, between 1799 and 1831, were intended to insure supplies of live oak for shipbuilding. During the nineteenth century several states inquired into the possibilities of action to protect their forest resources, and laws for the encouragement of tree planting were passed in a few states. In 1875 the American Forestry Association was founded to educate our people to the need for conservation measures. Not until 1891, however, when the national forest system was started, did the conservation movement get under way on a nation-wide scale. The act of Congress in 1891 which authorized the establishment of the Forest Reserves marked the real beginning of a national forest conservation policy.

1905. The Act of February 1, 1905, provided for the transfer of the forest reserves from the Department of the Interior to the Forest Service in the Department of Agriculture. Gifford Pinchot was appointed the first Chief Forester. The present Forest Service dates from this act. When the Forest Service took charge, there were 60 forest reserves with a net acreage of some 62 million acres of land. During his administration, from 1901 to 1909, President Theodore Roosevelt added a total of 128 million acres to the established reserves. The name "Forest Reserves" was changed in 1907 to "National Forests" because "reserve" implies that the area is withdrawn from use.

President Theodore Roosevelt held the famous White House conference of governors, May 13–15, 1907, to consider the fact that our natural resources were being consumed, wasted, and destroyed at a rate that threatened them with exhaustion. As a result, an inventory of our natural resources was published in 1909.

1911. A new national policy was established by the Weeks law, which authorized the purchase by the federal government of forest lands necessary to the protection of the flow of navigable streams.

1916. The National Park Service was organized in the Department of the Interior.

1924. The Clarke-McNary law extended the federal land purchase policy under the Weeks law of 1911. Lands necessary for the production of timber, as well as for the protection of navigation, within the watersheds of navigable streams could be purchased. This law also authorized the Secretary of Agriculture to enter into cooperative agreements with the states for the protection of state and private forests against fire. State and private owners were to contribute not less than half the total cost. Other sections of the law provided for studies of forest taxation, cooperation with the states for the establishment of shelterbelts, management of farm woodlands, and cooperative work in farm forestry extension.

1927. One of the first private sustained-yield management programs was adopted by the Goodman Lumber Company in Wisconsin.

1928. The Woodruff-McNary Act, approved April 30, authorized a series of yearly appropriations up to a total of $8,000,000 to protect watersheds of navigable rivers. The McSweeney-McNary Act of May 22 authorized a program of forest research to "insure adequate supplies of timber and other forest products, to promote the full use of timber growing and other purposes of forest lands in the United States, including farm wood lots and those abandoned areas not suitable for agricultural production, and to secure the correlation and the most economical conduct of forest research in the Department of Agriculture . . ." For the first time a forest inventory was authorized to establish basic facts on the forest resources.

1930. The Knutson-Vandenberg Act of June 9 authorized the Secretary of Agriculture to expand tree-planting operations on the national forests and pay for them out of receipts from timber sales.

1933. On March 21, President Franklin D. Roosevelt sent to Congress his message urging legislation to relieve unemployment, to build men, and to build up the nation's forest resources by the establishment of the Civilian Conservation Corps. During the life of the CCC program, more than two million young men participated, and a vast amount of forest protection, tree planting, watershed restoration, erosion control, and other resource improvement work was accomplished. The first major industrial effort to establish large-scale forestry on logging operations came about during the New Deal's National Recovery Act in 1933, when Article X of the N.R.A. Lumber Code included requirements for minimum forestry practices.

The Forest Service prepared and sent to the Senate "A National Plan for American Forestry," popularly known as the Copeland Report. The main recommendations for a satisfactory solution of the nation's forest problem were (1) a large extension of public ownership of forest lands, (2) more intensive management on all forest lands, and (3) public control over private forest cutting practices. The Tennessee Valley Authority (TVA), which was established in 1933, also developed an active forestry and watershed management program.

The Soil Erosion Service (which later became the Soil Conservation Service) and the Agricultural Adjustment Administration were also established in the middle 1930's. These agencies developed large-scale programs for the conservation of land and soil resources and helped many farmers improve their management of soil. The Taylor Grazing Act of 1934 established a permanent system of conservational management of the federal grazing lands in the West which were still held as Public Domain.

1937. The Norris-Doxey Cooperative Farm Forestry Act provided for increased technical forestry aid to forest owners.

1937. O&C Act of 1937. The Nation's first sustained yield forestry law was passed by the Congress to apply to western Oregon forest lands under BLM management.

1940. President Franklin D. Roosevelt combined the Bureau of Fisheries and the Biological Survey into a Fish and Wildlife Service in the Department of Interior, under Ira N. Gabrielson, its first chief. All wildlife programs—migratory waterfowl, fish hatcheries, and research—were brought under this bureau.

1941. The forest industry Tree Farm movement was born in the state of Washington. By 1967, owners of nearly 70 million acres of private forests (30,000 Tree Farms) were cooperating in this program.

1941–45. World War II caused heavy inroads on the nation's

forests, as wood became a critical war material. Although winning the war was the most important thing, more forestry legislation was passed by the 78th Congress (1943–45). The Clarke-McNary Act was amended to authorize increased appropriations for cooperative fire protection, and appropriations were made to keep forest surveys up to date.

Private industry, which had only begun to practice forestry on a portion of its own lands prior to World War II, began a program of management on an extensive basis. In addition, the paper industry was active in purchasing very extensive holdings in both the South and Pacific Northwest.

1944–46. An international organization for forestry was started under the auspices of the United Nations Food and Agriculture Organization (FAO).

A special amendment to the federal income tax favored private forestry and encouraged many landowners to begin a sustained yield program.

1946. The American Forestry Association called a postwar forestry conference to develop a program to meet the changing forestry problem.

1945–47. The Forest Service completed an appraisal of the forest situation, which showed that there had been a marked deterioration in quality as well as quantity of timber during the war. Cutting practices were poorest on small private forest lands and best on large private forests and public forests.

The forest industry responded to the growing need for more intensive forestry by establishing large acreages of well-managed company forests in every region of the country, and by developing an educational program through its American Forest Products Industries organization. Marked progress in better forestry on larger ownerships took place.

1947. Congress passed a Forest Pest Control Act which provided for federal cooperation with the states and private owners to control outbreaks of forest insects and diseases. Private consulting foresters became active in large numbers during the postwar period.

1952–57. The Forest Service undertook a new appraisal of the forest situation under the title *Timber Resource Review*. The details of the findings are set forth in a following section.

At the same time the strength of several forest conservation programs was tested by proposals in Congress designed to provide certain groups with special rights in the public forests. These measures met defeat partly because of organized resistance from the citizens' conservation movement.

In 1953 the American Forestry Association called an American Forestry Congress, which recommended a series of policy proposals, and Resources for the Future, sponsored by The Ford Foundation, called a "Mid-Century Conference on Natural Resources" which provided a forum for all proposals and suggestions on needed resource programs.

In 1956 the National Park Service embarked upon "Mission 66," a program designed to improve many of the park facilities needed for increasingly intensive uses. The Forest Service undertook "Operation Outdoors," a similar program for the national forests.

1958. The Outdoor Recreation Resources Review Commission, appointed by President Eisenhower and headed by Laurance S. Rockefeller, made very comprehensive surveys of the nation's future demands and needs for outdoor recreation facilities. Its work culminated in a large number of reports and recommendations including the establishment of a Bureau of Outdoor Recreation in the U. S. Department of the Interior in 1962.

1960. The Multiple Use Act and the Sustained Yield Act (P.L. 86–517) for National Forests broadened the authority of the Forest Service to manage National Forests for all consistent uses including timber, wildlife, grazing, watershed, minerals, wilderness, and recreation.

1964. The Land and Water Conservation Fund Act provided for new sources of revenue for the acquisition of national parks, national forest recreation lands, national recreation areas, and grants to states for state recreation lands and facilities.

1964. The Multiple Use and Classification Act authorized multiple use management on public domain lands under the Bureau of Land Management for a five-year period until the Public Land Law Review Commission recommendations determine the future of public domain lands.

The Wilderness Act, also passed in 1964, provides for preservation of a few million acres in National Forests and Parks and Wildlife Refuges as a remnant of the original frontier wilderness.

All of these great steps forward in building our conservation programs were brought about by the hard, patient efforts of a few farsighted men, often opposed by powerful forces who viewed them as radical visionaries. But for their persistent efforts and intelligent idealism, few of these programs would have developed.

OUR PRESENT FOREST SITUATION

Forest Area

Recent studies by the U. S. Forest Service show that there now remains about three-fourths of the original forest area, estimated at 759 million acres. Of this, 509 million acres are classed as commercial forest lands. The other, noncommercial forest land, is mainly in parks, wilderness areas, and protection forest cover, most of which is in the West (Table 2–1).

TABLE 2–1
The Forest Area of the United States
(thousands of acres)

Region	Total Land	Commercial Forest	Noncommercial Forest*	Total Forest
New England	40,401	31,451	435	31,886
Middle Atlantic	87,334	43,888	2,758	46,646
Lake States	209,151	52,392	2,819	55,211
Central	292,339	44,058	639	44,697
Southern	512,691	201,069	19,235	220,304
Pacific	204,500	63,514	32,816	96,330
Mountain	555,340	65,623	69,141	143,322
Alaska	365,481	5,761	112,726	118,487
Hawaii	4,106	1,089	893	1,982
Total	2,271,343	508,845	241,462	758,865

* Parks, nonproductive, etc.
Source: U. S. Forest Service.

About three-fourths of the forest-producing land area of the United States lies east of the Great Plains, and most of it is in second-growth or young timber. The other fourth, still with a considerable area of virgin timber, is located in the Rocky Mountain and Pacific Coast regions.

The commercial forest area is divided almost equally between softwoods (conifers) and hardwoods (broadleaved trees). The Western forests are nearly all softwoods, slightly more than half of the Southern forests are covered with hardwoods, and in the North five-sixths are hardwoods.

The U. S. Forest Service, with the cooperation of the states and forest industries, recently completed a new survey of our timber resources, which is called the *Timber Trends in the U. S.* This comprehensive report contains the most up-to-date information ever developed on forestry in the United States. Because of its length and detail, only the essential facts developed from the survey can be summarized.

In addition to examining our present forest situation, *Timber Trends* made a forecast of our future timber needs up to the year 2000. It found that if we continue to use wood in the same proportions as we now do, the greatly expanded population in the year 2000 will require an increase from 14 to 21 billion cubic feet, half again as much as our present growth. By greatly improving and extending our forestry programs above present levels, the United States can supply this much and more timber in the future. Growing this much timber presents a great challenge to present-day Americans because the trees must be started now to be available for the next generation!

A summary of our timber situation as found by the Forest Service's *Timber Trends* is as follows:

Timber Volumes

Three-fourths of the forest land is in the Eastern part of the United States, in the Southern, Northeast, Central and Lake

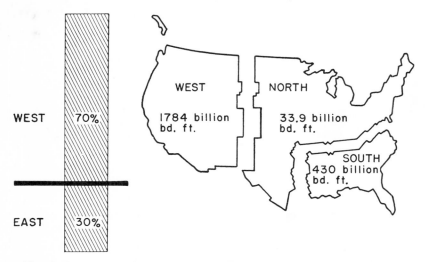

Fig. 2–2. Sawtimber volume. Three-fourths of this country's commercial forest land is in the East. However, in terms of sawtimber volume, almost the reverse is true: 70 per cent in the West and 30 per cent in the East. (U. S. Forest Service)

States, but two-thirds of the standing sawtimber is in the West, mainly in Oregon, Washington, and California. In the United States as a whole, a total volume of 2,544 billion board feet was standing in 1963, 33.5 per cent of which was Douglas fir and ponderosa pine. Southern yellow pines made up 8 per cent, oaks 6 per cent, and all other species accounted for the rest (Fig. 2–2).

Quality of Timber Stands

One-fourth of the forest land (117 million acres) is poorly stocked with trees. Ten per cent of the volume is in cull trees and the average tree size is less than it was in 1945. Poor management on smaller ownerships has permitted the cutting of the best trees and often left the land inadequately stocked for the next crop of timber. Fifty million acres are open land in need of planting.

Timber Growth and Cut

On the brighter side, total growth is increasing and is greater than it was in 1944. But much of the growth is on hardwoods and on small trees, whereas most of the cut is in softwoods and

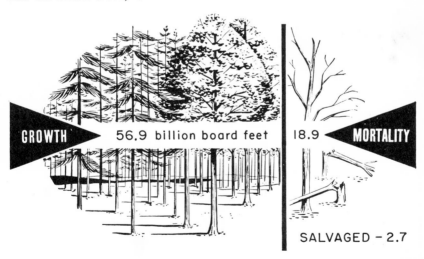

GROWTH ► 56.9 billion board feet 18.9 ◄ MORTALITY

SALVAGED − 2.7

Fig. 2–3. A volume equivalent to one-fourth of the net annual sawtimber growth in the United States is lost due to the killing or dying of trees. Mortality can be reduced by expanded protection facilities and more intensive forest practice to harvest weakened and threatened trees while they are still usable. Salvage of dead timber is often possible. (U. S. Forest Service)

in big timber. Today about as much sawtimber is being grown as is being cut (for the first time in recent history) and *more* growth is being laid on trees of less than sawlog size than is being cut! Better forestry on the same forest area could double our present growth, from 14 billion cubic feet to 28!

Fire, Insects, and Disease

These destructive agents kill nearly 19 billion board feet per year (one-third as much as the amount cut), only 3 billion of which were salvaged. If it were not for these mortality losses, sawtimber growth would have been 30 per cent greater (Fig. 2–3).

Forest Ownership

Three-fourths of the forest land in the United States is privately owned and one-fourth is owned by the federal, state, and local governments. Large forest products industries own 67 million acres; 97 million acres are in National Forests; the states control 21 million acres; counties and municipalities 8 million; three and one-half million farmers own 151 million acres in woodlots; and

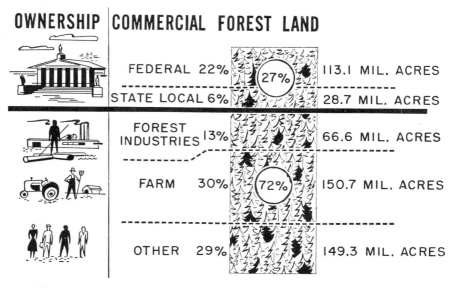

OWNERSHIP | COMMERCIAL FOREST LAND

FEDERAL 22%   (27%)   113.1 MIL. ACRES

STATE LOCAL 6%   28.7 MIL. ACRES

FOREST INDUSTRIES 13%   66.6 MIL. ACRES

FARM   30%   (72%)   150.7 MIL. ACRES

OTHER   29%   149.3 MIL. ACRES

Fig. 2–4. Ownership of commercial forest land. Private owners hold almost three-fourths of this country's commercial forest land. The rest is in public ownership. (U. S. Forest Service)

149 million acres are held by nonresident individuals. The best managed forests are in large industrial and governmental ownerships. The poorest management is found on farm and other small holdings (Fig. 2–4).*

TOWARD MORE INTENSIVE MANAGEMENT

It is generally agreed that the Forest Service *Timber Trends* figures on the basic forest situation are accurate and that they faithfully reflect the status of our timber resource so far as it is humanly possible to measure it. Differences have cropped up over the interpretation of some of the figures cited above, particularly over the timber production we shall probably need in the future. Some people feel that the United States will not use as much wood per person as the Forest Service estimates, particularly if wood declines in importance or because it is high priced. Others feel that more wood will be needed as our other resources become scarcer.

Regardless of whether the United States, in future years, has a high or low level of wood consumption, considerably more wood will be needed to take care of our expanding population. As a provident nation we shall need to undertake the following: a more complete job of protecting our forests from fire; a more intensive program for controlling insects and diseases; a still better job of managing our forest cutting so as to obtain prompt restocking of good species; a stepping up of our tree planting on bare lands; a vigorous program of thinnings, stand improvement, and other forest cultural measures in millions of acres of young forests; increasing salvage logging operations to pick up dying trees before they become too rotten to use; and accelerating tree growth by crossbreeding, as has been done with hybrid corn. These and other intensive forestry measures will make it possible to grow more timber from our present forest acreage, both public and private. And to do so we shall need thousands more technically trained men than are available today.

QUESTIONS

1. When were the Forest Reserves set aside from the public domain?
2. In what year did President Theodore Roosevelt change the name of the Forest Reserves to National Forests?
3. Who was the first Chief Forester of the United States?

* Data from *Timber Trends.*

4. What President started the Civilian Conservation Corps (CCC) and in what year was it begun?

5. When did the forest industries' Tree Farm Program begin?

6. What is the present acreage of commercial forest land in the United States?

7. In what part of the United States is most of the sawtimber found today?

8. Which part of the country has the largest area of forest land?

9. Are American forests growing about as much, more, or less sawtimber than we are cutting?

10. How does the acreage of forest land owned by public agencies and private owners compare?

EXERCISES

1. What is the principal kind of forest ownership in your locality? What is next in importance?

2. Are most forest lands in your locality held in large or small tracts?

3. Do the forest lands appear to be well managed or neglected?

3

Characteristics and Growth Requirements of Forest Trees

The study of requirements and processes of tree growth and the environment under which it takes place is called *silvics*. Intelligent management of the forest must rest upon a solid foundation of knowledge of silvical processes. Identification of trees according to species has been termed *dendrology* and includes a study of all the significant identifying characteristics. Both of these topics are the subject of this chapter.

A knowledge of tree names, of tree identification, and growth habits of trees are the ABC's of the practicing forester. It is absolutely essential that the technician be able to name the most important commercial trees in the part of the country where he lives or works, and to know the names of most other important timber trees in the United States. He can learn them with study and observation if he looks for a few of the distinguishing characteristics.

It is one thing to learn to identify the tree as it stands in the forest or park and quite another to learn to identify the wood. Just as there are key characteristics of leaves, bark, fruit, and twigs to indicate the tree species, so in the wood there are certain

31

indicators which tell the expert how to find the name. Because wood identification is a special technical study which this book does not treat, it is suggested that this subject be made a topic for future consideration. Close observation of different woods, in the meantime, will be helpful in making important distinctions.

IDENTIFICATION CHARACTERISTICS

A tree is usually defined as a perennial woody plant with a single main stem (bole or trunk) attaining a height of 20 ft. or more and a diameter of over 4 in. at maturity. Trees have three main parts: roots, trunk (or bole), and crown. Every tree has one or several common names, but only one scientific name in Latin. Latin is used the world over because it is a "dead" language and no longer subject to change by usage.

Tree Parts

Positive identification of plants is ordinarily made by tiny differences in the flowers, but leaves, bark, twigs, buds, and fruit (including nuts) are adequate for the practical forester. In summer one can identify a tree by the leaves or needles alone (in the great majority of species), but in winter, when the leaves of broadleaved trees have fallen, the other characteristics must be relied upon. Fig. 3–1 shows principal types of leaf forms for both hardwoods and conifers, which should be used as one important guide in identification. The identifying features of many important forest trees in the United States are set forth in Appendix B, "Characteristics of Important Commercial Timber Species."

The twigs of a tree may be helpful as a means of tree identification when the leaves are off (Fig. 3–1). Distinctive features of the twig are the bud, the bark, and the leaf scars formed after the leaf has fallen. Most of these features are sufficiently different in each species to be noted by close observation.

Bark is also one of the most important means of determining tree species, especially of mature trees when the leaves are off. As the new wood is made in the cambium layer, inner bark is pushed outward; the dead outer bark cracks into plates (or scales) and ridges in different ways for different species. In identifying both the bark and twigs there is no substitute for actual observation.

One of the best ways to learn to identify trees is to go on field trips with someone familiar with each species of tree. One can then keep a record of the characteristics in a notebook for future

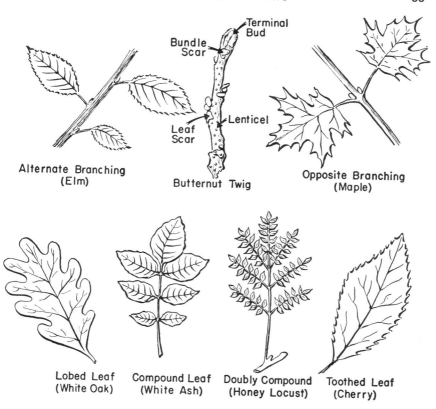

LEAVES AND TWIGS OF HARDWOOD TREES

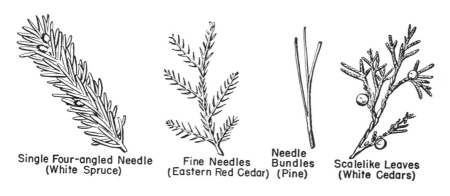

CONIFEROUS LEAF FORMS

Fig. 3–1. Leaf and twig forms.

reference. There are many books on tree identification which give the tree features, its range, and other pertinent information. Most states publish booklets describing the trees growing within their boundaries. It is suggested that the student write his state forester for one of these publications in order to develop his knowledge of trees in his part of the country. Appendix B describes briefly several dozen of the most important commercial trees and is primarily for reference rather than field use. This will be helpful in familiarizing oneself with the terms and descriptions used.

Tree Names

All timber trees are divided into two main groups: the conifers, which are the needle trees with cones, and the broadleaved trees. Deciduous trees drop their leaves in winter and are dormant, while evergreens do not. Most deciduous trees are broadleaved hardwoods; coniferous softwoods are evergreen with the exception of the larches and bald cypress. While the terms "softwood" and "hardwood" are commonly used in the timber trade, some hardwoods such as yellow poplar and basswood have *soft wood!*

Botanists have developed a systematic method of classifying plants by classes, orders, families, genera, and species. The conifers are in the class Gymnosperms, and the broadleaved trees are in the class Angiosperms. Individual kinds of trees are called species,* and their scientific names always include both the *genus* and *species*. As an example, all oaks belong to the genus *Quercus;* white oak is called *Quercus alba* and northern red oak is called *Quercus rubra*. The pines are easy because they belong to the genus *Pinus;* white pine is *Pinus strobus* and Virginia pine is *Pinus virginiana*.

FUNCTIONS OF TREE PARTS

Tree roots serve a double purpose—to anchor the tree to the ground against winds and to supply the tree with water and chemical nutrients. Some species of trees have deep roots going well into the subsoil, while others are shallow-rooted. Shallow-rooted species are usually found on moist sites where they do not have to reach far down for moisture. They are more subject to windthrow, especially when other trees are cut from around them and

---

* The term "species" is both singular and plural when used with plants and animals. The letter *s* is never dropped in the singular.

they are left to stand against the full force of the wind. Species which grow in swamps and bottomlands where surface moisture is usually present are generally shallow-rooted. Deep-rooted trees found on higher sites are more resistant to windthrow. Some species with "tap" roots are very well anchored and stand up well against wind even when other trees are cut away. Open-grown trees are generally more windfirm than forest-grown specimens. Conifers may be either shallow- or deep-rooted, while broadleaved trees often combine both root systems.

The root system of a tree consists of the large main roots, root branches which bear smaller rootlets, and in some species, additional fine root hairs. The root hairs and rootlets absorb water and dissolve soil nutrients which are carried up through the roots into the rest of the tree. Unlike most plants, some conifers and beech lack root hairs. This function is taken care of by mycorrhiza, associated organisms which attach themselves to the rootlets.

The trunk or bole of the tree contains layers of cells (see Appendix A for definition) which conduct chemical nutrients dissolved in water (sap) to the branches and leaves. It also acts as a storage area for some plant foods manufactured by photosynthesis (see below) and supports the whole crown. It is of course the most valuable part of the tree and the object of most foresters' attentions!

The tree trunk consists of heartwood and sapwood, which are made up of a series of concentric growth rings, one for each year of the tree's life. The sapwood often shows as the outer, light-colored or white layer nearest the bark while the heartwood is the darker center of the tree. Sapwood (xylem) is made up of live growing cellular tissues which carry the sap up the tree. The heartwood of a tree is made of dead sapwood cells which have ceased to function, but continue to provide mechanical support. It frequently contains mineral or chemical deposits which give greater durability. Between the inner layer of bark (phloem) and outer layer of sapwood is the cambium layer, a thin layer of cells which does the growing for the trunk and lays on the diameter growth. On the outside of the cambium the inner layer of bark (the phloem) conducts the food made in the leaves down to the branches, trunk, and roots for growth tissues. Just outside the inner bark may be found a special cambium layer which makes bark tissue alone.

The crown of the tree is made up of branches, twigs, and broad leaves or coniferous needles. Larger twigs and branches have a wood structure similar to that found in the tree trunk. The smaller twigs contain conduction cells which carry the dissolved nutrients brought up from the roots to the leaves. With the aid of sunlight, the green-colored chemical in the leaves (called chlorophyll) absorbs carbon dioxide (CO_2) from the air and combines this with the water and nutrients to make carbohydrates in the form of sugars and starches. This process is called *photosynthesis*. Carbohydrates, often with nitrates and minerals, may be converted into proteins, fats, and other substances such as oils, resins, latex, pigments, tannins and other acids, vitamins, and alkaloids. The wood itself is a carbohydrate in the form of cellulose plus a chemical complex called lignin which binds together the wood cells.

One major use for the water carried up from the roots is for the manufacture of foods. Water serves also for the upward transportation of minerals and the downward transportation of the manufactured sugar and other chemicals for storage in the trunk and roots. Another function of water is to maintain an even temperature for the tree through transpiration and evaporation of moisture from the pores (stomata) of the leaves. The leaves, which break down carbon dioxide through photosynthesis, also return to the air the oxygen in excess of that used in the manufacture of carbohydrates.

FALL COLOR

The colored substances in plants are known as pigments. In summer the bright green of plant life is caused by the pigment chlorophyll. During summer nights the sugars pass through the leaf veins into other parts of the plant.

There are pigments other than chlorophyll in green plants. If you place an object through which light cannot pass, such as a board, on your lawn for two or three days, the covered grass will become yellow. Chlorophyll is destroyed by the prolonged absence of light. Yellow pigment, *xanthophyll,* and orange-yellow pigment, *carotene,* become apparent. These yellow pigments are present in the green leaves, but chlorophyll is the conspicuous one. In Indian summer, when night temperatures are in the 40's, photosynthetic activities in leaves cease. The plants lose much or all of the chlorophyll, and yellow pigments become dominant, as in the autumn foliage of the cottonwood, aspen, birch, hickory, tulip poplar, oak, maple, and others.

Leaves of maples, especially the red maple, also develop a red pigment, *anthocyanin,* and may retain a little chlorophyll. In Indian summer anthocyanin pigments also develop in the leaves of scarlet oak, sourwood, dogwood, and certain other trees, shrubs and vines. Brown color in the leaves of beech and some oaks is caused by tannin in the leaves.

Our deciduous or broadleaf forests are found in the region southward from southeastern Canada through our eastern states to Georgia and Alabama. In this region there are many different kinds of trees, shrubs, and vines, and this is where you will find the most colorful array during Indian summer.

In New England the maples are especially colorful. From New England southward, especially along the mountains and foothills where there are numerous kinds of woody plants, the autumn coloring is unequaled anywhere in the world. In the central and western states, south of the Great Lakes, the yellow of cotton-woods and birches, and red of the oaks dominate. These, mixed with evergreen conifers, are very attractive.

HOW TREES START

Seed

Most people know how farm crops grow and produce seed. Trees, which go through exactly the same sort of process, have many ways of producing seeds. Some grow inside of fleshy fruits: the persimmon, plum, apple, pawpaw; some have wings: the elms, pines, and maples; some occur in cones: pines, hemlocks, firs, and spruces; and others have the form of nuts: walnuts, hickory, basswood, and butternuts; some produce male and female organs in the same flower: apples, black cherry, elms, basswood; some produce the male organs and female organs in separate flowers: walnuts, hickories, maples; some have male and female trees: ashes, holly. Our pioneer fathers knew when good and bad seed years came for the oaks, hickories, walnuts, and beeches because the hogs that ran in the woods depended upon the tree seeds or "mast" for sustenance. The factors that determine a good or poor seed year vary according to the species of the tree, and they often occur in fairly regular cycles.

Birds and rodents help a great deal in spreading the larger-seeded species. Squirrels often bury quantities of acorns and nuts in various places. Seeds from some light-seeded species, such as maples, elms, ash, yellow poplar, sycamore, and cottonwood catch the wind, which spreads them far beyond the limits possible for heavier-seeded species. Seeds from oaks, walnuts, hickories, basswood, pines, beech, maples, and black cherry are food for wildlife, which carry them considerable distances from the parent tree, thus spreading the species. However, distribution of seeds is not enough. They must have proper conditions for germination, and only a very, very small percentage of the seeds that are produced ever develop into seedlings.

Just as with any other seed that goes into the ground, tree seeds are specific in their requirements for germination. Most of them, for example pine, elm, ash, yellow poplar, and birch, do much better if they lie next to the mineral soil and are covered up a little. Many seeds do not germinate unless they go through a very cold winter, as for example, thornapples, dogwood, and some pines. Some of the small, harder-shelled species, if passed through the digestive tracts of birds or animals, are in better condition for germination than before they were eaten. Thus, the fruits of honey locust and Osage orange are eaten by cows; red cedar, hackberry, and black cherry are eaten by birds, and the germinating quality of the seeds is improved.

Each species has its own definite requirements which must be met before the seed will germinate and become established. A proper supply of moisture is essential to good germination.

Sprouting

Most hardwoods reproduce not only from seed but also from sprouts. Examples are all species of oak and black locust. Redwood, bald cypress, pond and shortleaf pine are the only important conifers in this hemisphere which sprout new growth from stumps. The stumps of young trees sprout much more vigorously than those of mature trees, and old stumps of many species do not sprout at all. Sprouts may come from both the stumps or the roots, but those of most value come from the stumps. Black locust and aspen are the exceptions.

THE BATTLE FOR SURVIVAL

After seeds have once germinated, they are influenced by all the variations in conditions around them. Some species, such as cottonwood, willow, ash, white elm, sycamore, and hemlock thrive in moist sites; other species, such as black walnut, southern yellow pines, and black locust, grow in full light and warm temperatures; still others, the hard pines* and many oaks, do well in dry situations. Species characteristic of moist shady sites and moderate temperatures are beech, sugar maple, dogwood, and hemlock. All sorts of combinations of these factors are found as requirements of different species.

Only a small proportion of the seedlings that germinate and get above the ground continue to grow. Many seedlings are apparently able to grow in competition with other types of vegetation such as weeds and shrubs. But they require light, moisture, and fertility to survive and develop. In the heavy competition of nature only those plants best fitted to compete will survive. Seedlings that come through and finally outgrow the competing vegetation are usually in good condition and grow to maturity.

"Ecology" is defined as the study of all forms of life in relation to environment. Nut trees which depend on squirrels to plant their seeds and squirrels which eat some of the nuts have an ecological relationship. Hemlocks are dependent in their early years upon shade-giving species for protection. The world of nature is full of ecological relationships. Birds feed upon insects for food and nest in trees; outbreaks of damaging insects are often kept under control by birds. Ecology is a highly complex subject but one which the forester must be aware of in handling a community of trees, plants, and animals.

HOW GROWTH TAKES PLACE

All new growth each spring comes from the *buds, cambium,* and *root tips* (see Fig. 3–2). From the buds come leaves, flowers, and new twig growth. A good observer who is out in the woods frequently during early spring has seen the buds slowly open and new leaves appear. The new terminal growth on pines is often called a "candle" and is a lighter green color than the old growth of previous years.

Growth in tree diameter is due to the division and growth of the cambium cells which, as we have learned, occur just inside the bark and form a cylinder around the tree. As these cells divide, new cells are formed and increased diameter results. Cells formed in the spring, when growth is rapid, are larger than those

* Hard pines include practically all pines not of the five-needle white pine groups: eastern and western white pines and sugar pine.

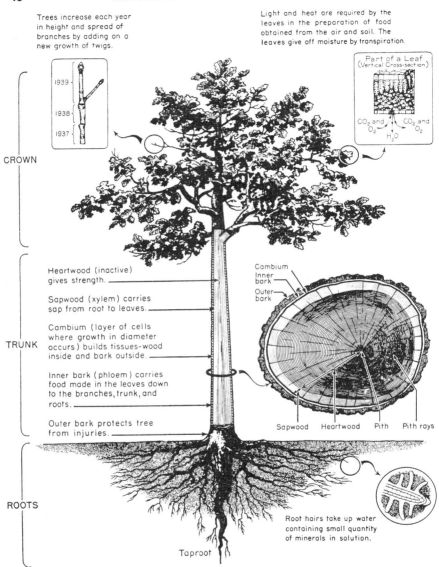

Trees increase each year in height and spread of branches by adding on a new growth of twigs.

Light and heat are required by the leaves in the preparation of food obtained from the air and soil. The leaves give off moisture by transpiration.

Part of a Leaf
(Vertical Cross-section)

CO_2 and O_2 CO_2 and O_2
H_2O

CROWN

1939

1938

1937

TRUNK

Heartwood (inactive) gives strength.

Sapwood (xylem) carries sap from root to leaves.

Cambium (layer of cells where growth in diameter occurs) builds tissues-wood inside and bark outside.

Inner bark (phloem) carries food made in the leaves down to the branches, trunk, and roots.

Outer bark protects tree from injuries.

Cambium
Inner bark
Outer bark

Sapwood   Heartwood   Pith   Pith rays

ROOTS

Root hairs take up water containing small quantity of minerals in solution.

Taproot

The buds, root tips, and cambium layer are the growing parts. The tree takes in oxygen over its entire surface through breathing pores on leaves, twigs, branches, trunk, and roots.

Fig. 3–2. How a tree grows. (U. S. Forest Service)

formed in the summer. In the "diffuse-porous" group of hard-woods (birch, maple, beech, and red gum), however, the vessels (pores) are usually of uniform size. It is the difference between spring wood (lighter and wider) and summer wood which shows up as annual rings so clearly on the stump of a tree. "Ring-porous" hardwoods, such as elms, oaks, and ashes, have distinct rows of tiny vessels at the edge of the spring wood.

The variations in the annual ring widths tell the story of a tree's growth. Thin rings can mean that the tree has been crowded, if it is in a dense forest, or that there has been a dry year, if it is in the open (see Fig. 3–3). Wider rings show that plenty of sunlight

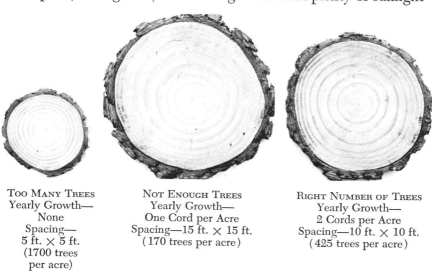

TOO MANY TREES
Yearly Growth—
None
Spacing—
5 ft. × 5 ft.
(1700 trees
per acre)

NOT ENOUGH TREES
Yearly Growth—
One Cord per Acre
Spacing—15 ft. × 15 ft.
(170 trees per acre)

RIGHT NUMBER OF TREES
Yearly Growth—
2 Cords per Acre
Spacing—10 ft. × 10 ft.
(425 trees per acre)

Fig. 3–3. Variation in tree growth rings. These trees were ten years old when cut. (U. S. Soil Conservation Service)

and moisture are available to the tree. Well-spaced trees generally grow faster and produce wider rings than do those under crowded conditions. When a tree is released from overtopping by another tree, its rings begin to widen within a year or two as it responds to the better growing conditions.

Young trees are vigorous and fast-growing. Old trees slow down in growth, eventually become overmature, and die if not cut. Overmature trees are less resistant to disease and insects and are therefore a poor risk. Rot frequently increases in old trees more rapidly than volume growth. The rate of growth of trees varies with species, with conditions of soil and moisture, and with the way in which the forest is managed and cutting is done.

Since photosynthesis takes place in the leaves, the number of leaves and the amount of light that they get determines, to a large extent, the rate at which trees grow. Therefore, the size of the top of a tree is important. It must also have plenty of room in which to expand and have a good chance at the available sunlight (see Fig. 3–3) if it is to reach optimum size at maturity for the site.

Tree Age

The age of a cut tree can be determined by a careful count of annual rings from the middle of the stump to the outside bark. Several years should be added to the number of rings to account for the growth of the tree from ground level to stump height. To find the age or rate of growth of a tree without cutting it, foresters use a thin hollow auger (increment borer). It is drilled into the tree to the pith and the count of rings on the extracted cylindrical core shows the age.

Many conifers, such as red (Norway) pine, white pine, spruces, and firs produce one whorl of new branches each year near the top. The age of such trees, especially if they are not very old, can be found simply by counting whorls. This does not hold true with southern pines, however, which may form two or more whorls of new branches each year. Two periods of growth are not uncommon in the South, especially when growth is interrupted by a drought. As a result, two growth rings are occasionally produced in one year.

FACTORS OF SITE

The rate at which trees grow and the kinds of trees that grow on a given area depend upon the factors of *site*, which is defined as the combination of soil, moisture, and climatic factors present. Foresters have classified sites for tree growth based on the heights which trees will grow in a given time. Site quality is measured by the height to which each species grows in a given period of years, usually fifty. Trees grow taller on good sites than on poor ones. *Site index* tables have been constructed so that it is possible to determine what the site quality may be for trees at any age beyond sapling stage.

Light Requirements

In managing a forest and applying forestry measures, one of the most important considerations is the degree of tolerance of each tree species to shade. Some trees require bright open sunlight and even a little shade will prevent them from growing. Others require much shade, especially in their early years, or they soon die. In deciding what species to plant, which trees to favor in thinning, and what trees to harvest and what to leave, tolerance is the primary factor to be considered. The classification of important timber trees according to a scale of tolerance is given in Table 3–1, at the end of this chapter.

Air

Trees growing in the open obtain plenty of oxygen, nitrogen, and carbon dioxide from the air. However, in cities and near some types of industrial plants, waste gases from smoke will adversely affect tree growth. Where there is too much waste gas, as there is around some nickel and copper smelters, all vegetation may be killed. Air movement, especially high winds, often affects tree form. Timberline trees are bent and twisted by constant winds of the high mountains. Windstorms often blow down large stands of trees. The amount of moisture held in the air (humidity) affects the rate of moisture loss from the leaves and often proves to be a limiting factor for some species.

Temperature

Air temperature is especially important for tree growth. Some species can stand cold winters; others will soon die in prolonged cold spells. Likewise, some trees can grow in hot dry climates and others must grow in climates with more humidity. Some need cool fog belts to survive. Cool north slopes favor certain species; on exposed southern slopes only species which can live in the hot, direct rays of the sun will survive.

Growing Season

Long growing seasons (as in the South) make for more tree growth than the shorter seasons of the North. The volume of growth in any season is directly related to the amount of rainfall.

Plenty of rainfall during the spring and summer produces more wood than does precipitation deficiency. Tree growth stops when annual rainfall is less than 20 in., as in the case in the Great Plains of the West. In the Tropics, where there are balmy temperatures and adequate rain all year, trees grow the year around. No annual rings are to be found!

Soil Requirements

The soils on which forests grow vary greatly in texture, fertility, and water-holding capacity. Because the most fertile soils have largely been taken over for agriculture, forests now occupy more of the sandy, heavy, poorly drained, clay, rocky, swampy, and other kinds of soils unsuitable for farming. Silty soils are usually found in river bottoms; rocky and gravelly soils in glaciated areas of the northern states. Most other soils are derived from parent rock material which has been deteriorated by water, weather, and other natural actions.

Forest soils consist of several distinct layers or horizons, which are classified in the following manner:

1. Surface undecomposed and partly decomposed organic material, such as leaves, twigs, decaying wood and bark, unmixed with mineral subsoil.
2. Decomposed humus mixture with mineral particles of the subsoil.
3. An intermediate horizon of organic material and soluble salts carried down by water from the above layers and largely composed of mineral matter.
4. Several deeper layers which shade from those containing small quantities of dissolved organic chemicals on down to the basic subsoil derived from the parent rock material.

The surface soil acts like a sponge which absorbs water from rains or melting snow, stores some for future plant use, and permits the balance to filter down through to the subsoil where it eventually penetrates the ground water table. In open soils, where cover is absent and the soil particles are compacted, water tends to run off more rapidly, much less of it infiltrating to the subsoil. Soil erosion, siltation, and floods are more common on bare soil than where forests protect the surface. Soil characteristics strongly

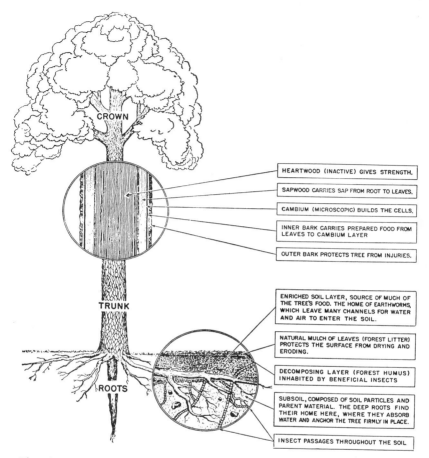

CROWN

HEARTWOOD (INACTIVE) GIVES STRENGTH.

SAPWOOD CARRIES SAP FROM ROOT TO LEAVES.

CAMBIUM (MICROSCOPIC) BUILDS THE CELLS.

INNER BARK CARRIES PREPARED FOOD FROM LEAVES TO CAMBIUM LAYER

OUTER BARK PROTECTS TREE FROM INJURIES.

ENRICHED SOIL LAYER, SOURCE OF MUCH OF THE TREE'S FOOD. THE HOME OF EARTHWORMS, WHICH LEAVE MANY CHANNELS FOR WATER AND AIR TO ENTER THE SOIL.

NATURAL MULCH OF LEAVES (FOREST LITTER) PROTECTS THE SURFACE FROM DRYING AND ERODING.

DECOMPOSING LAYER (FOREST HUMUS) INHABITED BY BENEFICIAL INSECTS

SUBSOIL, COMPOSED OF SOIL PARTICLES AND PARENT MATERIAL. THE DEEP ROOTS FIND THEIR HOME HERE, WHERE THEY ABSORB WATER AND ANCHOR THE TREE FIRMLY IN PLACE.

INSECT PASSAGES THROUGHOUT THE SOIL

TRUNK

ROOTS

Fig. 3–4. The tree and the soil. (U. S. Forest Service and Soil Conservation Service)

influence the rate of growth and distribution of different tree species. Fertility, composition, texture, water-holding capacity— all strongly influence forest yields.

Different tree species have varying soil requirements. Pines, for example, are best suited to light sandy or gravel soils whereas hardwoods require heavier and richer soils. There are exceptions to both generalizations. The data below set forth the soil requirements of many important commercial species which should be kept in mind, particularly on reforestation plans:

1. *Light upland soils* (sandy, gravelly, or other well-drained soils). Jack, Virginia, red (Norway), lodgepole, loblolly, shortleaf, long-leaf, and ponderosa pines. Oaks often occur on these sites also.
2. *Slightly more moist but well-drained poor upland soils* (mixed with clay or loam). Eastern and western white pines, sugar pine, eastern and western hemlocks, Douglas fir, balsam and other true firs (oaks also found here), red and white spruce.
3. *Upland moist, well-drained better soils* (clays and loams). Birch, beech, cherry, elm, hickory, maple, aspen, sweet gum, Sitka spruce, western larch.
4. *Bottomland and cool rich silty moist soils.* Cottonwood, yellow poplar, sycamore, western red cedar, Port Orford cedar, coast redwood, walnut.
5. *Swampy mucks and peats* (the better the drainage the better the site for growth). Black spruce, bald cypress, eastern and southern white cedars, tamarack.

Slope or aspect is an important determining factor in tree location. Dry south- and west-facing slopes may support species which can live only in the full sunlight. Cool moist north and east slopes are favored by shade and moisture-loving trees.

OTHER SILVICAL FEATURES

Some characteristics of individual species have been discussed —tolerance for shade, root systems, preferred kinds of soil conditions, and locality of growth. These are inherent in the nature of the species just as some birds, such as quail, prefer fence rows whereas others, such as the ruffed grouse, like the deep woods. Some species of trees live longer than others. Some reproduce quickly and easily; others are very demanding in the seedbed requirements for young seedlings. Certain species are quite temporary, giving way to species which are relatively permanent elements of the "climax" forest.

Some species have a long life span; for others, it is quite short. Aspen, paper birch, jack and Virginia pine, for example, seldom live much more than 50 years. This is generally true of species found in "temporary" types. Climax species such as oak, maple, white pine, elm, and hemlock, which grow to larger sizes, live much longer. This aspect of ecology, of great importance to the forester, is called "ecological succession." Table 3–1 shows the relative position of many important species in the scale of succession.

The growth habits of trees are important in shaping their development. Black cherry, for instance, will bend and twist toward open sunlight in the forest canopy, often developing a crooked trunk. Some species grow much more rapidly than others on the same site. White pine will grow 2 to 4 ft. a year, whereas hemlock may put only 4 to 6 in. on its height. Black walnut seldom grows in groups, more often with other species.

TABLE 3–1

Some Silvical Characteristics of Important Forest Trees

Species	Rate of Growth	Reproduction	Succession Place	Longevity	Tolerance
Pines (Eastern)					
Jack	R	E–M	P–S	M–S	I
White	R	E–M	S–C	L	M
Red (Norway)	R	D	S–C	M–L	I
Shortleaf	R	M	P–S	M–L	I
Slash	R	E	P–S	M	I
Longleaf	R	D	P–S	L	I
Loblolly	R	M	P–S	M–L	I
Virginia	M	E	P	S	I
Pines (Western)					
Ponderosa	M	M	P–C	L	I
White	R	E	S	L	M
Lodgepole	M	E	P	M–S	I
Other Conifers (Eastern)					
Balsam fir	R	E	S–C	S	M–T
Black spruce	S–M	E	S–C	M–L	I
White spruce	M–R	M	S–C	L	M
Red spruce	R	M	S–C	L	M
Hemlock	S	M	C	L	T
Tamarack (larch)	R	M	P–S	M	I
Northern white cedar..	S	M–E	S–C	L	T
Bald cypress	S	M	C	L	I–M
Other Conifers (Western)					
Larch	R	E	P–S	L	I
Engelmann spruce	S	D	C	M–L	T
Douglas fir	R	M	S	L	I
Western red cedar	M–R	E	C	L	T
Western hemlock	M	E	C	L	T
White fir	R	E	S–C	M	T
Coast redwood	R	D	C	L	T

TABLE 3–1 (Continued)

Species	Rate of Growth	Reproduction	Succession Place	Longevity	Tolerance
		Hardwoods (Eastern)			
Sugar maple	M–R	E	C	M–L	M–T
Beech	M	E	S–C	M	T
Black cherry	S	D	S	M	M
Northern red oak	R	D	S–C	M	I
Basswood	R	M–D	S	M	M
American elm	R	M	S	M–L	M
Yellow birch	M–S	M	S–C	L	M–I
Black walnut	M–R	D	S	M–L	I
Shagbark hickory	S	M	S	M	I
Tulip (yellow) poplar..	R	M	S	L	I
White oak	S	M	C	L	I
Red gum	R	E	P–S	M	I
All aspens	R	E	P	S	I
All ashes	M–R	M–E	S	M	I\

Rate of Growth: R (Rapid), M (Medium), S (Slow).

Rate of Reproduction: E (Easy), M (Medium), D (Difficult).

Place in Succession: P (Pioneer or Temporary), S (Sub-climax or Transition), C (Climax).

Longevity: S (Short, up to 50 years), M (Medium, 50 to 100 years), L (Long, over 100 years).

Tolerance of Shade: I (Intolerant), M (Intermediate), T (Tolerant). Tolerance applies largely to trees in early growth stages. Even the most tolerant species in youth require full sunlight to attain optimum growth during maturity.

SOURCE: Adapted from Reginald D. Forbes and Arthur B. Meyer (eds.), *Forestry Handbook* (New York: The Ronald Press Co., 1955), Section 6, Table 2.

In Table 3–1, above, five important silvical characteristics are set forth for a number of commercial species as a guide to the forestry technician and forest owner. This information applies entirely to those parts of the tree's range and those sites where it makes its best growth.

QUESTIONS

1. What is the definition of a tree?
2. Name the three main parts of a tree and give the functions of each.
3. Why do trees have scientific (Latin) names?
4. What does the process of photosynthesis do for plants?
5. What parts of the tree are used to distinguish one species of tree from another?
6. How can one tell the age of a tree from the stump?
7. Give the definition of "site" as used by foresters.

8. What function does the cambium layer have in a tree?

9. What do wide annual rings show about a tree's growth. What do narrow rings show?

10. Name one species of tree with a compound alternate leaf. Name one with a simple opposite leaf.

11. What is meant by "tolerance" in a tree?

12. Why do shade-tolerant species form all-aged forests and intolerant species even-aged forests?

EXERCISES

1. Collect and identify the leaves or needles of twelve trees growing in your locality.

2. Name three tolerant and three intolerant local species.

3. Identify three species growing on moist soils (river bottoms or swamps) and three growing on light upland soils.

4

The Composition and Distribution of Forests

The forest is more than a group of individual trees—it is a complex plant community. Since the community includes not only trees, but shrubs, annual plants, soils, and animal life of many kinds as well, it might be compared with the obvious community relationships in a city or town. The individual trees in a forest are as interdependent with other living things as are the people in a community.

To be classed as a forest, a group of trees must have crowns close enough to encourage natural pruning by shading the lower limbs and an accumulation of undecomposed and decomposed material overlying mineral soil. Other associated elements usually include smaller plants and many forms of animal life. A new plantation of small pines cannot meet these standards, nor can trees in a city park, nor scattered remnant trees after heavy logging.

CLASSIFICATION OF TREES WITHIN A FOREST

Within the forest it has been found helpful to classify individual trees in a number of ways as an aid to forest management. The most important are shown in the following groupings.

Classification by Size

Beginning with the smallest and youngest size classes, the following groupings are based upon d.b.h. (diameter breast high) and height of the tree:

Seedlings, up to 3 ft. high
Small saplings, 3 to 10 ft. high
Large saplings, 10 or more ft. high and up to 4 in. in diameter
Small poles, 4 to 8 in. in diameter
Large poles, 8 to 12 in. in diameter
Standards, 12 to 24 in. in diameter
Veterans, over 24 in. in diameter

Classification by Position in the Stand

Another basis for classification of trees is by the relative position of their crowns in the general level of the forest canopy (the covering formed by the interlacing of tree tops). This crown classification is mainly of value in even-aged forests (see Fig. 4–1):

Fig. 4–1. Tree crown classes: D, dominant; CD, co-dominant; I, intermediate; and S, suppressed.

DOMINANT: Trees with wide crowns above the level of the forest canopy, receiving sunlight from above and partly from the sides.

CO-DOMINANT: Trees large-crowned at the general level of the forest canopy, receiving direct sunlight from above and partly from the sides. Crowns somewhat smaller than dominants but healthy and vigorous.

INTERMEDIATE: Trees with much of crown below general level or pinched at general canopy level, receiving some sunlight from above with little or none from sides.

SUPPRESSED: Trees overtopped by large trees and receiving no full, direct sunlight from above or the sides.

In addition to the above classifications there are these which consider tree quality:

WOLF TREES: Trees which hinder the growth of thrifty trees and are of little value themselves.

CROOKED AND FORKED TREES: The forms of which render them poor merchantable material.

FIRE-SCARRED, HOLLOW, OR ROTTEN TREES: Also of little value.

CLASSIFICATION OF FORESTS

For purposes of mapping forests for forest management, forests may be grouped according to composition of species, density of stand, age composition, and forest type. Each of these classifications is set forth in the following paragraphs, followed by a discussion of the distribution of the several forest types and where they are to be found.

By Species Composition

A *pure forest* is one in which all or nearly all trees are of the same species. A *mixed forest* is one consisting of trees of two or more species. Pure or mixed forests may be either even-aged, uneven-aged, or all-aged.

Intolerant species such as pines, tamarack, yellow poplar, basswood, or yellow birch often begin in pure, even-aged stands. Later on, the hardwoods tend to evolve toward an all-aged, mixed condition. Trees in dense, young, even-aged forests compete so fiercely that their growth is slow and mortality is very heavy. In dense forests on poor sites most trees tend to stagnate; on good sites dominant trees will develop which crowd out competitors. Shade-tolerant species, such as the hemlocks, beech, and the true firs, usually grow well either in pure, preferably all-aged forests, or with other species. Intolerant species cannot withstand competition from tolerant trees and cannot successfully reproduce under their cover except in large openings.

By Stand Density

Because forests vary considerably in numbers of trees, volume per acre, basal area, and other criteria, it is important that we find a means of expressing differences. The difference between a dense stand and an open one is obvious to the eye when it is expressed on the basis of the amount of crown opening. The density as expressed in other ways (volume, basal area, number of stems per acre) must be measured in order to detect the actual differences. But for purposes of convenience, three classes of crown density have been recognized:

Dense or well stocked, over 70 per cent of crown closure.
Thin or medium stocked, 40–70 per cent of crown closure.
Poorly stocked, under 40 per cent of crown closure.

One way to determine crown density rapidly is by measuring the amount of shade and open sunlight in a stand at midday. There is often so much variation within a stand that occular judgment is accurate enough for most purposes.

It is apparent that any forest which has less than a dense crown is functioning below the most efficient level *unless* there are young trees coming up to fill the openings. If a stand is too dense, it may become stagnant, and growth will slow down because the competition for light, water, and soil nutrients is too great. Extremely slow growth is the result. But a forest does not usually long stay this way. Competition between trees will result in the elimination of the weaker ones and the dominance of the stronger.

Likewise, a stand that is too open (understocked) will produce large-crowned, limby trees with short trunks. A well-managed forest is one in which the density is kept at the optimum level so that the trees can make full use of water, sunlight, and soil chemicals. In some forests underbrush occupies much good growing space and only through its elimination will trees develop and grow.

By Age Composition

When practically all the trees are of the same age, even though they may vary in size because of their different rates of growth, a forest is *even-aged*. An *all-aged* forest is one in which the trees range from seedlings to big merchantable timber, with all age and size classes represented (Fig. 4–2, A, B).

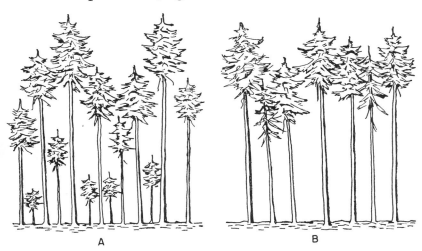

Fig. 4–2. All-aged and even-aged forest profiles. In the all-aged forest (A), the trees range from small seedlings to mature and over-mature veterans. In an even-aged forest (B), the trees are all about the same age. Some are dominant, some are co-dominant, and the remainder are intermediate or suppressed.

In some stands there may only be two size classes, seedlings and standards, without pole-sized trees; or there may be overmature, defective trees along with saplings and nothing in between. Forests which may have only two or three distinct age or size groups are commonly referred to as being uneven-aged.

All-aged forests have a more uniform distribution of sizes and generally include more of the shade-tolerant species (usually hardwoods), while even-aged stands are most often made up of intolerant conifers. There are exceptions such as ponderosa pine, which grows in both uneven-aged and even-aged stands, and sugar maple, which starts off on cutover lands in even-aged stands and gradually develops into uneven-age distribution. Windstorms, overcutting, fire, and other losses create openings in the forest and create uneven-age groupings. The endless variety of situations found in every forest makes it difficult to standardize or classify each one, and this complicates the practice of silviculture.

By Forest Types

Natural groups or associations of different species of trees which commonly occur together over large areas are called forest types. Forest types are defined and named after the one or more dominant species of trees, such as the spruce-fir and the birch-beech-maple (northern hardwood) types within the Northern forest region. Other examples are the Douglas fir-western hemlock types of the Pacific Coast forest region, and the longleaf pine type in the Southern region.

Many of the forest types are only "temporary" types which in time will give way to another completely different group of transition (or subclimax) species and finally the climax type. For example, white pine on old fields of heavy soils in New England will be replaced by climax northern hardwoods. Aspen-birch on the Lake States cutovers is being replaced in some soils by white pine or by northern hardwoods, which are climax species for these soils. Thus, types which are strongly influenced by underlying soils change, over time, both by man's disturbance and nature's evolutionary development.

Common Forest Types of Continental United States

It is possible to describe a wide number of combinations of species which occur in nature and call each one a forest type. In fact, the Society of American Foresters recognizes 106 different types in the eastern United States and 50 in the western. Most forest types are mixtures of species, although some are in pure stands, e.g., lodgepole pine, redwood, Engelmann spruce, white pine, and others. In general, eastern types are more complex than western, and coniferous types less complex than hardwood forests. The number of species appears to increase as one proceeds from north to south.

Because of the large numbers of forest types which are found with greater or lesser proportions of different species, an effort has been made to set forth a few of the more common forest types found over each of the major regions. Most of the other forest types contain various combinations of these species in addition to others less commonly found.

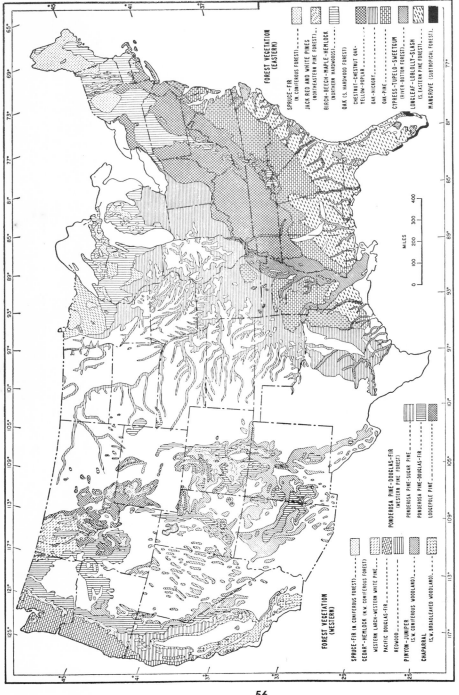

Fig. 4–3. Forest vegetation of the United States. Adapted from Shantz and Zon's "Natural Vegetation" map in the *Atlas of American Agriculture*. (U. S. Forest Service)

FOREST VEGETATION (EASTERN)

SPRUCE-FIR (N. CONIFEROUS FOREST)

JACK RED AND WHITE PINES (NORTHEASTERN PINE FOREST)

BIRCH-BEECH-MAPLE-HEMLOCK (NORTHERN HARDWOODS)

OAK (S. HARDWOOD FOREST)

CHESTNUT-CHESTNUT OAK-YELLOW-POPLAR

OAK-HICKORY

OAK-PINE

CYPRESS-TUPELO-SWEETGUM (RIVER-BOTTOM FOREST)

LONGLEAF-LOBLOLLY-SLASH (S. EASTERN PINE FOREST)

MANGROVE (SUBTROPICAL FOREST)

MILES
0   100   200   300   400

PONDEROSA PINE-DOUGLAS-FIR (WESTERN PINE FOREST)

PONDEROSA PINE-SUGAR PINE

PONDEROSA PINE-DOUGLAS-FIR

LODGEPOLE PINE

FOREST VEGETATION (WESTERN)

SPRUCE-FIR (N. CONIFEROUS FOREST)

CEDAR-HEMLOCK (N.W. CONIFEROUS FOREST)

WESTERN LARCH-WESTERN WHITE PINE

PACIFIC DOUGLAS-FIR

REDWOOD

PINYON-JUNIPER (S.W. CONIFEROUS WOODLAND)

CHAPARRAL (S.W. BROADLEAVED WOODLAND)

56

Eastern United States	*Western United States*

Northern:
- White pine
- Norway (red) pine
- Jack pine
- Hemlock–yellow birch
- Spruce–fir

- Aspen–birch
- Birch–beech–maple (Northern hardwoods)
- Black spruce–tamarack–white cedar (swamp conifers)

Central:
- Oak–hickory (also in South)
- Oak–pine
- Elm–ash–cottonwood (bottomland hardwoods)

Southern:
- Loblolly–shortleaf pine
- Longleaf–slash pine
- Cypress–southern hardwoods
- Oaks–pine
- Oak–gum–yellow poplar

Rocky Mountain:
- Ponderosa pine
- Western white pine
- Lodgepole pine
- Spruce–fir
- Western larch

Pacific Coast:
- Douglas fir–western hemlock
- Ponderosa pine
- Sugar pine–ponderosa pine
- Western white pine–western larch
- Spruce–fir
- Redwood
- Western red cedar

AMERICAN FOREST REGIONS

Different combinations of species of trees are found in natural associations or mixtures in various parts of the United States. Varying conditions of temperature, precipitation, and of soil are the major determinants of the six major forest regions in the continental United States and two in Alaska. Most of the trees in a forest region differ from those in the others, yet a few overlap in two or three regions, especially in the eastern part of the United States.

The four forest regions of the eastern half of the United States are the *northern, central hardwood, southern,* and *tropical* and the two western regions are the *Rocky Mountain* and *Pacific Coast,* as shown in the map, Fig. 4–3. The forests of Alaska are divided into the *coast* and *interior* forest regions. There are many local variations, as for example along the central portion of the East Coast where northern, central, and southern species often intermingle.

The Northern Region

Covering most of New England and New York, this region extends southward over the Appalachian Mountain highlands to northern Georgia, and westward into the Lake States, including most of Michigan, Wisconsin, and Minnesota.

The Northern Forest Region is characterized by the predominance of northern white pine, red or Norway pine, eastern hemlock, red and white spruces, gray, paper (white), sweet, and yellow birches, elm, beech, sugar maple, basswood, and northern red and scarlet oaks. Each of these species varies in abundance in different parts of the region, and many of them are absent in other parts.

The more abundant or valuable trees composing the two divisions of the northern forest region are as follows:

Northern Portion (Northeast and Lake States):

Red, black, and white spruces
Balsam fir
White, red (Norway), and jack pines
Hemlock
Sugar and red maples
Beech
Northern red, white, black, and scarlet oaks
Yellow, paper, and gray birches
Aspen, quaking and largetooth
Basswood
Black cherry
American, rock, and red elms
White, green, and black ashes
Shagbark and pignut hickories
Butternut
Northern white cedar
Tamarack

Southern Portion (Appalachian region; includes most species in northern portion and in addition):

Chestnut oak
Chestnut (nearly extinct)
White, shortleaf, pitch, and Virginia pines
River birches
Beech
Red spruce
Southern balsam fir
Yellow poplar (tulip poplar)
Black walnut
Pignut, mockernut, and red hickories
Black locust
Black gum
American, red, and rock elms

The Central Region

This region covers a large amount of the central portion of the eastern half of the United States, almost to the Atlantic Coast. It extends from southern Minnesota eastward to Connecticut, and, excluding the southern Appalachian Mountain country, south through the Piedmont area and the Cumberland Plateau to the northern parts of the Southern states. The region includes an abundance of different oaks and hickories, and, on the better soils, yellow or tulip poplar and black walnut.

The principal kinds of trees that make up the central forest region are:

White, black, northern red, scarlet, bur, chestnut, and chinquapin oaks
Shagbark, mockernut, pignut, and bitternut hickories
White, blue, and green ashes
American and red elms
Red and silver maples
Black cherry
Basswood
Dogwood
Eastern red cedar
Beech
Pitch, shortleaf, and Virginia pines
Yellow poplar (tulip poplar)
Sycamore
Chestnut
Black walnut
Cottonwood
Black locust
Willows (many species)

The Southern Region

The yellow pine forests of the Southeastern states provide the most important source of sawtimber in the eastern United States. Mixed stands of hardwoods and cypress are found on river and creek bottom lands and in swamps. The region extends along the Atlantic and Gulf Coastal Plains from eastern Maryland to eastern Texas, and includes portions of Missouri, Arkansas, and Oklahoma. The natural conditions are a soil of relatively low agricultural value, abundant rainfall, and a long growing season. The region contains about 30 per cent of all our forest lands, made up largely of southern pines and with smaller acreages of lowland hardwoods and cypress. The four most important species of pines (shortleaf, loblolly, longleaf, and slash, in this order) are found in journeying from north to south across the region.

The principal trees which compose the forest of the Southern region are as follows:

Longleaf, shortleaf, loblolly, and slash pines
Southern red, black, post, laurel, and willow oaks
Winged, American, and cedar elms
Eastern red cedars
Pond and sand pines
Red, tupelo, and swamp black gums
Water, laurel, live, overcup, Texas red, and swamp chestnut oaks
Bald cypress
Pecan, water, and pignut hickories
Beech
River birch
Water, green, pumpkin, and white ashes
Red and silver maples
Cottonwood and willows
Sycamore
Evergreen magnolia
Southern white cedar

The Rocky Mountain Region

Spread over a vast extent of mountains and high plateaus in the central-western part of the United States, the Rocky Mountain forest region reaches from Canada to Mexico, a length of about 1,300 miles, and from the Great Plains west to the great basin of Nevada and eastern parts of Oregon and Washington, a breadth of 800 miles.

The total area of the many separate divisions or blocks of the Rocky Mountain region amounts to about one-eighth of the total forest land in the United States. The most extensive forest type is the ponderosa pine, followed by lodgepole pine, western white pine, western larch, and finally Douglas fir and Engelmann spruce.

The principal species of the region are as follows:

Lodgepole pine	Aspen and cottonwood
Douglas fir	Ponderosa pine
Western larch	Western red cedar
Engelmann spruce	Lowland white and alpine firs
Western white pine	Western and mountain hemlocks
Limber pine	Oaks and junipers

The Pacific Region

Stands of very large firs, pines, hemlock, and cedars characterize this westernmost area. The dense coastal forests of Washington, Oregon, and the Sierra Nevada mountains of eastern California are dominant features of the landscape.

The California big trees, or Sierra redwoods, and the redwood of central and northern California coasts reach over 300 ft. in height with diameters up to 40 ft. The western red cedar, Douglas fir, and sugar pine of California all grow to heights of over 200 ft. with diameters up to 15 ft.

The Pacific Coast forest region also contains about one-eighth of the commercial forest area in the country. The Douglas fir-western hemlock types contain the largest acreage, followed closely by ponderosa (western yellow) pine. Other important types are the sugar pine, western white pine, western larch, spruce-fir, the coast redwood, and the big tree. Principal species are:

Douglas fir	Western white pine
Western hemlock	Port Orford and Alaska cedars
White, noble, red, and silver firs	Oaks, ash, maples, birches, alders,
Western red cedar	cottonwood, madrone
Ponderosa and Jeffrey pines	Knobcone and digger pines
Sugar pine	Western juniper
Redwood and bigtree sequoias	Western larch
Incense cedar	Lodgepole pine
Sitka and Engelmann spruces	

The Forests of Alaska

Along the southeastern coast of Alaska, stretching for more than 1,000 miles, is a gradually narrowing belt of dense forest (about 5 million acres) made up of trees of good size. This is the most northern extension of the coniferous forest found in Oregon, Washington, and British Columbia. About three-fourths of the total stand of timber consists of western hemlock and the remainder is mostly Sitka spruce, with small amounts of western red cedar and Alaska cedar. In the interior are more than 100 million acres of spruce-birch forest land—much of it small in size and subject to recurring forest fires.

QUESTIONS

1. (a) Give the term used to describe a forest with many sizes and ages of trees. (b) Give the term used for forests in which the trees are nearly of the same size and age.

2. What is the difference between a *pure* and a *mixed* forest?

3. Name the four classes used to classify trees according to their crowns.

4. Give the three classes used to describe stand density.

5. What is the definition of a forest type?

6. Name two important forest types in the South.

7. Name two important forest types in the Northern states.

8. Name two important Western forest types.

9. In which of the six major forest regions of the United States do you live?

EXERCISES

1. Visit a nearby forest area and locate an *even-aged* and an *all-aged* stand.

2. In each of the above stands determine in which *stand density class* they fall.

3. Identify the forest type of each of the above stands.

5

The Practice
of Silviculture

Silviculture may be defined as the art of reproducing and managing forests continuously to obtain high yields of forest crops through the application of a knowledge of silvics.* A forest can grow up naturally without interference by man and still produce timber, but by applying what we have learned about forest growth we can produce greater amounts of the desired kinds of timber in shorter periods. This is the heart of the practice of forestry. It is a conscious, intelligent use of man's abilities to assist nature, in contrast to careless cutting and lack of foresight. The techniques used by foresters in managing forests are governed both by a knowledge of silvics and an understanding of the forest as a plant community. Most of this knowledge has been obtained by scientific observation, research, and experimentation.

The several stages of forest development require different kinds of treatments to obtain the desired results. The economic objectives of forest owners in obtaining certain kinds of forest products (sawlogs, pulpwood, Christmas trees, etc.) strongly govern the silvicultural treatment to be followed. Forest types, size and species composition, and silvical characteristics are the basic determining factors, however. Taken together, the silvical characteristics which govern the handling of a particular forest type or species are: (1) degree of tolerance to shade, (2) windfirmness of root system, (3) ability to grow in pure or mixed stands, (4) growth in even-aged, all-aged, or uneven-aged stands, and

* See also the definition in Appendix A.

(5) relative ease or difficulty of obtaining reproduction. Silvicultural measures can be separated into two major groups: those which are applied to young growing stands, and those which are followed in harvesting mature stands.

INTERMEDIATE CUTTINGS IN IMMATURE STANDS

The term "intermediate cuttings" refers to those cuttings made in a stand of timber from the time of its formation until it is ready for harvesting. This group of measures includes a number of practices designed to improve the quality of the stand by removing the poorer trees and to increase the rate of growth of the residual trees in the stand. Other terms used for intermediate cuttings include "timber stand improvement" (t.s.i.) and "cultural measures." Essentially, the purpose of intermediate cuttings is to achieve the proper growing space for the best trees in the forest by favoring them and limiting competition. Salvage of trees which might otherwise be lost through mortality is another important result of t.s.i. work.

The spread of roots of a forest tree often is approximately the same as that of its branches, so that when the crowns of adjoining trees get too crowded, their roots also are in conflict; tree growth greatly suffers for both these reasons. Trees should not be too close together nor should there be too much space between them.

As the forest grows, the number of trees decreases. In a seedling stand 20,000 or more small seedlings may be found on an acre. Usually from 1,000 to 1,600 seedlings per acre properly spaced will produce a well-stocked stand. After 20 or 30 years only 400 to 800 trees will remain. A well-stocked, mature, even-aged forest may contain 150 to 200 large and evenly distributed trees an acre. The amount of space needed between trees increases with their age and size. Shade-intolerant trees need more room than those which are tolerant of shade.

Forests in the eastern part of the country are largely second- and third-growth woodlands which have sprung up from cutover land or land which has been both cut and burned. Fortunately, fire protection has been extended over wide areas during the past quarter century so that nature's recuperative powers have restored trees to much land which was nearly barren not too many years ago. Forest plantings begun on a wide scale by the Civilian Conservation Corps in the 1930's have developed to the point where they need attention just as much as the millions of acres of wild new forests. At each stage in the development of the young forest during its life cycle, silvicultural measures will be required (Figs. 5–1 and 5–2). Those described in the following pages would be applied at various stages of growth and to the several forest types as indicated.

Fig. 5–1. A white pine stand marked for thinning. The trees marked are those which are to be left standing. (Champion Paper & Fibre Co.)

Weedings or Cleanings

A new forest just starting from the seedling stage may have a variety of undesirable species present which may overtake and crowd out the more valuable trees. Young pines can exist for a short time in shade, but undesirable weed-tree sprouts and reproduction will soon get the upper hand. Cleanings can be accomplished easily through the use of brush-killing chemicals such as 2, 4, 5-T in mixed hardwood-pine stands but is more difficult in mixed hardwood stands where elimination of poor hardwoods is desired.*

*See especially, "Caring for the Young Forest Plantation" near the end of this chapter for information on some of the newer techniques used for weedings and release cuttings.

Fig. 5–2. The same stand, after thinning. The heavy volume re-moved (about 41 cords per acre) can be seen in the cut timber. Note the good spacing in the residual stand. These trees will accelerate rapidly in growth for nearly a decade. (Champion Paper & Fibre Co.)

Release or Liberation Cuttings

Young sapling stands often start under weed or wolf trees, which cause suppression and stagnation of the new growth at its most rapid stage of development. Much cutover land coming up to new forests has these overtopping trees, and they will soon take over the site unless removed. In many areas where wildlife man-agement is practiced, however, these wolf trees are selected to be left as den trees for wildlife or because they produce needed food, especially nuts. Removal of wolf trees can be done either by cutting where there is a market for the wood or by girdling and poisoning where there is not. Girdling is accomplished by cutting a V-shaped notch into the cambium layer, either with a mechani-cal girdler or with an axe. Sometimes the notches are filled with a poison to prevent sprouting or to insure rapid death, because some species will linger for a long time after girdling. Release cuttings probably will require more time and attention from forestry-trained men during the next several decades than any other single forestry measure.

Sanitation Cuttings

Trees are sometimes attacked by insects or diseases which may kill infected trees and spread to uninfected trees. Trees with a heavy infestation of bark beetle, for instance, will die and the insects harbored by them will attack other trees. Sanitation cuttings remove the source of trouble from the stand and leave the healthy trees to grow. Sanitation cuttings to control diseases are usually carried out as part of the regular improvement cutting program. If diseased trees are not removed in the regular commercial operations, they may be removed as soon as possible thereafter in order to free the ground for new growth.

Sanitation cuttings to control infestations of bark beetles are emergency measures to be undertaken as needed. Infested trees are often felled and removed from the stand. In case the outbreak is severe, it may be necessary to spray unremoved tops and stumps with benzene hexachloride to prevent further spread and damage by the insects.*

Salvage Cuttings

Timber stands are sometimes so severely injured by fire, insect attack, or by windstorm or sleet that it is necessary to salvage the damaged timber. Occasionally a single tree of large value and high quality is killed by lightning. Salvage operations remove the merchantable dead and damaged trees, leaving the uninjured trees to grow. In the case of fire-injured trees, salvage cuttings remove the weakened trees which will not recover and if left, might be an invitation to attack by insects or disease.

Thinnings

Since trees cannot be moved to provide proper spacing as they grow, some of the trees must be cut to "thin" the forest where crowding becomes too great. Thinnings are mainly made in *even-aged stands of young timber.* Good trees that die naturally mean that much wood volume is lost. Thinnings anticipate this loss and provide usable posts, pulpwood, fuel, or mine props. Thinning is usually needed when the trees are between 15 and 25 years old.

* See Chapter 9, "Protection," for detailed discussion of techniques used.

By then the crowns of the trees grown are closed in and lower branches have begun to die. The need for thinning is obvious when there is severe overcrowding of tree crowns, spindly stems, narrow growth rings, and frequent dead and dying trees. Although foresters have developed several methods of thinning for intensive forestry, the two most commonly used are low thinning (or thinning from below), and high or crown thinning.

Crown Thinning. Thinning from above is a cutting of the larger (dominant) trees in young stands with rapid recuperative powers. By removing some of the larger trees more space is made available to the smaller trees for additional growth. This method is used extensively in jack, Virginia, and lodgepole pines, balsam fir, and aspen (and other short-lived species in temporary forest types). Pulpwood can often be harvested by this method, but care must be taken to leave enough residual trees to form a closed stand and to permit the smaller residual trees to continue growing (Fig. 5–3). This kind of thinning removes dominant, suppressed, and

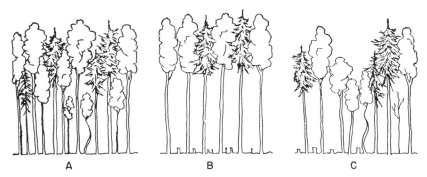

A   B   C

Fig. 5–3. Thinning from above and below. The stand before thinning (A) has many intermediate and suppressed trees. Thinning from below (B) removes most of the poorer trees and leaves the best for future growth. Thinning from above (C) removes the larger trees and only the poorer small ones.

some intermediate crown classes and leaves co-dominants to grow for a time.

Low Thinning (Thinning from Below). When the object of thinning is the maximum future benefit, the practice is to "thin from below"—i.e., provide for proper spacing by cutting the inferior, smaller, or defective trees, leaving the best and most vigorous trees to grow. Such thinnings will develop the best trees into sawlogs much sooner than without this treatment. Low thinnings are best applied to older stands and to species with a long growing life, usually 75 years or more.

When marking trees for thinning from below, *dominant* and *co-dominant* trees are the most desirable to save. All the *suppressed,* poor *intermediates,* and some of the limby or crooked *dominant* trees are cut.

Low thinnings are most commonly practiced today. It is best to thin not too heavily but to do it often. Not more than one-third of the trees should be cut at one time, unless overcrowding is serious. Cutting should be repeated at five- to ten-year intervals, when the crowns become crowded again. Properly done in a dense young forest, thinnings will greatly increase the growth rate of residual trees and yield higher quality material on shorter rotations. Larger volumes can be harvested, in total, because of the salvage of much wood which would otherwise be lost through mortality.

One way to check on a stand to determine whether it needs thinning is to take increment borings in a number of the best trees (dominants). If the annual rings indicate that growth has slowed down in the past five years compared with the previous five years, thinning is needed. Where the stand has been thinned previously, the technician will note from the borings that the annual rings become much wider a year or two after the thinning and then become gradually narrower as the stand closed in again. Another means of determining the need for thinning is by comparing basal area, stocking density, and volume distribution of the stand in question with data from yield and other data tables for normal stands (see Chapter 6).

Nine rules to keep in mind when thinning from below are:

1. Mark the stand carefully *before* cutting. Do not make marking and cutting one job.
2. Mark all trees to be cut on one side only. Marks should be clear so they can be easily seen by the loggers.
3. Plan the marking to secure the best development of the most promising trees rather than the removal of the poor trees.
4. Look *up* rather than down when marking. Remember that it is the size, shape, and spacing of the crowns which count as much as the spacing of the stems.
5. Do not mark trees if there is no definite beneficial purpose in their removal.

6. Always mark whips, but do not always mark butt-scarred or wolf trees. Removing them may sometimes cause more harm than good to the stand.

7. Concentrate the thinnings on areas to which one can easily return for another cut. Frequent and light thinnings are far better than heavy thinnings with long intervals.

8. Do not let the best trees develop into wolf trees. Keep sufficient trainers to prevent this.

9. Know the silvicultural properties of the species and the quality of the site before thinning is started.

Spacing Determinations in Improvement Cuttings

Foresters have devised some simple "rule-of-thumb" spacing guides that are fairly accurate and easy to apply in thinnings. These rules, which have come to be known as the "D plus" rules, are simple guides for determining the spacing between trees left standing after a thinning operation in a young stand. Here is what they are and how they work.

"D" is the average diameter of the trees to be left, and for trees 6 in. and over, d.b.h., the rule is D plus 6. This gives the average spacing in feet. For instance, if the diameters of the trees to be left average 10 in., then 10 plus 6 equals 16. So the average spacing between the trees left is 16 ft.

This rule is useful for most types in the eastern United States. For the West, the principle of "D plus" rule is the same, but the "6" is reduced. The spacing requirements for some of the western types for trees left after thinning are:

Pure ponderosa pine	D plus 4
Mixed conifers (white pine, larch, Douglas fir, ponderosa pine)	D plus 3
West Coast Douglas fir and redwood	D plus 2

For stands under 6-in. diameter, use D plus 4 in the East, and D plus 2 in the West.

These rules are no substitute for common sense. Rules-of-thumb should be used only as a guide which needs to be well seasoned with judgment. Proper marking cannot be done entirely mechanically. For example, a clump of eight or ten good trees with room on the outside, but crowded in the center, might be thinned to two or three according to the rule. Actually, wise selection and cutting of three trees might give the whole group enough room. In short, each tree should be sized up individually for its chances of growing into profitable timber. Generally, not more than one-quarter of the wood volume is taken out at any one thinning so as to avoid producing too great a shock to the remaining trees.

Pruning

High-grade logs with wood largely free from knots are an important forestry objective. In its early life a stand must be kept sufficiently dark under the crowns so that shade will kill off branches on the lower trunks of the trees. The small branches rot and fall off, and the trees grow clear wood. If the forest is not sufficiently dense when it is young, large branches develop and, even though they are later killed by shading, persist for years, thus forming knotty logs and lumber.

To produce high-grade lumber or veneer logs when natural

Fig. 5–4. Pruning thinned ponderosa pine stand to improve lumber quality. (U. S. Bureau of Land Management)

pruning has been unsatisfactory, the best trees should be selected and pruned by cutting the lower branches. Pruning should be started when the trees are about 4 in. d.b.h.; and only about 200 crops trees which are straight, sound, and fast growing, and which will develop into high-quality sawlogs, should be pruned. Pruning trees which are crooked, or which have very thick branches, does not pay if they are over 8 or 10 in. in diameter. Pruning usually pays only on the better conifers—white pine, Douglas fir, red pine, longleaf pine, and on hardwoods of value for veneer.

Pruning live branches should be done during the dormant period in the winter (Fig. 5–4). The first pruning should remove branches up to one-half log above stump height on the bole. As growth continues, pruning should be extended to 12 ft. above the ground. After another interval, the pruning may be extended to a height about 17 ft.—if a 16-ft. clear log is desired. No more than one-third of the height of young trees should be pruned at any time.

An axe is not suitable for pruning because it leaves spikes and pitch hollows. The best tool is a sharp saw with from 6 to 8 teeth per inch, mounted on a pole, when pruning above the hand's reach. Cut the branches cleanly, flush with the trunk so that no stubs are left, to provide good healing and to prevent rot. Live branches over 1½ in. thick should not be pruned.

SILVICULTURAL SYSTEMS USED IN HARVEST CUTTINGS

Applied forestry differs from unplanned logging in that specific systematic methods are followed in choosing the trees to be cut. A number of silvicultural systems originally developed in Europe are being adapted to the requirements of our own forests as they are put under management programs. Properly managed forests yield much greater volumes of better quality wood over the long run than do lands on which unplanned logging is done. But destructive cutting usually yields a heavier immediate volume, and that is why so much of it is still done, especially on small holdings. Many years elapse before such timber lands may again be harvested.

The objective of a silvicultural system is to obtain new forest growth through natural means. Reproduction of the forest may be obtained either from seed, stump sprouts, or root suckers. Silvicultural systems take into account one or more of these by securing new growth after cutting. The principal systems most generally followed on managed forests are: clearcutting either in strips or blocks; the seed tree method; the shelterwood system; the selection system; and clearcutting and planting, or direct seeding.

These silvicultural systems are intended for forests which have a volume of mature timber ready for harvesting. Because so many American forests have been carelessly handled in the past, the systems which are described may not always fit every situation to be found. Variations using several systems are frequently employed to fit timber type and species combinations, topography, and local market conditions. Each system must be considered a theoretically ideal procedure, needing modification in actual practice on the ground. Natural reproduction, if inadequate, is often supplemented by planting young trees in open spaces.

The choice of the proper harvesting method depends upon a number of factors, of which the following are of major importance:

1. It must fit the peculiar characteristics and silvical requirements of the forest type and species.
2. It must supply a sufficient volume of forest products to permit efficient logging and favorable marketing.
3. It should result in prompt restocking of desirable species and have a beneficial result on all valuable residual trees on the land, so far as possible. (An exception to this last factor is the several clearcutting systems which do not leave any residual trees of value.)

Some species reproduce themselves quite easily from seeds or from sprouts; others are slow and difficult and often require supplemental forest planting if the right proportions of desirable species are to be obtained. As a practical matter, the kind of silvicultural system to be followed on any tract should be chosen to obtain restocking at the earliest possible time after cutting, or to do the least damage and give the greatest stimulus to residual trees; but if the area does not restock naturally, supplemental planting will be required. The following description of each method sets forth the types and species to which it is best suited, its advantages and disadvantages, and other pertinent information.

Clearcutting Systems

When clearcutting is used in the management of a forest, it may be done in a variety of ways, each one of which is designed to bring about a new growth of reproduction following cutting.

The variations of this method described below are usually applied to forest situations which meet one or more of the following conditions:

1. Intolerant trees which need full sunlight for germination of the seed and development of the seedlings.
2. Shallow-rooted species or those growing in exposed places where there is danger of the whole stand being thrown by the wind.
3. Even-aged stands of species which must develop uniformly in order to provide merchantable growing stock.
4. Success can be achieved only where there are light-seeded species easily windborne into the cutover areas.
5. Where whole stands are overmature, clearcutting is needed to utilize the merchantable material without wasting it.
6. Where opening up the site does not encourage a growth of shrubs before valuable tree seedlings become established.

Clearcutting of any type has the disadvantages (a) of overexposing some sensitive sites to drying out by the sun and wind, (b) of gravely impairing natural reproduction (often causing planting costs), (c) of leaving large areas of slash which are a fire hazard, and (d) of leaving the soil susceptible to erosion. In spite of these disadvantages, which at first appear quite serious, the method can be useful when it is properly applied and modified in the following ways:

Clearcutting in Strips or Blocks. In order to avoid some of the disadvantages resulting from clearcutting large areas, some forest types may be handled by cutting alternate strips or blocks and patches. Areas of uncut timber on the side of the prevailing winds are left standing for a time long enough to reseed the cutover areas, after which they are cut. For species which reproduce easily, such as jack and lodgepole pine, Douglas fir, western larch, and black spruce, the clearcutting method in strips or blocks not too large to allow for quick blowdown is acceptable forestry practice (Fig. 5–5).

Southern pine has been successfully regenerated by clearing and disking strips 200 to 300 feet wide and leaving intervening seed source strips of standing timber about 66 feet in width. Livestock must be kept out of young seedling areas for 8 to 10 years to avoid serious losses.

The Seed-Tree Method. This variation of the clearcutting system leaves scattered windfirm trees at intervals close enough

Fig. 5–5. Block clearcutting in Douglas fir in the Pacific Northwest. Block cutting is necessary because Douglas fir seedlings will not grow in the shade of larger trees. (American Forests Products Industries, Inc.)

to provide adequate seeding for establishment of the new crop of trees. It has the disadvantage of loss of seed trees by blowdown and difficulty of salvage of the seed trees after the new growth has started because of the damage caused in logging. In some of the northern pine types the seed-tree method has been tried without much success because of heavy invasion of brush. Longleaf pine in the South has been managed with good results by this system.

It is essential that sound, large-crowned windfirm trees be left standing if maximum seeding is to be obtained. Seed trees may be left singly or in small groups in order to have the advantages of mutual protection. The required number of seed trees depends upon the species and its ability to produce seed. In most cases five or ten trees per acre are the minimum needed. They should be left for at least five years, or until adequate reproduction is established.

Clearcutting and Planting. Some species, such as Norway (red) pine, do not reproduce very quickly and are soon prevented from doing so by the invasion of brush. If clearcutting is practiced, the only sure way of obtaining reproduction with this situation is to follow immediately with planting. In some forest types it is more satisfactory and economical to plant immediately after cutting because of the time saved in establishing the new forest and the assurance of proper density of stocking. This method is widely practiced with Douglas fir in the Pacific Northwest.

The Coppice System. This system of silviculture is applicable only to species which sprout easily from both the stumps and roots. Essentially, it is a variation of the clearcutting method except that sprout reproduction is relied upon entirely to bring about the next stand.

The coppice method is successful in the aspen type of the Lake States because this species begins to put up root sprouts (suckers) the first year after cutting. It has been found that better sprouting takes place on winter-logged areas than on those where summer logging has been followed.

The Selection System (Selective Cutting)

Cutting is called selective when each tree cut is chosen with regard to its present position in the stand and future possibilities for growth. This system is naturally suited to all-aged and uneven-aged woodlands, especially the hardwoods. Clearcutting, high-grading (removing the best and leaving the poorest trees) and diameter-limit cutting* usually are a drastic shock to the forest, whereas properly conducted selective cutting merely works with Nature by removing the older trees to make room for the younger ones.

The selection system has many silvicultural advantages. It affords good site protection, windfall is kept to a minimum, reproduction is easy and certain, fire hazard is kept low and slash is scattered, and cutting can be adjusted to fit market conditions. Its main disadvantages are economic: logging costs may increase

---

* Cutting all trees above a certain diameter and leaving all others below, regardless of quality, condition, or position in the stand.

because light volumes are removed at frequent intervals and heavy investments in growing stock are required. Furthermore, damage to residual trees may be severe at times.

Selective cutting is very simple in a well-stocked, all-aged forest. The older and larger trees are marked and cut as they reach maturity. The growth of younger adjacent trees is accelerated while the seedlings readily develop in the small openings made by cutting. Frequent light cuttings at five- or ten-year intervals tend to keep up the quality of the growing stock.

Unmanaged and neglected woodlands often contain some trees of inferior species, as well as deformed, diseased, and partly decayed trees. Trees may be too scattered or be so crowded that their growth has almost stopped. Selective cutting in such cases offers excellent opportunities for harvesting wood while at the same time improving the spacing and increasing the rate of growth (Fig. 5–6).

Under careless cutting, which removes the best trees and leaves the worst, the forest would cease to be an efficient wood producer. The aim of selective cutting is just the opposite; such poor mate-

Fig. 5–6. All-aged northern hardwood–hemlock stand. *Above*, before selective cutting. The trees to be felled are those with a line drawn through the trunk. *Below*, residual stand ten years after selective cutting.

rial as can be used should be taken along with "the cream." How far this should be carried depends upon the kind of forest, on the availability of markets, and on the need for improving the forest in order to improve future yields in both quality and quantity.

Proper cutting in an overcrowded forest releases the best trees and improves their growth. Cutting too heavily so as to leave only a few trees exposed has just the opposite effect. They receive a shock from which they may not recover. Trees need the protection of one another. Trees suddenly released from the protection of other trees removed by heavy cuttings may be blown over by the wind or injured by frost or sun scald. A high wind can uproot shallow-rooted species or trees growing on shallow or wet soil; prolonged exposure to wind may weaken or kill them gradually by weakening their roots and increasing evaporation from their foliage. Slender tall trees with brittle wood (such as spruce or fir), break off easily. All of these reasons dictate the desirability of partial cuttings.

The following rules will be helpful in choosing the right trees in selection cuttings:

1. Mark for harvest all overmature trees which are making little if any growth.
2. Immature, thrifty, fast-growing trees of better species should be left standing.
3. In clumps of trees growing too thickly, remove the poorer specimens and inferior species.
4. Aim for proper spacing even if it means leaving a few trees which should ordinarily be cut. This will assure continuation of proper forest conditions.
5. Remove defective, poorly formed trees of valuable species for which there is a market. Leave one per two acres (or girdle but leave standing) for den, nesting, or wildlife food.
6. Try to release the maximum number of thrifty young saplings and poles without too sudden an overexposure to sun and wind.
7. Make light cuts at frequent intervals (five or ten years). This will encourage regular growth acceleration and greater growth rate. Heavier cuts at long intervals disturb a forest more severely.

The Shelterwood System

This method combines some of the features of clearcutting with those of selective cutting and is applied to even-aged stands or uneven-aged stands with large trees in the majority. Some of the more shade-tolerant species such as white pine, sugar pine, red-wood, etc., need to have some shade during their first years, and a partial cover supplies this. Under the shelterwood method the stand is removed in two, three, or more cuts several years apart, with the poorest timber being taken first. The best trees which are left may put on some fast growth for a period but, more important, they continue to supply seed so as to assure an adequate growth of seedlings on the ground. The system is used mainly in pon-derosa, Norway (red), and white pine and in the southern pine forest types.

The series of shelterwood cuttings is divided into three phases: *preparatory cutting, seed cutting,* and *removal cutting.* The pre-paratory cutting removes only the most mature, defective, and other trees whose absence will benefit the residual stand. Open-ings are created which are not so large as to encourage undesir-able brush but large enough to allow enough light to stimulate seedling growth. Usually not more than one-third to one-fourth of the volume in the largest trees is removed in the preparatory cut. The residual trees serve as continual sources of new seed to assure adequate restocking.

The seed cutting is the heaviest harvest cutting and is usually timed right after a good seed year so as to encourage the most abundant reproduction in the additional open space made avail-able. The trees marked in a seed cutting include all of the remain-ing slower growing and intermediate trees, while the very best windfirm dominants are left to stand. About 30 to 60 per cent of the remaining volume is taken in this cutting (Fig. 5–7). Natural regeneration can often be greatly stimulated by mechanical scari-fication of the soil to improve the seed bed and reduce brush invasions.

The final or removal cutting takes place after reproduction is well established. All merchantable timber is cut from the area.

The shelterwood system has several advantages. Brush and un-desirable hardwoods can be kept fairly well under control while seedlings start up; reforestation is accomplished by nature; seed-lings develop from the choicest seed trees, thereby giving some control over the quality of the new forest; the change in forest conditions is gradual, not sudden, so the seedlings and the soil can adapt themselves more readily to the change in the forest environ-ment; and finally, the trees left standing after the first and second cuts will accelerate in growth and produce wood more rapidly as

Fig. 5–7. Shelterwood cutting in southern pine in which 15 to 20 of the best trees are reserved per acre for seed production shelter and long rotation quality growth. After seedlings are established, the overstory will be removed. (U. S. Forest Service)

a result of increased light and lessened competition for moisture and soil nutrients.

The shelterwood system's disadvantages are that it takes considerable skill, reproduction may be damaged in the second and third cuts, prices and markets may not fit silvicultural timing, and logging may be more expensive.

OTHER ASPECTS OF HARVEST CUTTING

Marking Mature Timber for Harvest

Proper selection of the trees to be cut and those to be left under any partial cutting system is one of the most critical and responsible of forest jobs. It should be done with care, well in advance of cutting, and by experienced men. The importance of proper marking is so great that the time it requires certainly should be considered well invested. It takes the forest many years to replace wasted timber. The trees to be cut are marked by axe blazes or spotted with paint on the trunk *and* on the butt (to serve as a check on loggers). Although axes are still used for marking timber, paint guns make it possible for a good marker to cover a larger forest area in a day. Most paint guns are simply quart cans equipped with a nozzle and a handle. The paint (usually yellow) is diluted 50 per cent with kerosene to make a freer-flowing liquid (Fig. 5–8).

Blazes or paint spots should all face one direction, preferably toward the nearest logging road. Ordinarily only trees to be cut are marked, but in dense stands those that are to be left standing are marked. Under this system, blazes should not go into the wood because injury to the tree may result.

The external evidences of trees to be marked are:

1. Dead limbs in the top of the tree
2. Sparse and yellowish foliage
3. Abnormally rough bark
4. Large size (growth rate should be checked)
5. Crown of tree thinning out noticeably

The other trees which must be considered in timber cutting operations are the damaged or defective trees. These are trees which have been damaged by grazing, fire, insects, or disease, or injured by some other cause such as lightning or previous logging. Some of the things to look for are:

1. The presence of shelf fungus (conks) or decay on the trunk
2. Rotten spots, or hollows, at the base of the tree trunk
3. Many dead limbs in top

Fig. 5–8. Cruising and marking mature 64″ ponderosa pine for timber sale south of Bly, Oregon. (U. S. Bureau of Land Management)

4. Swollen areas on the trunk of the tree indicating internal defect
5. Holes in the trunk
6. Hollow trunk (can be determined by pounding on the trunk)
7. Loose bark or other indications of injury
8. Frost cracks and fire-scarred butts

Defective or damaged trees should be given first consideration in timber harvesting so that they can be removed while there is still a chance to obtain sound logs above or below the point of damage. Also, the removal of defective or damaged trees makes more room for sound, vigorous trees of desirable kinds which will produce high returns in future growth.

Keep the following factors in mind when selecting trees to be harvested under partial cutting systems:

1. Leave the woods borders as dense as possible. This reduces wind damage to trees in the woods and provides cover for wildlife.
2. Remember that cutting too heavily will open the woods to drying sun and wind and will cause mortality.
3. Remember that *condition* of the tree, and not *size*, should be the first consideration as to whether to cut it or leave it.
4. If the stand is understocked, the volume of timber cut in any one period should be slightly less than the net growth for the same period. This method of cutting will insure continuous timber crops.

Except for stands with undergrowth, it is preferable to mark while the trees are leafed out, so that dead and dying trees can be easily recognized. But be sure to leave occasional nesting and den trees to maintain a good ecological balance between trees and wildlife.

To control the volume and species of wood to be marked for cutting from an area, the trees should be tallied, according to their size and species, as they are marked. This is explained in the next chapter.

Preparation of the Soil for Natural Reproduction

Skidding logs in many types of forest with an open soil free of brush before cutting will make a perfect seedbed for germination of seeds. But in many areas underbrush of various kinds such as hazel brush in the Lake States and inferior oak sprouts in the South soon invade after cutting and take over good forest growing soil. A number of measures have been developed to eliminate brush and open up the soil for reception of tree seeds.

Just prior to or immediately following logging (if slash is not too abundant), it has been found that disking the cutover areas with a large bull disk pulled by a crawler tractor will turn up subsoil essential for a good seedbed while setting brush back quite effectively. This is called *mechanical scarification*. From here on it is a race between the regrowth of the inferior tree sprouts and brush and the development of the new seedlings.

Chemical Control of Brush Species

If sprouts are already present in addition to brush, a much more difficult problem must be dealt with. Chemical brush killing is the quickest and most satisfactory method of controlling these unwanted growths, but this must be done with care. Hormone-type herbicides (2,4-D and 2,4,5-T esters)* are commercially available and, when diluted as sprays, are effective in killing most types of shrubs and sprouts. The sprays are applied either as a mist on the foliage, or at the base of the tree or shrub. Consider-able research has been done with these sprays by the Forest Service Experiment Stations and manufacturers.

There are some secondary aspects to brush control over wide areas which need to be carefully considered. The danger of de-stroying wildlife habitats and their supply of food for birds and animals, plus other secondary ecological unbalances which may occur, dictate very careful brush removal plans which give con-sideration to all these factors.

In the South and other areas where young hardwoods of weed species may dominate the site, the use of ammonium sulfate (a yellow crystalline, toxic salt) is applied to stumps to stop sprout-ing and to girdled trees to bring rapid death. Since this salt is not poisonous to animals, it is less dangerous to use than sodium arsenite, another chemical used for this purpose.

The following directions have been developed by the Soil Con-servation Service for use by landowners and technical men in the field:

Method 1. *Basal wetting.* Use on trees 2 in. or less and small stumps. Apply solution of 1 part 2,4,5-T to 20 parts diesel fuel or kero-sene, saturating bark and exposed roots all around up to knee height. When applied to stumps, a paint brush will waste less solution; the number and vigor of sprouts will be reduced.

Method 2. *Frilling.* Make a ring of overlapping axe cuts around the tree at a convenient height. Wet the frill by pouring in one of the following solutions: (a) Four lbs. of Ammate crystals per gallon of water; or (b) 1 part 2,4,5-T to 20 parts diesel fuel or kerosene. To re-duce waste, apply oil solution with hand gun. Kills trees in one to three years. A mechanical girdler can be used instead of an axe.

Method 3. *Foliage Spray.* To release pine seedlings from brush competition, spray leaf surface of brush in August or September with 1 part 2,4,5-T to 100 parts of water. The leaves of the brush should be wet, but try to keep spray off the pines, although a little is not harm-ful. Brush will be killed or stunted so pine can get through.†

* See section on "Caring for the Young Forest Plantation" in this chapter.
† See weed control methods under "Caring for the Young Forest Plantation" in this chapter.

ARTIFICIAL REFORESTATION

When nature has failed to seed in a new crop of trees on cut-over land, where forest lands are too thinly stocked, or where it is desired to reforest open lands such as old fields, artificial planting is needed. More than 10 million acres are presently in need of planting if they are to become productive. Some of this acreage may not be needed for future timber crops and some of it may be too poor to yield profitably, but much of it will eventually be restored to tree growth by planting. Prior to World War II, federal and state forestry agencies did most of the planting, but today small owners and big companies are engaged in extensive planting efforts amounting to hundreds of thousands of acres annually. Reforestation is an expensive operation and is undertaken to speed up restocking more rapidly than under natural conditions.

Choice of Species for the Planting Site

Before starting out on a reforestation program, a good deal of advance planning is essential. Proper choice of tree species depends upon location of the area and the kind of soils available. Generally speaking, coniferous seedlings or transplant stock are favored because most hardwoods reproduce well naturally. Fig. 5–9 shows the species which are generally adapted to planting in the several climatic areas in the United States. However, the planting of species native (indigenous) to the area, grown from seed collected from nearby stands, offers the surest road to success in forest planting. If nonnative, exotic species are planted, they should be only those which have already been demonstrated to be successful on other nearby forest plantations.

The soil preferences of the different species are given in Chapter 3, which may serve as a guide in selecting proper species at each location. Failure to fit species to the site may result in losses, and advance soil tests should be carried out if any doubt exists. One of the best soil tests is to learn which species grew on the area previously even though it may now be too exposed to replant the same species. Keep in mind species found in temporary or transition types for planting on open lands. Climax species often do well for underplanting in poorly stocked stands.

Seasons for Tree Planting

Seedlings should be ordered weeks, months, or even a full year ahead of the date desired; they should be lifted and distributed

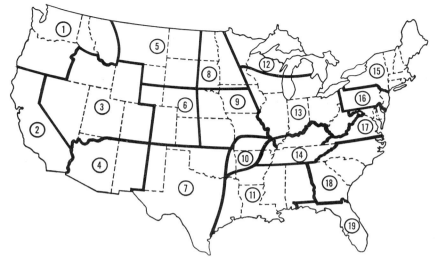

1. Douglas fir, western white pine, ponderosa pine.
2. Redwood, ponderosa pine, Douglas fir, white fir, Sitka spruce, Monterey pine, Monterey cypress, sequoia.
3. Ponderosa pine, Douglas fir, blue spruce, white fir.
4. Ponderosa pine, blue spruce, Arizona cypress, Rocky Mountain red cedar, Austrian pine, Chinese arborvitae.
5. Jack pine, white spruce, eastern red cedar, ponderosa pine.
6. Jack pine, ponderosa pine, eastern red cedar, western white spruce.
7. Eastern red cedar, ponderosa pine, Arizona cypress, Chinese arborvitae, one-seed juniper.
8. Ponderosa pine, white spruce, jack pine, European larch, northern white cedar.
9. Norway spruce, white spruce, blue spruce, eastern white pine, western white spruce, European larch, northern white cedar, eastern red cedar.

10. Shortleaf pine, eastern red cedar.
11. Loblolly pine, shortleaf pine, slash pine, longleaf pine, eastern red cedar, southern cypress.
12. Eastern white pine, red pine, jack pine, white spruce, balsam fir.
13. Eastern white pine, jack pine, Norway spruce, white spruce, blue spruce, northern white cedar, European larch, Douglas fir.
14. Shortleaf pine, eastern white pine.
15. White spruce, Norway spruce, eastern white pine, red pine, jack pine, European larch, northern white cedar.
16. Eastern white pine, red pine, pitch pine, northern white cedar, Norway spruce, European larch, white spruce.
17. Shortleaf pine, loblolly pine, eastern white pine, southern cypress, Norway spruce.
18. Loblolly pine, shortleaf pine, longleaf pine, slash pine, eastern white pine, Norway spruce, eastern red cedar, southern cypress.
19. Slash pine, longleaf pine, loblolly pine, southern red cedar, southern cypress.

Fig. 5–9. Recommended species for forest planting, by climatic zones. Where exotic species are listed, planting stock should come from seed collected from locally proven trees.

from the nursery during the dormant period for tree growth. Late winter (in the South) or spring planting (in the North) is usually preferable to fall planting because the small trees have more opportunity to develop their root systems during the ensuing growing season.

The seedlings should be planted promptly after they are received from the nursery. If planting cannot be done within a day or two, the seedlings should be "heeled in" temporarily and lifted again as needed. Early planting is desirable because the small trees can become established, ready for growth when warm weather starts. Late plantings may suffer loss of advance root growth.

Reforestation Methods

The two methods most commonly used in artificial reforestation are (a) direct seeding (sowing the area to be reforested with seeds), and (b) planting nursery-grown seedlings. The choice of the method depends on several important factors such as expense, time required, availability of seedlings, and chances of success. The two methods are described as follows:

Direct Seeding. Until recently direct seeding of pine and Douglas fir has been considered quite risky with heavy losses of seedlings. However, with proper ground preparation and the use of chemical repellents, which discourage birds and rodents from eating the seed, survival is more successful. This is especially true on recently logged or thoroughly scarified land where mineral soil or churned-up humus provides a favorable seed bed. Tractors with bull discs are used in heavy brush on recently cut areas to prepare the seed bed particularly in the Southern pine and West Coast Douglas fir areas. On extensive areas, seed is distributed by special attachments to helicopters, airplanes, or tractors. Hand seeding from old fashioned cyclone seeders is commonly used in smaller patches where thorough ground scarification has been done in advance.

The direct seeding method lends itself to use of machinery and reduction of hand labor. In addition to high machinery costs seed must be distributed abundantly in order to obtain desirable stocking of seedlings. This method can be considered most economical on large private or public forest tracts. Smaller tract owners are better advised to use seedling trees for planting success—especially where brush and predators interfere with seedling germination. Spot planting of oak, walnut, or other hardwoods is frequently used by small owners in the Central hardwood regions.

Optimum conditions for seeding occur either in late autumn or early spring for previously disked sites. Moisture will have thoroughly penetrated the soil and new seedlings are thus able to resist drought should dry weather follow. A sowing rate of 3 pounds of dewinged and chemically treated coniferous seed per acre has been found to give full stocking of seedlings on undisked lands; whereas 1½ pounds will suffice on scarified areas.

Field Planting. Planting of nursery-grown stock gives the best results. Seedlings can be grown to the proper size and with proper root development in nursery beds. The whole process of gathering seed, preparing soil, seeding, protecting the seedlings from insects and diseases, and lifting and packaging can be efficiently organized so as to produce seedlings in abundance and at a reasonable cost. Nursery-grown seedlings* have been used with very little failure, due to their vigorous root systems. The forest manager can decide on the number of seedlings to be grown per acre and act accordingly. This measure of control may save the cost of the early thinning of young natural stands or direct-seeded stands, as well as the loss of growth due to overcrowding.

By obtaining stock from a forest nursery many problems involved in obtaining seed and growing seedlings are eliminated. Large state, federal, or company nurseries produce high quality stock, relatively free of injury and disease, and of the proper size and development for planting. Consideration is given to selection of tree seed from quality parent trees adapted to local conditions. The large nurseries produce many million seedlings at a cost lower than most owners can grow them. Nursery stock comes properly wrapped and in excellent condition for planting and gives results that are simpler and surer, on the average, than from home-grown seedlings.

Preparatory Considerations

Proper Spacing. The spacing to be followed in planting tree seedlings depends on the cost of planting, the rate of growth of the trees, and the nature of the products for which the trees are to be used. Close spacing gives a quicker cover of the soil. Therefore, spacings such as 4' × 4', 4' × 5', and 5' × 5' are used for Christmas trees and erosion control plantings. Close spacing up to 6' × 6' results in early killing of the side branches and hence permits the development of trees with a greater percentage of clear wood free of knots.

Close spacing utilizes the available soil, water, air, and sunlight more fully, and hence produces a greater volume of wood in a

---

* The term "seedlings" as used here also includes transplanted nursery stock. A seedling which has been in the seedbed 2 years is called 2–0 stock. Stock which has been in the seedbed 2 years and in the transplant bed 2 years is called 2–2 transplants, and so on.

shorter period. If a close-spaced stand is kept properly thinned, it will produce a greater volume of usable wood products. If such a stand is not thinned, it will become crowded early and will require more years to make merchantable size in either pulpwood or sawlogs than a more open or thinned stand. By planning the spacing so that an early thinning will be required, the trees to be removed can be used or sold. Close spacing, such as 4′ × 4′ and 5′ × 5′, will usually benefit from early thinnings for Christmas trees before the trees can be sold for pulpwood. A 6′ × 6′ spacing is often used when no early thinnings are planned. The optimum number of seedlings for different spacing, per acre, is as follows:

Spacing	Number of Seedlings
4 ft. × 4 ft.	2,722 per acre
5 ft. × 5 ft.	1,742 per acre
6 ft. × 6 ft.	1,210 per acre
8 ft. × 8 ft.	680 per acre

Wide spacing allows each tree more room in which to grow and the tree does not shed its lower branches as early or as thoroughly. As a result, the trunk has more and larger limbs, and the forest products, such as lumber, have more knots. Products from limby trees are of lower quality and value.

Preparing the Land. Seedlings grow faster in old fields than in land not previously cultivated because there is usually less competition from grass and brush. Where heavy sod or brush is encountered, the land is usually furrowed with a plow in advance of hand planting. If this is not possible, the tree planter usually "scalps" off sod with a mattock to lessen competition. Areas with very heavy growths of such undesirable species as scrub oak may have to be killed by chemicals or partially cleared prior to planting. When there is no use for the wood, killing by girdling or felling is often done.

Caring for Nursery Planting Stock. Seedlings from private and state nurseries come properly packaged with the roots moistened and protected against drying. The tree roots must be kept cool and moist. Purchased seedlings represent an expenditure which should be safeguarded. This can best be done by the proper care of planting stock, as follows:

1. Be on the lookout for the shipment of seedlings and accept them promptly.
2. Do not let seedlings freeze or heat up while in bales, or dry out as they are opened.

3. Carry seedlings to the planting site without delay, or "heel in" in a cool, moist place protected from the sun and wind. They will keep well for several weeks.
4. Use the following practices when "heeling in":
   a. Dig a V-shaped trench in a moist, shady place.
   b. Break bundles and spread roots out evenly.
   c. Cover roots with loose soil at the same level as they grew (do not bury tops) and dampen with water.
   d. Complete filling in soil and tramp firmly with feet to pack soil on roots.

Handling Seedlings at Planting Time.
1. When ready to plant be sure to have sufficient tools, water, and buckets for handling and planting.
2. Keep the seedling roots moist until planted.
3. Do not unnecessarily delay or prolong planting.
4. Read the planting instructions carefully and follow them closely.

Field Planting Methods

Tree seedlings may be planted with the use of hand tools such as a dibble, shovel, mattock, or post-hole augur. They may also be planted with a tractor and planting machine. For small areas, and where labor is available, hand planting will serve. It can be hastened if the ground is furrowed with a plow ahead of the planting. For large areas, machine planting may prove less expensive and equally successful. Whatever the planting method, use precautions to get the correct depth of planting. A safe rule is to put the tree in the ground with the roots at the same depth as they grew in the nursery. Most trees will die if planted too high or too low.

Mixed plantings of most species of conifers are considered to be more insect- and disease-proof than pure stands. Furthermore a loss of one species—if infestation hits a mixed stand—does not wipe out the years of work and growth that have taken place.

On slopes where trees are often planted to control soil erosion it is very important to place furrows and plant trees on the contour. Furrows off the contour can lead to serious gullying. Furthermore, contoured furrows will not only prevent erosion but act as water catchments essential to the life of a new struggling seedling.

Hand Planting. Methods of planting by hand are shown in Figs. 5–10 and 5–11.

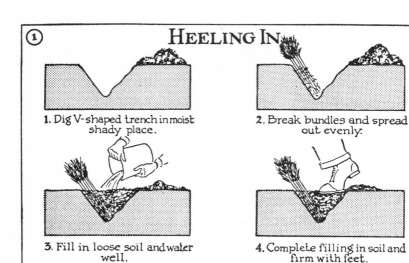

HEELING IN

1. Dig V-shaped trench in moist shady place.

2. Break bundles and spread out evenly.

3. Fill in loose soil and water well.

4. Complete filling in soil and firm with feet.

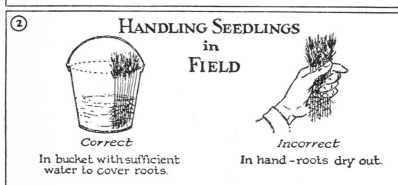

HANDLING SEEDLINGS
in
FIELD

Correct
In bucket with sufficient water to cover roots.

Incorrect
In hand - roots dry out.

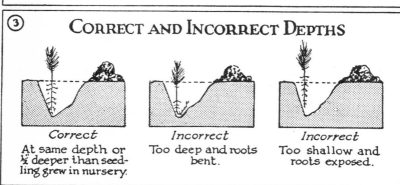

CORRECT AND INCORRECT DEPTHS

Correct
At same depth or ½ deeper than seedling grew in nursery.

Incorrect
Too deep and roots bent.

Incorrect
Too shallow and roots exposed.

Fig. 5–10. Hand-planting methods. (From *Forestry Handbook*, edited by Reginald D. Forbes and Arthur B. Meyer for the Society of American Foresters. Copyright, 1955, by The Ronald Press Company, New York)

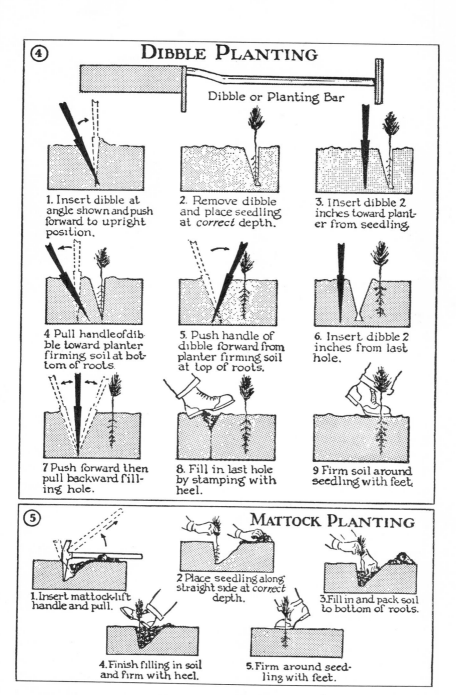

④ DIBBLE PLANTING

Dibble or Planting Bar

1. Insert dibble at angle shown and push forward to upright position.

2. Remove dibble and place seedling at *correct* depth.

3. Insert dibble 2 inches toward planter from seedling.

4 Pull handle of dibble toward planter firming soil at bottom of roots.

5. Push handle of dibble forward from planter firming soil at top of roots.

6. Insert dibble 2 inches from last hole.

7 Push forward then pull backward filling hole.

8. Fill in last hole by stamping with heel.

9 Firm soil around seedling with feet.

⑤ MATTOCK PLANTING

1. Insert mattock-lift handle and pull.

2 Place seedling along straight side at *correct* depth.

3. Fill in and pack soil to bottom of roots.

4. Finish filling in soil and firm with heel.

5. Firm around seedling with feet.

Fig. 5–10. *(Continued)*

91

Fig. 5–11. Southern farmer plants loblolly pine seedlings in gully on his farm. (U. S. Forest Service)

Machine Planting. Several planting machines are now on the market, and in some areas such machines are available for hire. In many localities, banks or other civic-minded groups will furnish a planting machine at a modest charge. Use of the machine is recommended for a large area where there are not too many obstacles such as standing trees, gulleys, stumps, or rocks. Seedlings may be planted by machinery at the rate of about 1,000 per hour. The costs are relatively lower than for hand planting. The principles given for hand planting should be followed when using machine planting (Fig. 5–12).

Until recently most tree planting was done in old fields but new machinery using crawler tractors with brush cutters and heavy plows are successfully converting low quality brush and poor tree areas to productive forests. The higher cost of this method is offset by low land costs and thus makes it economically feasible. This one process of brush clearing-tree planting is also useful in recently logged areas where heavy slash would prohibit use of the standard equipment.

Fig. 5–12. Typical tree-planting machine. (From *Forestry Handbook*, edited by Reginald D. Forbes and Arthur B. Meyer for the Society of American Foresters. Copyright, 1955, by The Ronald Press Company, New York)

Chemical Fertilizers to Stimulate Growth

Because some forest soils (especially sandy plains) are often deficient in certain plant nutrients, growth rates are slow. Research has found that providing supplemental nourishment through chemical fertilizers will stimulate growth for periods up to ten or twelve years. Before using fertilizers forest owners should have their soils tested (collected samples should be taken to the County Agricultural Agent) to determine what deficiencies exist. Forest soil fertilizers are available in pellet or cake form inserted through a hole punched in the ground near the trunk.

Soil tests may show a lack of trace elements needed for tree growth. These can be easily supplied through the powdered chemical in the form most easily available to the tree. It is not yet clear through research whether chemical fertilizers are economical to use—that is, whether their costs are equal to or exceed the value of the growth increase.

Taking Soil Samples

Methods and procedures for taking soil samples vary considerably depending upon the purpose and information desired. However, for routine testing to obtain information regarding lime requirements, organic matter, and the amounts of available nutrients in the plow layer, the following procedure is recommended:

1. Take samples with a soil auger, sampling tube, or a spade to a depth of 6" or 7" (see illustrations).

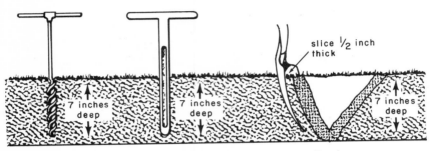

Wood Auger   Soil Sampling Tube   Spade

2. Collect samples, 4 to 6 sites from fields that are relatively uniform as to soil type (color, texture, drainage, and productivity). Thoroughly mix and place portion (about a cupful) in the sampling bag to be sent to the laboratory.
3. Never mix samples from soils of distinctively different color, texture, drainage, or productivity. These samples should be taken and tested separately.
4. Avoid unusual spots, such as dead furrows, near fences and roads, and places which may have received excessive amounts of crop residues, manure, lime, or fertilizer.
5. Clean paper or cloth bags are most convenient containers for soil samples. It is very important to number or mark these bags or containers so that there will be no question as to the farm, field, and portion of the field from which the sample came. Where forest maps are available the sampling spots should be indicated by number on this map.

CARING FOR THE YOUNG FOREST PLANTATION

Young trees, whether they are planted or grown naturally, require special care, such as:

1. Young seedlings are easily killed by fire and must be protected. A good road system in and around the plantation assures points from which to backfire. Firebreaks through the planted area

serve to localize possible fires and reduce the chances of complete loss.

2. New plantations usually do not have a 100 per cent "catch" of planted seedlings. This may be due to poor planting methods, dry weather, or other causes. In order to assure complete stocking, these "fail" spots should be replanted by hand the following spring.

3. The young trees should be protected from damage by grazing. Light grazing by cattle may do little harm, but grazing by sheep, goats, and hogs can seriously injure the seedlings. Where the damage from grazing could be serious, livestock should be excluded by fencing. Trampling in clay soils will greatly reduce the capacity of the soil to absorb and store water and will adversely affect tree growth.

4. As the trees grow and become crowded, the forest should be thinned and weeded of the poorly formed, diseased, and otherwise undesirable trees.

5. In some instances it may be necessary to release young seedlings from overtopping by undesirable trees.

6. If early thinnings for Christmas trees are desired, shaping of crop trees by pruning is a highly desirable practice, described later in this chapter.

Forest planting in plantations is increasingly becoming a more important aspect of forestry. This is apparent in the large number of Christmas tree plantations which each year supply a large portion of the national production.

Of great importance, especially during planting time and the early years, is the control of weeds which compete for mineral nutrients, water, and growing space. The fight for survival if the weeds are uncontrolled materially lengthens the maturity and rotation age and results in lower stand densities. This may contribute to the failure or success of a plantation venture.

The weeds can be controlled by mechanical means such as disks and cultivators; however, this type of control after planting, can injure the root systems.

Many new weed control chemicals or herbicides are on the market and the list continues to grow. Some eliminate all vegetation for many years while others are selective and affect only certain groups of plants or certain species within a group. All *must* be used with extreme caution and within the special state laws and manufacturer's directions.

The newer materials available do not destroy the living tissue itself but interfere with various growth processes, such as blocking the making of chlorophyll, breaking down enzymes necessary for certain functions, or blocking some other process.

These materials also have the advantage of being effective in small quantities per acre and may be easily and cheaply applied by mechanical means.

Four well-tested materials—2,4,5-T, amitole, delapon, and simazine—either alone or in combination are quite effective in controlling weeds. These materials are quite safe to handle and with the exception of simazine, they do not accumulate in the soil. If chemicals are applied *after* mowing and *prior* to mid-summer, the best results can be obtained. Annual applications in early summer will be necessary for a year or two on better soils.

2,4,5-T was developed in 1940 and is now a widely accepted silvicultural tool for selective control of woody species with only insignificant effects on most conifers. Generally it is applied with an oil carrier and in some cases an oil and water emulsion. In all operations care should be exercised to avoid having the spray drift to the desirable crop trees or adjoining crop lands.

Delapon is effective against the annual and perennial grasses. It is most effective when the weeds are growing vigorously. A small amount of a wetting agent (detergent) helps to increase the rate at which the plant absorbs and transmits the solution through the plant. Application in late summer will eliminate sod from the area. Over winter the material will decompose or leach out of the soil.

A second application immediately following planting and before new grass emerges should effectively eliminate the weeds during the critical first growing season. It is absorbed readily through the foliage and root system.

Amitole is effective on a large group of broadleaf weeds and grasses and on some woody plants, such as poison ivy and poison oak. It is absorbed readily through the root system and foliage. It is rapidly deactivated by organisms in the soil with little if any remaining. It is usually applied as a direct spray on the weeds to be killed, with care taken not to get the spray on the trees.

Coniferous stands can be precommercially thinned and undesirable hardwoods controlled at a lost cost per acre for labor and chemicals, by using Cacodylic acid and the new "Hypo-Hatchet" or "Hypo-Drill" injectors.

One or two shots kill the crowns of hardwoods within two to

four weeks during the growing season. Dormant season injections produce kills the following spring. The injector or hatchet can be adjusted to inject a predetermined quantity of the chemical into the sap stream of the tree with each blow.

Soil type, climate, species to be controlled, and conditions of growth all affect the rate of application and method used. Recommendation of the manufacturer should be read very carefully and followed. Use for purposes other than that intended by the manufacturer and concentrations other than those which have been proven can lead to unsatisfactory or disastrous results.

Christmas Tree Plantation Management

Plantation-grown Christmas trees are competing with such wild trees as balsam fir, white, black, and red spruce, and red cedar in many large city markets. Scotch, red, and white pine, Douglas fir, Norway spruce, and other species have been extensively planted in old fields for this market. Many people feel that large sums can be made easily in Christmas trees by figuring that in 8 to 12 years 1,200 trees per acre can be sold for $.50 to more than $1.00 each. Too often forgotten is the cost of production, losses, and poor unsalable trees, and the often glutted market for Christmas trees!

In addition to the cost of establishment—often $50 to $100 per acre—taxes, fire protection, pest and weed control, fertilizers, and, particularly, the hand labor required for pruning and shearing in shaping trees should be considered. Shearing to proper shape which is an annual process between the third or fourth year (24" to 30" in height) after planting up to the second year before harvest provides a full well-shaped tree preferred by the consumer. The Virginia State Extension Service gives the following instructions to Christmas tree growers:

Pruning or shearing of pines should be done in the spring and early summer when the new growth (candles) is still soft and succulent, and before it hardens. This period usually ranges from June 1 to July 15, depending upon the section of the United States. It is recommended that white pine be sheared as early as possible. Studies now being conducted at Virginia Polytechnic Institute will add new information as to the optimum time for pruning and shearing.

One method to determine whether height and lateral growth has slowed down or stopped is to observe the needles on the new growth. If the needles lie close to the stem, growth is still active. When the needles start to stand away from the stem cell enlargement is near completion and there will be no further lengthening of the terminal or lateral branches. Too early pruning will result in few buds, slow growth, and dead stubs. In most pine plantations there will be a period of about ten to fifteen days when conditions are ideal for pruning or shearing. If the trees are pruned too late, the new buds will be small, and new growth the following year will have a bird's nest effect. The pruning or shearing of spruce or fir can be done at any time of the year, but best results are obtained if the work is done while the trees are dormant during late fall and winter.

How to Prune

Pine. Start by cutting the terminal (leader) branch to desired length, usually about 12"; make the cut at a 45° angle; then clip the laterals of the terminal whorl so that they are 3" to 5" shorter than the terminal. Next, proceed around the tree and prune or shear all laterals so as to shape the tree into an inverted cone. Any branches that are too long or irregular may need to be removed back to second-year wood. In most instances, no pruning or shearing should be done during the growing season prior to harvest.

Spruce and Fir. Start pruning by cutting the terminal to proper length, usually eight to twelve inches. Make the cut at a 45° angle at a point just above a good, live single bud. If the cut is made above two or more buds in a cluster, a multiple terminal will develop. To prevent multiple terminals, remove extra buds by pinching or twisting them off. After the terminal is cut, prune the lateral branches so the tree is cone shaped. If there are extra long branches, cut them back.

It must be remembered that the tree needs a handle of approximately 1" for each foot of tree height, plus a little allowance for a fresh cut for mounting the tree in its holder. Some producers, however, speed and improve their harvesting operations by selecting the tree bases and cleaning handles as a routine part of their pruning or shearing operations.

Pruning or shearing is done to develop quality trees. Its refinements are developed through practice, observation of results, and more practice. The producer must develop and maintain a sense of good tree balance and proportion. By following the standards adopted by the Agricultural Marketing Service of the U. S. Department of Agriculture, producers can be assured of the development of the best possible trees.

Tree Color and Fertilizers

The color of Christmas trees corresponds to the total nitrogen content of the needle foliage in combination with trace elements of iron and molybdenum. When total needle nitrogen values are in the vicinity of one per cent, tree color is yellow and needle loss occurs. Trees with dark green foliage have total needle nitrogen values in the vicinity of 1.7 to 1.8 per cent.

Consumer acceptance is greatest for trees with dark color. These are the trees with high needle nitrogen content. The buying public does not care for light-colored, yellowish green trees. Thus many trees that are otherwise acceptable are discarded or never harvested because of inadequate color. With fertilizer treatment, most cases of color deficiency can be overcome, but it should be done experimentally on a few trees to determine the degree of success attainable.

Trees with low needle nitrogen content lose their needles quickly at room temperature. Needle retention is important to the housewife who dislikes the litter of fallen needles around the Christmas tree. Fertilized trees hold up better during shipment into warm areas than nonfertilized trees.

Tree Growth Is Also Related to Nitrogen Supply

Christmas trees can grow from 12″ to 14″ per year without becoming too sparse and losing the desired shape. In many areas, however, the trees fail to grow a foot a year. In some areas, growth is only 3″ to 6″ a year.

The time needed to produce a crop of trees can be greatly reduced by keeping the trees growing as near the allowable maximum of 12″ to 14″ a year as possible. In many cases, this would double the production presently obtained per acre.

For example, if the normal growth rate is 6″ per year, it will take twelve years to grow six feet of tree. With the use of fertilizers, a tree of the same height could be ready for market in seven years. Here soil tests will be needed to assure the proper kind and amount of fertilizers to apply.

QUESTIONS

1. What is the definition of silviculture?
2. What are the two major silvicultural practice groups?
3. Name three kinds of intermediate cuttings in young forests.
4. Select one of the above intermediate cuttings and explain how it will improve the forest.
5. What are some of the benefits of thinning young, even-aged stands?
6. What is the purpose of thinning "from below"?
7. Is clearcutting an accepted forestry practice in some cases? If so, name one species or forest type where it is used.
8. Name three systems of harvesting a forest which leave residual trees on the ground and a forest type in which they are used.
9. What are benefits from pruning young stands?
10. What is meant by "heeling in" nursery seedlings?
11. When planting trees, what is the best depth for setting them?
12. Why should roots of coniferous nursery stock always be kept moist?
13. Give two reasons for close spacing of tree plantations.
14. What benefits come from thinning a dense plantation?

EXERCISES

1. Find an immature forest in need of immediate cuttings, then decide which method is best suited to the situation.
2. On a small part of the tract, using thumb tacks and small squares of white paper, mark those trees which you feel should be removed to improve the stand.
3. Visit a mature stand of timber and decide what silvicultural system is the best method to apply.
4. If it is possible to participate in a reforestation project in your area, spend a day or more planting trees.
5. Examine a recently logged area and determine if the proper cutting method was used.

6

Measuring the Forest

Forest measurements include map making, measuring land areas, and determining timber volumes. Prior to carrying out any forestry program, accurate information on timber supplies, boundaries, and location of the important features of the forest tract is essential.

Forest surveying is usually less intensive and exacting than that on lands which have high values such as city lots and farm lands. Because of this it is usually possible to use a hand or staff compass instead of a transit and to pace distances rather than measure them precisely with a tape. However, in the case of disputes over forest property boundaries, road layouts, and condemnations, transit and tape surveys are made. But for most purposes of forest management, including forest-type mapping and timber cruising, the hand compass and pace, or the staff compass and chain tape methods, make it possible to do much more rapid work. Since these methods can give reasonable accuracy as well as speed, they are the ones which forest technicians are expected to know.

LAND SURVEYING SYSTEMS

There are two major systems for subdividing lands in the United States: the irregular *metes and bounds* method used in the original thirteen colonies, and the *rectangular surveys* which were applied to most of the public lands over the rest of the country. Thomas Jefferson is credited with having been the originator of the rectangular surveys adopted by Congress in 1785.

Metes and bounds survey lines either follow along ridges,

streams, roads, etc., or they follow lines of a specified angle (bearing) and distance from one established corner to the next. Since there is no general system, surveyors must depend on old field notes, titles, etc., for guidance. Forest surveys can be made with only a general knowledge of boundaries, which the owner can usually furnish. Boundary lines, such as roads and fences, which have long been accepted by owners on both sides, become legal boundaries if neither party objects. Often owners must agree arbitrarily on a boundary line.

The rectangular survey system is laid out into square areas (specific exceptions are noted later), the largest of which is a *township* of 6 miles square (23,040 acres), containing 36 sections of 1 square mile each (640 acres). Sections are in turn divided into four quarter sections, and these into 40-acre tracts one-fourth of a mile square (see Fig. 6–1). Forties were not surveyed out in the early surveys, but as land became subdivided, their lines have been "run out." There are exceptions to the above definitions which are discussed in detail in the *Forestry Handbook.**

The basic system in laying out the public lands includes guide lines or *meridians* running north and south, which are crossed by base lines (*parallels*) running east and west. Between the guide meridian lines, the north-south boundary lines of townships are called township lines; and between the *base lines*, the east-west boundary lines are called *range lines*. Townships are described with reference to the *initial point* where the base line crosses the *principal meridian,* as Township 3 North, Range 4 West (T3N R4W).

Because the north-south meridian lines converge at the poles, they are not quite parallel (as are the base lines) and thus require corrections in laying out the townships. This is accomplished by reducing the areas of outside "forties" of the 11 sections on the north and west boundaries of each township.

Boundaries of forest land are marked, at section corners and sometimes at quarter corners, by iron or concrete posts capped with a brass marker indicating their specific location. The earliest surveys were marked with wooden posts, blazed trees, or piles of rock, but most of these have disappeared east of the Great Plains, though many remain in the Western timber country. Early surveys done with a compass instead of a transit were often inaccurate due to local magnetic attraction or error. Since these incorrect corners are the legal corners unless corrected by the

* See Bibliography.

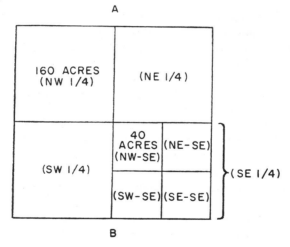

6	5	4	3	2	1
7	8	9	10	11	12
18	17	16	15	14	13
19	20	21	22	23	24
30	29	28	27	26	25
31	32	33	34	35	36

A

B

Fig. 6–1. Subdivisions of government survey lands. (A) Township divided into sections; (B) section divided into quarters and forties.

Bureau of Land Management, many of them still stand today. They can result in greater or lesser acreage in a given forty or section and thus increase or decrease the timber volume present on the description. Blazed trees usually facing the corners were called "witness trees," and "bearing trees" showed the direction and distance to the established corner.

Obtaining base maps for the general area in which the property is located is a first step. These provide the orientation needed in making a forest-cover-type map. Usually the county surveyor or other county official with this duty can obtain maps of the county showing the subdivisions from records in the county court house.

In map making on forest lands, the primary concern is with sections and forties within sections. It will be recalled that groups of four "forties" are called quarter sections. Forties are described as NW-SW, SW-NE, SE-NW, etc. A single forty in a certain section may be described as NE¼ of the SE¼ of Section 9, T2N R1W, with the name of the county often included. These are called "legal descriptions."

MAPPING FOREST AREAS

Measuring Direction

The first rule in mapping an area is accuracy in direction and distance. Direction is determined with a compass, and distance is measured with a surveyor's tape or by pacing. Since forestry maps are *extensive* and not *intensive,* pinpoint accuracy is not required, but the limit of tolerance in error is only within that attributable to the instruments used—not carelessness! A forester's compass is accurate to the degree but not to minutes, and pacing can be reasonably accurate only if constantly checked. Compass and pacing are the most common methods used in forest mapping.

Accurate surveys can be made only when starting from a known point. Established sections or quarter-corners are the most accurate, in areas where they are available. Elsewhere, known property corners or other permanently located points can be made to serve.

Compasses used in forestry are either hand (Fig. 6–2) or staff, the principal difference being that a staff compass is a little steadier and more accurate, but their operation is similar. Since a compass is used to maintain a specific direction, this is always expressed as a *bearing* or as an *azimuth.* The azimuth may be read clockwise from the compass, which shows North as 0 degrees, East as 90°, South as 180°, and West as 270°. Bearings never exceed 90°, are measured from North or South, and divide the circle into quadrants. (See Fig. 6–3.)

To use a hand compass, hold it in both hands with elbows against the body. The needle will usually swing back and forth some time before coming to rest so that a reading must be taken

Fig. 6–2. Standard forester's hand compass, showing bearings and azimuths in compass circle, with township-section grid on inside of cover.

quickly when an average can be sighted. With a levelled staff compass one can let the needle come to rest on the exact bearing being sought. In both types, after locating the bearing through the sighting vane, pick out an object (a particular tree, rock, etc.) toward which one proceeds to the point for the next compass reading.

The better silva compasses make use of sighting, similar to sighting a gun, and a reflecting mirror. The bearing is translated into azimuth and the azimuth is set on the compass. Sighting is

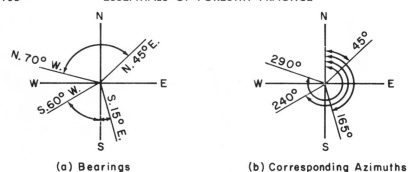

(a) Bearings　　　　　　　(b) Corresponding Azimuths

Fig. 6–3. Bearings and azimuths. (From *Forestry Handbook,* edited by Reginald D. Forbes and Arthur B. Meyer for the Society of American Foresters. Copyright, 1955, by The Ronald Press Company, New York)

done by lining up the compass needle with the arrow etched in the top glass of the compass. This is done by use of the mirror in the hinged cover of the compass, then sighting through the "gunsight" notch to a particular object. The compass is held at eye level.

The construction of a forester's compass (Fig. 6–4) requires

Fig. 6–4. Forester sighting staff compass through sighting vanes on a timber survey. (U. S. Forest Service)

little elaboration here except to draw attention to the 360 degrees shown on the outer circle, to the floating needle which points to magnetic North, and to the sighting vane. Three kinds of errors develop in using a compass: inaccurate readings, accidental, and systematic errors. By taking backsights as well as foresights at each station, with intermediate "ties" to corners and other known points wherever available, systematic errors can be checked (Fig. 6–4). Accidental errors can occur only through failure to read the correct bearing or failure to follow a correct one. Systematic errors can creep in if a compass is out of adjustment, if it has not been corrected for declination, or if it is too close to metal, such as a knife, which may swing the needle from its course. The student is referred to a text on surveying or the *Forestry Handbook** for such information as the correct bearing for adjusting the compass for declination (the magnetic bearing is not quite true North in most places so that the compass must be corrected), for methods used in surveying metes and bounds (traverse running and calculation), and for answers to other problems which may be encountered on different assignments. The forester with whom the technician works can usually be helpful in special field problems which develop on the job.

Measurement of Distance

This is done either with a 2-chain tape, or by pacing at the same time the compass is being used to measure direction. Pacing is the least accurate method but is most commonly used because it is faster and can be done by one man working alone. Here are a few rules for pacing that help to do it accurately:

1. A pace in surveying means two steps. Count double steps only— when your left or your right foot hits the ground, not when each hit.
2. Measure your pacing over known distances (checked by a tape) and through the type of terrain in which you are apt to be working and at a speed which you will normally proceed through the woods. The tendency is to go at a slower, more calculated pace over the measured distance than when pacing in the woods.
3. Keep track of your paces systematically and develop a system such as picking up a small twig for each hundred paces you make. A suggestion is to pace in chains. Keep track in 5 chain intervals as one tally. This makes it easier to measure the dis-

* See Bibliography.

tance. Four tallies or 20 chains to ¼ mile, 8 tallies or 40 chains to ½ mile, 16 tallies or 80 chains to 1 mile.

4. On rough terrain with slopes you will cover less straight-line distance (on the map) than you will be pacing. A rule of thumb is to drop every fifth pace on steep slopes, every tenth on moderate slopes, and on gradual slopes about 1 in 25 will do.

Using a surveyor's tape will give more accuracy but it takes a little more time. Most commonly used is the 2-chain tape with a trailer for compensating on slopes. A chain is 66 ft. in length and graduated into 100 links. Since a "forty" is 20 chains in length (1,320 ft.), the chain tape is a convenient measure. It always requires a two-man crew because the rear end of the tape must be snubbed each time it is moved a full length.

Useful Land Measurement Data

1 chain equals 66 feet.
1 rod equals 16½ feet.
An acre is approximately 208.7 feet square.
An acre contains 43,560 square feet.
A ⅕-acre plot has a radius of 52.7 feet.
A ¼-acre plot has a radius of 58.9 feet.
A ½-acre plot has a radius of 83 feet.
16 forty-acre squares equal 1 section.
36 sections equal 1 township.

Drawing the Map

Mapping the forest area in which one is working is usually done at the same time as estimating the volume of standing timber. More often than not the boundaries of the property are not distinctly marked, so it is necessary to locate corners. In the Eastern states, where metes and bounds are used, the boundary lines will be irregular and will be described as bearings and distances. An example of property lines where metes and bounds prevail is shown in Fig. 6–5.

Mapping such an area requires that one locate the boundaries by starting at the known corner, sight in each bearing as shown, pace the distance to the next corner and repeat the process until one arrives back at the starting point. Use of previous survey notes is invaluable in locating corners in any survey. Surveyors use a mathematical process for "closing" a "traverse" to make sure of accuracy in legal surveys. However, unless there is some question over the boundaries (and a registered surveyor should handle this), the map should serve its purpose, both as a base map and a means of determining the acreage of the tract.

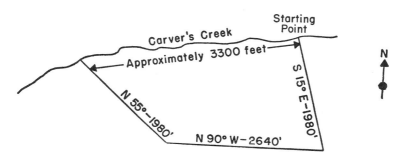

Fig. 6–5. Traverse of property surveyed with metes and bounds.

On lands under the rectangular survey system, the boundaries are run mainly to establish ownership lines for timber sale jobs. The procedure followed in running boundaries is as follows: Starting from an established section corner, the technician simply runs his line on the cardinal points of the compass, measuring distance as he goes, until he reaches the corner of the forty on which he is working. Then he proceeds 20 chains (1,320 ft.) along each side of the forty until the four sides are "boxed."

Forestry maps are drawn in the field and are carried in a clipboard suspended from the shoulder with a leather thong. A map sheet such as that shown is one form similar to those used in rectangular surveys. On more intensive surveys a plane table on a tripod is used for mapping. In addition to determining the area to be covered by the survey, maps serve two other main purposes: the location and extent of the different forest types and the location of important surface features (both man-made and natural) such as roads, power lines, lakes, streams, etc., for future management and logging plans. Maps are always drawn to scale, as for example, 8 in. equal one mile. The symbols used in mapping forest land are shown in the cover-type map in Fig. 6–6. On all forestry maps North is at the top.

All maps should contain the following information:

1. The name or initials of the map maker and the date of the survey.
2. A legend showing the symbols used.

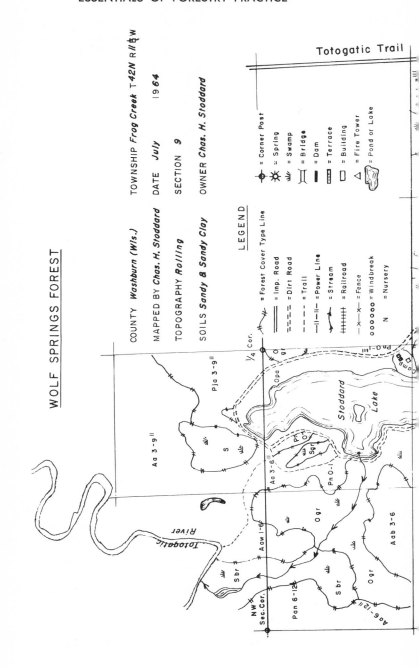

WOLF SPRINGS FOREST

COUNTY *Washburn (Wis.)*   TOWNSHIP *Frog Creek* T *42N* R *11* $\frac{1}{2}$W

MAPPED BY *Chas. H. Stoddard*   DATE *July*   19 *64*

TOPOGRAPHY *Rolling*   SECTION *9*

SOILS *Sandy & Sandy Clay*   OWNER *Chas. H. Stoddard*

LEGEND

= Forest Cover Type Line
= Imp. Road
= Dirt Road
= Trail
= Power Line
= Stream
= Railroad
= Fence
= Windbreak
N = Nursery

= Corner Post
= Spring
= Swamp
= Bridge
= Dam
= Terrace
= Building
= Fire Tower
= Pond or Lake

Totogatic Trail

Totogatic River

Stoddard Lake

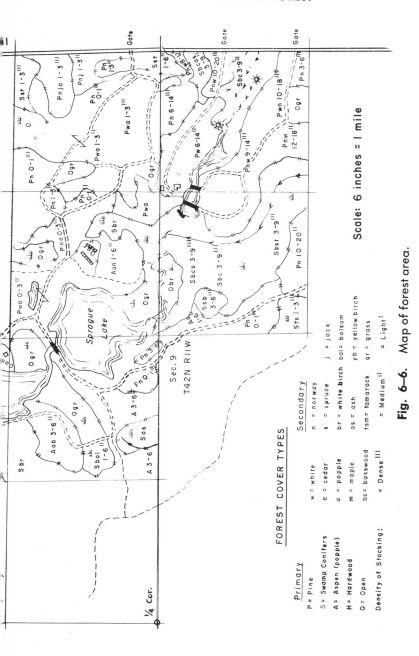

Scale: 6 inches = 1 mile

Fig. 6-6. Map of forest area.

FOREST COVER TYPES

Primary	Secondary	
P = Pine	w = white	n = norway
S = Swamp Conifers	c = cedar	s = spruce
A = Aspen (popple)	a = popple	br = white birch
H = Hardwood	m = maple	as = ash
O = Open	bs = basswood	ram = tamarack
Density of Stocking:	= Dense III	= Medium II

j = jack

bal = balsam

yb = yellow birch

gr = grass

= Light I

   3. The scale used on the map, i.e., 8 inches = one mile, etc.

   4. A title such as "Forest Type Map," "Topographic Map," etc.

When sketching in the forest type symbols such as those shown in Fig. 6–6, stand density and the range in tree sizes are also shown. Along with the symbol of the pine types P, the small letters n and w are shown to indicate that Norway and white pine are the principal species. An aspen type A accompanied by w means an understory of small white pine. The range in diameters is shown simply as 3–9 or 9–12, etc. Stand density is expressed by underlining with one, two, or three bars under the type lettering to show poor, medium or well stocked stands. Thus a completed symbol for a pine type containing Norway and white pine ranging in d.b.h. from 9–12 inches and well stocked would be Pnw 9–12. Medium-stocked long leaf and slash southern pine ranging from 12 to 16 in. d.b.h. would be Pls 12–16. Slash marks as in Pls 12–16″ are often used also.

   One of the important tasks in making forest maps is to keep an accurate check of the distance as one proceeds across forest type boundaries. On the map shown in Fig. 6–6, note how type lines are used to denote a change from pine to swamp conifers. Each of these lines must be drawn in and connected on the map.

   To determine the area enclosed within an irregularly bounded property or within a forest type, the most common procedure used by foresters is the "grid" method (small squares). Although a planimeter is more accurate, it is not always available. Knowing the scale of the map drawn (for example, 8 in. = 1 mile), draw a grid on transparent paper (or take transparent cross-section paper). Each square in the grid represents a known area, such as ½ in. square, which in this case is equal to 2½ acres. Then place the transparent grid upon the map and count all of the grids wholly within the area to be determined and add up the acreage. Then, count all the grids which fall only partly within the boundary line, estimating the proportion lying inside. If it is half, it will be 1¼ acres, and so on. Other fractions must be estimated proportionately if they are more or less than half of the area. Keep an accurate count on a separate sheet of paper and then add up all squares and fractions of squares to arrive at the total acreage. A transparent Modified Dot Acreage Grid, which can be used to determine acreage on maps and aerial photos of any scale, may be purchased through firms that handle forestry supplies.

Aerial Photographs

These can be of inestimable value in making field maps and in demarcating forest types. Practice in their use, followed by ground checking, will disclose the relative ease with which different forest types can be delineated. An example is shown on Fig. 6–7, with

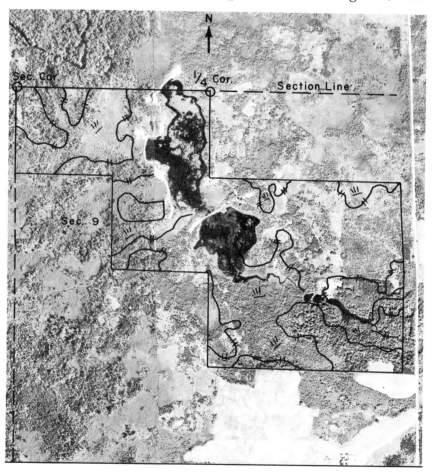

WOLF SPRINGS FOREST
Sec. 9 –T42N, R11W
Washburn County, Wisconsin

Scale: 4" = 1 mile

⁀—H⁀— Forest Type Line

Fig. 6–7. Aerial photograph of forest area mapped in Fig. 6–6, with compartments delineated.

lines added to show compartment boundaries. Roads, waterways, and railroads as well as buildings can be identified on aerial photos. Foresters are developing methods for estimating timber volumes from aerial photos for extensive surveys. Forest types can be determined easily by the use of a stereoscope, and even by the naked eye—especially the type lines between conifers and hardwoods. Small crowned spruce is distinguishable from large crowned pines, for example. Since this use of aerial photos is a highly technical one, detailed study of special texts on this subject is suggested.* Aerial photos are usually "read" with the aid of a stereoscope which shows up depth-surface detail through magnification, including hills, valleys, and even tree heights. In reading aerial photos, they should be placed so that the shadows of objects fall toward the reader; otherwise valleys may appear as ridges, and ridges as valleys. The stereoscope is made up of two magnifying glasses mounted on an adjustable frame which can be raised or lowered to bring desired parts of the two matching photos into focus. Acreage in aerial photos is also determined by the transparent grid method. The central clearing house for information concerning aerial photographic coverage is the Map Information Office, U. S. Geological Survey, Washington, D. C., 20242. It publishes, at approximate 18-month intervals, a "Status of Aerial Photography," in which a map of the United States is cross-hatched to represent areas of primary photography, and indicates the agency possessing the photographic negatives.

The procedures for securing aerial photographs are:

1. Delineate the area of photographic coverage desired.
2. Locate available photography of the area.
3. Order photo indexes of entire coverage.
4. Determine the area covered by each contact print.
5. Order individual photographs.
6. If necessary, reorder photographs omitted from the first order.

Electronic Surveying

Electronics is another space-age science that has revolutionized surveying. Cadastral surveyors are now leapfrogging from mountain to mountain with electronic distance-measuring outfits which can measure up to 50 miles and not be off more than a few inches. And they do this remarkable feat with signals that travel at the speed of light.

* See Bibliography.

To clear line and chain distance by hand would take 5 or 6 men a whole day to run 1 mile of section line through scrubby timber. The electronic method not only saves time; it also saves thousands of dollars in surveying costs. For instance, it would be virtually impossible to survey much of Alaska by standard methods.

The electronic outfit consists of two units, a master unit that sends out the electronic signal and the remote unit that receives the signal and rebroadcasts it back to the master unit. Both units are portable and can be mounted on tripods. Power is supplied by nickel-cadmium batteries. Both units are equipped with two-way radios so that the operators can talk to each other as they record the measurements, even though they are several miles apart.

The signal beam received at the master unit is made visible on a small cathode ray tube (a cousin to the picture tube in a TV set). By measuring electronically to the billionth of a second the time interval between impulses and its radar-like return, the surveyor can calculate the distance between the master unit and the remote unit. Like light, the beam travels in straight lines and normally must be unobstructed. Ordinarily, it cannot shoot over ridges or through dense timber.

But the flying surveyors have licked this problem, too. They have mounted a master unit in the nose of a helicopter with a built-in hover sight. The hover sight is an arrangement of bubble tubes and prisms developed by the Geological Survey. It enables the hovering helicopter to sight in directly over a marked point on the ground. When the vertical position is all right, the operator sends out the signal to the remote unit. This hover sight method gives the surveyor a giant set of stilts and enables him to "see" over the board fence into the ball park.

Topographic Maps

Occasionally, topographic maps will be needed in rough or mountainous country. These maps differ from land use cover maps by showing contour lines of known elevations on a surface base map. Topographic mapping is a complex field operation requiring the use of levels and other refined instruments. Foresters frequently make use of existing local topographic maps for laying out new roads, bridges, or other improvements, but it is not often that they make these maps themselves. Topographic maps have been made for much of the forested area of the United States by the U. S. Geological Survey and may be ordered by sending information on the exact description (section, town, range, county, state) of the area. Fig. 6–8 shows a portion of a topographic map.

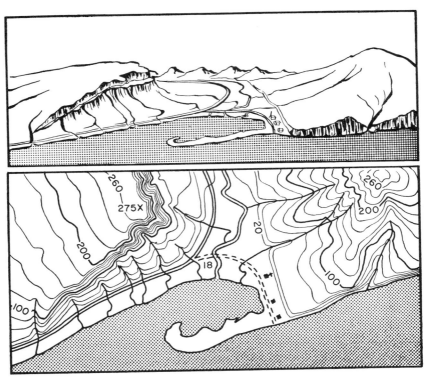

Fig. 6–8. How relief, hydrographic, and cultural features are shown on a topographic map. *Above,* a perspective view of a river valley that lies between two hills. In the foreground is the sea with a bay partly enclosed by a hooked sandbar. On each side of the valley are terraces through which streams have cut gullies. The hill on the right has a gradual slope with rounded forms, while the hill on the left rises abruptly and ends in a sharp precipice from which it slopes gradually away, forming an inclined tableland that is traversed by a few shallow gullies. *Below,* a topographic map of the same area with the ground forms represented by contour lines. The contour interval used here is 20 feet, which means that the vertical distance between one contour and the next is 20 feet. (Redrawn from U. S. Geological Survey)

ESTIMATING STANDING TIMBER VOLUMES

Timber Cruising

This is the process by which an estimate of the number of board feet, cords, or pieces (as in the case of posts, poles, piling, etc.) is determined. On large tracts this determination of the volume of forest products standing in the woods is either by random or systematic sampling of a percentage of the total, multiplying this sample by whatever factor is necessary to determine 100%. All the trees in a series of circular plots, usually of one-fifth or one-quarter acre in size, are tallied by diameter (and merchantable height). One tally sheet is used for each plot. Ordinarily the decision as to which method (random or systematic sampling) to use will depend upon the forester in charge, the agency, or the company's forestry manual, which will have the details spelled out. Random sampling requires considerable judgment and experience; systematic sampling is a mechanical process which can be done by less experienced men.

A simpler method of judging volume, often used on small tracts (less than 100 acres), is to count and keep a record of every tenth tree. Trees should be marked after tallying to avoid double counting. Multiplying the total volume of the samples by 10 gives the estimated volume of the entire stand. While this has the advantage of less complexity than the sampling systems, it may actually require more field work.

Most timber cruising is done by a party of two men—the *estimator* and the *compassman*. The estimator makes the map as he walks along the line which the compassman indicates for him to follow and notes forest-type changes and other symbols at points on the map measured by the compassman's paces. A beginner on a timber survey party starts as the compassman; the more experienced man is the estimator. Fig. 6–9 shows types of equipment used for timber cruising.

The timber estimator also measures and tallies the trees in the strips or sample plots by diameter at breast height (d.b.h.) $4\frac{1}{2}$ ft. above the ground, and the merchantable height by species. He records these facts on tally sheets supplied for this purpose (Fig. 6–10). Most tally sheets provide for 2-in. diameter (d.b.h.) classes—6", 8", 10", 12", etc. A dot is made for each tree in a box

Fig. 6–9. Instruments and equipment used in forestry practice. On the forester's vest: increment borer, scribe, compass, and diameter tape. Below the vest: a hypsometer stick. Nails. On the forester's belt (from bottom to top): plot pins, hatchet, first aid kit, a 50-foot steel tape, and a spiegelrelaskope (a German device used for determining tree heights and basel area). On the right of the belt are an IBM punch card holder and stylus, a Tatum Board with aerial photo, pocket stereoscope, and punch cards used for IBM data processing. (U. S. Forest Service)

of four, then the four dots are connected with straight lines to make eight trees; and finally, crossed lines are put in the center of the box for the last two trees, giving a total of ten for each box. The estimator then repeats this process for additional trees, as shown on the tally sheet. Merchantable height is estimated as the number of 16-ft. logs and 8-ft. half logs, or as the number of pulpwood and sticks in lengths common to the region.

Symbol	. . . . . .									
Number	. . . . . .	1	2	3	4	5	6	7	8	9	10

Under mechanical sampling, plots in the property are established at regular intervals so as to cover a predetermined percentage of the area. Let us use a "forty" as an example. Fig. 6–11 demonstrates the spacing of 20 fifth-acre plots which are needed to obtain a 10 per cent sample (4 acres). A larger percentage would require more sample plots.

The spacing of each plot is shown on the map, and it will be noted that these plots must be taken at these predetermined points wherever they fall. When there are two or more forest types within a forty, there must be a note on each plot tally sheet identifying the forest type in which the plot was located. The

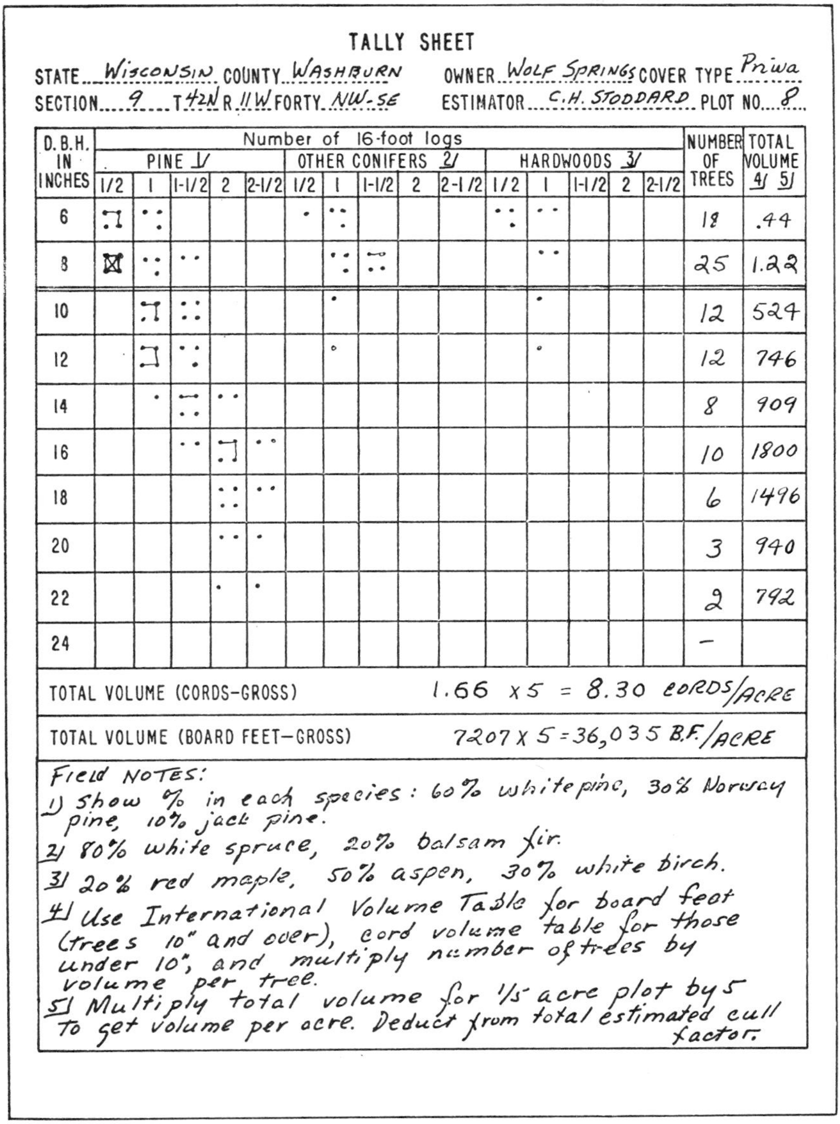

TALLY SHEET

STATE _Wisconsin_ COUNTY _Washburn_ OWNER _Wolf Springs_ COVER TYPE _Pn-wa_

SECTION _9_ T _42N_ R _11W_ FORTY _NW-SE_ ESTIMATOR _C.H. Stoddard_ PLOT NO. _8_

| D.B.H. IN INCHES | Number of 16-foot logs | | | | | | | | | | | | | | | NUMBER OF TREES 4/ | TOTAL VOLUME 5/ |
| | PINE 1/ | | | | | OTHER CONIFERS 2/ | | | | | HARDWOODS 3/ | | | | | | |
	1/2	1	1-1/2	2	2-1/2	1/2	1	1-1/2	2	2-1/2	1/2	1	1-1/2	2	2-1/2		
6	⦂I	⦂⦂			⦁	⦁	⦂⦁				⦁⦁	⦁⦁				18	.44
8	⊠	⦂⦁	⦁⦁			⦁⦁	⦂⦁				⦁⦁					25	1.22
10	⦂I	⦂⦂			⦁						⦁					12	524
12	⦐	⦂⦁			∘						∘					12	746
14	⦁	⦐	⦁⦁													8	909
16		⦁⦁	⦐	⦁⦁												10	1800
18		⦁⦁	⦁⦁													6	1496
20		⦁⦁	⦁													3	940
22		⦁	⦁													2	792
24																—	

TOTAL VOLUME (CORDS—GROSS)	1.66 x 5 = 8.30 CORDS/ACRE
TOTAL VOLUME (BOARD FEET—GROSS)	7207 x 5 = 36,035 B.F./ACRE

FIELD NOTES:

1) Show % in each species: 60% white pine, 30% Norway pine, 10% jack pine.

2) 80% white spruce, 20% balsam fir.

3) 20% red maple, 50% aspen, 30% white birch.

4) Use International Volume Table for board feet (trees 10" and over), cord volume table for those under 10", and multiply number of trees by volume per tree.

5) Multiply total volume for 1/5 acre plot by 5 to get volume per acre. Deduct from total estimated cull factor.

Fig. 6–10. Standard tally sheet used to record trees on a sample plot. With regard to Field Note No. 4, see Tables 6–1 and 6–2.

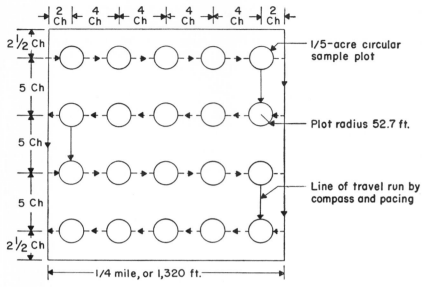

Fig. 6–11.   Plot spacing for a 10 per cent sample of a 40-acre tract. (*Note:* Ch is abbreviation for chain, 66 feet.)

forest-type map, which is prepared as the field work progresses, will show type boundaries so that their areas may be determined later. The volumes present on tally sheets for the same type can thus be brought together and calculated. When the total volume of timber tallied on plots in one type, the total area of the plots, and the area of the forest type within the forty are known, the total volume of timber within the type can be computed. The volumes of timber in each type are then added together to give the total volume on the forty. All tally sheets applying to each description are assembled at the end of the day and separated by type so that the volumes can be calculated.

When estimating timber within an irregularly boundaried property, random sampling is often the most practical method. The number of plots is determined in relation to the percentage sample to be made and the plots are located throughout so as to cover adequately all parts of the area. Where mechanical sampling is used, the procedure just described for irregular types is followed.

In *point sampling* cruising the predetermined number of photos are located on the type map or aerial photo to adequately cover and sample all parts of the area to be cruised. Care must be taken to be sure to locate the plots on the ground in the same place they appear on the map or photo, to prevent bias.

Plot lines should be laid out to run perpendicular to the topography. This will insure a sample of all of the area. If the lines are parallel to the topography, all plots in a line may fall on a ridge or in a valley and one or the other area will be missed.

Equipment Used in Estimating Timber

Several different kinds of tools are used in determining diameter and height of forest trees. Diameters may be measured with *calipers,* with a *diameter tape* which goes around the circumference, or with a *Biltmore stick.* Heights may be determined with the Biltmore stick or with several other kinds of instruments (hypsometers) designed for this purpose. The Abney hand level is also used where accuracy is essential. Both diameter and height are often estimated occularly in the eastern United States. The use of the diameter tape and the calipers to determine d.b.h. are self-explanatory. Fig. 6–12 illustrates how the Biltmore stick is used (see also Fig. 1–1). Tally sheets and base maps are carried in a clip board or aluminum tally-sheet holder which protects them from the weather.

In determining merchantable height, it is important to know how the timber is to be utilized and the standards used in the volume tables. Sawlogs usually are taken to a 6-in. top d.i.b. (diameter inside bark) at the small end and pulpwood to 4-in. d.i.b. Measurement of diameters is shown in Fig. 6–12. Using the hypsometer scale on the Biltmore stick one can then determine the merchantable height by counting the number of 16-ft. logs and fractional merchantable material in half logs, if they are 8 ft. or more in length. A *Pocket Cruiser Stick* is the shortened version of the Biltmore stick hypsometer scale and is often more convenient to handle in the woods. Experienced estimators measure only occasional "check" trees with instruments because they become quite accurate with occular estimates.

Determining Sawtimber Volumes

Since trees vary according to size, the volume of wood they contain will increase as tree diameter and height increases. Large trees are cut into sawlogs, usually measured in board feet of lumber, whereas small trees used for pulpwood and firewood are figured in cords. A board foot is 12 in. by 12 in. by 1 in. thick,

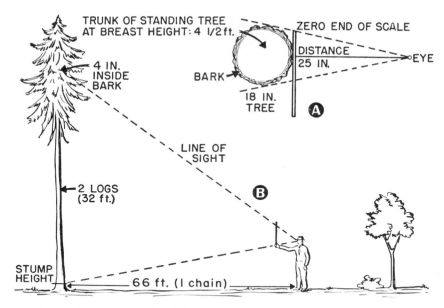

Fig. 6–12. Using the Biltmore stick. (A) To measure a diameter, hold the scale horizontally against the tree, 25 in. from the eye, chest high (4½ ft.), with the *Biltmore side* of the scale facing the operator. Close one eye and visually line up the zero end of the scale with one side of the tree. Then, holding steady, sight toward the other side of the tree. At the point where the line of vision intersects the scale, read the diameter of the tree. (B) To measure merchantable height, stand at a distance of 66 ft. from the tree. Hold the Biltmore stick vertically, 25 in. from the eye, with the *hypsometer side* facing the operator. Close one eye and visually line up the zero end of the scale with the stump height. Then, holding steady, sight to the top of the usable trunk length. Where the line of vision intersects with hypsometer scale, the large vertical figure will represent the length, in logs or half logs, of the usable trunk.

or 144 cu. in. of any dimension. To determine board feet use the following formula: Width in inches times thickness in inches times length in feet divided by 12. Standard cords contain 128 cubic feet and are 4 feet by 4 feet by 8 feet in dimension.

Sawlogs are usually cut into 8-, 10-, 12-, 14-, or 16-ft. lengths (up to 32 ft. in the West) whereas pulpwood is most frequently cut into 4-, 5-, or 8-ft. (100-in.) lengths (there are local exceptions). Poles, posts, and piling vary according to specification. In determining board foot volume in the East, trees 8- to 10-in. d.b.h.

are considered as sawtimber (depending upon local merchantability standards) and hence are measured in board feet. Frequently, those less than this are computed in cubic feet or cords.

Volume tables have been constructed (see Chapter 8) which make it possible to determine the number of board feet in standing trees. Trees may vary in form and hence in the volume of board feet or cubic content. Some trees have a relatively large diameter at breast height and become smaller (taper) relatively fast up the stem. Other trees of similar diameter may taper more slowly and consequently have a greater volume of wood. Thus the first log may vary from 80 b.f. in a rapidly tapering tree to 110 b.f. in a slowly tapering tree. Local volume tables have been developed in some areas to account for these differences. Most volume tables specify the conditions and assumptions which went into their construction. A ccmmonly used table is the "composite," in which variations are averaged out for wide areas (Table 6–1).

Volume tables based on three principal log rules are used in the United States: the International, the Scribner (Decimal C), and the Doyle. In a few localities other log rules are still in use. The International is the most accurate and corresponds closely to the actual amount of lumber a tree will yield. The Scribner, which is the official Forest Service log rule, is next in accuracy and is based on geometrical construction. When the second digit is dropped from the Scribner and rounded off to the nearest even 10, it is called Scribner Decimal "C." While the Doyle is still used mainly in the South, it is least accurate and consistently underestimates volumes of small logs.

To find the total volume of the trees tallied on a plot tally sheet, multiply the number of trees in each size class by the volume of a single tree of the same class as shown in the appropriate volume table. When this has been repeated for all size classes represented in the tally, sum up the volumes of each to obtain the plot volume.

Estimating or Cruising Pulpwood Timber

The procedure used in estimating standing pulpwood timber is much the same as for estimating sawtimber except that the trees are smaller and measured in cords. Plot tallies are obtained in the same fashion. Trees are measured and tallied by (1) d.b.h. classes only, or (2) by d.b.h. classes and merchantable height classes in terms of 8-ft. bolts, or (3) by d.b.h. classes and merchantable

TABLE 6–1

Composite Volume Tables

Utilization standards: Stump height is one foot. Height is the number of usable 16-foot logs to a variable top diameter not smaller than 8 in. inside the bark.

Diameter Breast High (Inches)	½	1	1½	2	2½	3	3½	4	4½	5

International ¼″ Kerf, Log Scale Volume Table

Number of 16-ft. logs per tree

Volume in Board Feet—International Rule

Diameter	½	1	1½	2	2½	3	3½	4	4½	5
10	17	39	53	68						
12	30	57	80	100	115					
14	42	79	110	140	163	181	205			
16	59	105	147	180	213	247	278	309		
18	74	135	188	235	278	320	360	400	445	490
20	92	170	236	295	350	402	450	499	552	605
22	112	209	290	362	430	494	555	613	676	704
24	133	252	346	431	512	594	665	742	821	900
26	158	300	409	508	604	698	786	880	980	1080
28	187	348	478	597	705	812	918	1025	1137	1250
30	220	408	552	687	811	934	1061	1180	1315	1450
32	256	471	643	794	935	1077	1216	1358	1519	1680
34	292	534	730	900	1060	1222	1380	1538	1724	1910

Volume in Board Feet—Scribner Rule

Diameter	½	1	1½	2	2½	3	3½	4	4½	5
10	14	30	40							
12	28	48	66	78	97					
14	40	70	96	116	141	165	190			
16	54	93	129	158	191	224	252	280		
18	72	122	168	207	248	292	323	355	400	445
20	90	156	212	262	317	366	407	451	502	553
22	111	194	262	328	392	452	505	563	620	678
24	137	236	319	399	472	549	613	687	754	822
26	165	281	381	478	566	653	730	820	901	982
28	195	331	448	559	665	764	857	959	1054	1150
30	227	383	522	648	772	886	995	1112	1228	1345
32	260	439	598	746	888	1019	1140	1278	1424	1570
34	294	500	678	847	1009	1159	1292	1455	1619	1783

Volume in Board Feet—Doyle Rule

Diameter	½	1	1½	2	2½	3	3½	4	4½	5
10	10	16	21							
12	18	29	38	46	52					
14	28	49	66	79	90	104	114			
16	42	71	98	121	142	162	176	189		
18	60	99	134	165	196	224	249	268	296	325
20	80	130	177	220	260	297	330	360	390	420
22	101	170	230	284	336	383	427	464	507	550
24	129	215	292	360	428	486	541	600	655	710
26	160	265	355	436	518	594	667	740	810	880
28	192	320	428	520	620	708	800	888	984	1080
30	228	377	507	626	738	840	949	1040	1170	1300
32	266	440	591	732	862	988	1118	1227	1363	1500
34	305	508	681	849	999	1142	1293	1430	1590	1750

Source: Lake States Forest Experiment Station.

height classes in 4-ft. bolts. The choice of either the first, second, or third method of measuring or estimating and tallying will depend on whether a local volume table (the one that gives volumes by d.b.h. classes only), or one like Table 6–2 (giving volumes by d.b.h. classes and merchantable height classes in 8-ft. lengths), or one which gives volumes by d.b.h. classes and 4-ft. lengths is available. If tables of all three methods are at hand, one will have a choice and, other things being equal, should select the local volume table because the work in the field and office will be easier and cheaper.

TABLE 6–2

Cordwood Composite Volume Table

Utilization standards: Volume is stem volume above 1 ft. stump in standard unpeeled cords.* Height is number of usable 8-ft. bolts to a variable top diameter not less than 4 in. inside the bark.

Cordwood Volume Table (applicable to all species except cedar).

D.B.H. (Inches)	Used height in number of 8-ft. bolts							
	1	2	3	4	5	6	7	8
	Volume in Cords							
6	.02	.03	.04	.06				
8	.03	.05	.07	.09	.12	.14		
10	.05	.07	.10	.13	.17	.20	.24	.27
12	.07	.10	.14	.18	.22	.27	.32	.36
14	.10	.13	.18	.23	.29	.35	.42	.47
16	.12	.17	.22	.29	.36	.44	.52	.59
18	.15	.20	.27	.35	.44	.53	.63	.72
20	.18	.25	.32	.42	.52	.63	.76	.85
22	.22	.29	.38	.49	.61	.74	.88	1.00

SOURCE: Lake States Forest Experiment Station.

* The standard cord is 4 ft. × 4 ft. × 8 ft. To find the approximate *peeled volume*, subtract 12 per cent.

Table 6–2 gives volumes in terms of cords, but sometimes the only table that can be secured will give volumes in solid cubic feet. If a table of the latter variety *is* the only one available, the total cubic-foot volume of the trees tallied on a tally form must be divided by the number of solid cubic feet of wood in the average stacked standard cord (4′ × 4′ × 8′ = 128 cu. ft.). This will give the plot volumes in terms of standard cords, the common unit of measure of pulpwood. The average standard cord contains about 80 solid cubic feet of wood, and this figure is a safe one to use as a converting factor, i.e., 128 cu. ft. in a stacked cord contains approximately 80 cu. ft. of solid wood.

Deductions for Defect and Cull

The tree volumes obtained and recorded by the previously described methods are *gross* volumes, with no allowance for defect. Many trees, especially in old or poorly managed stands, contain some rot or other defective material. If a tree is obviously not sound, it is the usual practice to make arbitrary deductions for the defect. For example, if the first 8 ft. in a tree are hollow, this length should be deducted from the total merchantable log length in the tree.

There will also be *hidden* defects which will show up when the logs are sawed even though they are not visible when the trees are marked and measured in the woods. To compensate for these hidden defects, a certain per cent of the total gross volume of the trees should be deducted. Usually, the amount of hidden defect varies between 10 and 25 per cent. If some timber has been cut and the logs scaled from this or a similar local stand, a close estimate of the defect can be made (see Chapter 8). This percentage deduction is subtracted from the total volume and is usually *in addition* to the allowance made for visible defect at the time the tree is measured.

Pulpwood is often cut either as 5 ft. 3 in. or 4-ft. bolts in the South, 4 ft. in the Northeast, and 8-ft. (or 100 in.) long in the Lake States.

Cumulative Volume Tally Sheets

Another development that is a real time saver is called the cumulative tree volume tally sheet. Note in the sample shown in Table 6–3 that each tree in the diameter class is crossed off and the last one shows the total volume in that class. Adding the total for all the diameter classes gives the total volume for the plot on a one-per-acre basis. It simplifies the whole process greatly but has some limitations if detail or a high degree of accuracy are desired. Instructions for using the cumulative volume method are shown at the bottom of the tally sheet.

MISCELLANEOUS FORESTRY MEASUREMENTS

Growth Rates

Quite frequently foresters need to know how fast trees are growing over specific periods of time, either for research data or for planning the allowable cut. The rate of growth of individual trees is largely controlled by age, species, site quality, and nearness to surrounding trees. The factors which affect the growth rate of individual trees determines the growth of forest stands. To attain maximum growth of a stand, the stand must approach a fully stocked condition where trees have adequate room to grow and yet where there is a maximum number of trees.

Trees grow in both diameter and height. Repeated measurements of these two variables at five- or ten-year intervals can provide accurate estimates of growth during the period between measurements. The difference in volume of the tree or stand at the time of the two measurements can be expressed as either annual or periodic growth.

Past growth rates are most often used to evaluate the rapidity of growth in an individual tree and also as a means of predicting future growth of entire stands. Growth of the individual tree may be used to indicate its growth rate as compared to other trees in the stand and indirectly its maturity or desirability as future growing stock. Growth of the entire stand can be used as a rough guide in setting allowable cut.

Growth rate of an individual tree is evaluated on the basis of the width of the annual rings and on changes in its merchantable height. Diameter measurements are made at $4\frac{1}{2}$ feet from the ground d.b.h. with the use of an increment borer; or by counting and measuring the annual rings on the stump. Height may be measured directly in the case of a felled tree or estimated in a standing tree.

Growth of a forest stand is expressed in board feet, cords, or any other common forest unit of measure and may be indicated as a per cent of the original volume. Growth in a forest stand is often considered to have two basic elements: growth of the merchantable trees; and growth of trees which are approaching merchantable size or ingrowth. Only the better trees, trees considered to be desirable growing stock, are used either to predict growth of the stand or as sample trees.

Growth in the forest stand is usually predicted on the basis of sample tree measurements taken in the process of making a timber inventory. It is common practice to measure one or two such trees on each inventory plot.

The diameter of sample trees is measured at d.b.h. with a diameter tape or calipers. The merchantable height is measured or estimated and an increment core is taken and measured. In the

TABLE 6–3

CUMULATIVE – VOLUME TALLY   NW¼E, SEC. 9 _ T42N R11W ____   DATE 7/10/57 _ _

LINE NO. __ 2 _ _ PLOT NO. _ 8 _ _ BY C.S. ____

USE ⅕ ACRE PLOTS. VALUES SHOWN IN TABLES ARE PER ACRE VOLUMES

LEGEND — X white Pine — 1 Norway Pine — ⊗ Aspen — ② White Spruce — ESTIMATED CULL % 10

NUMBER OF 16 FOOT LOGS PER TREE — **VOLUME IN HUNDREDS OF BOARD FEET (INTERNATIONAL ¼)**

DBH	½	1	1½	2	2½	3	3½	4	4½	5	TOTALS	ESTIMATED CUT
8	1 2 4 5 6 7 / 8 10 11 12 13 14 / 16 17 18 19 20 22 / 23 24					5 10 15 / 20 25 30 / 35						
10	2 4 5 7 9 12 15 / 18 21 24 27 30 / 32 35 38 41 44 / 47 50 53	2 4 6 8 12 16 / 18 20 24 28 32 / 36 40 43 47 / 51 55 59 63	2 4 6 8	4 9 14 / 18 22 27 / 32 36 40 / 45		8 16 23 / 31 39 46 / 54 62	9 18 27 / 35 44	10 19 27 / 39 48	12 23 35 / 47 58	18 36 53	3000	
12	2 5 7 9 12 14 16 18 / 20 22 23 25 27 / 29	10 12 14 16 / 18 20 23 25 27 / 29 31 33	6 12 17 23 / 29 35 41 46 / 52 58 64 70	7 14 20 / 27 34 41 / 48 54	9 14 / 18 22 27 / 32 36 40 / 45	11 22 33 / 43 54 65	12 25 37 / 50 62 74	14 27 41 / 54 68 81	16 33 50 / 66 82 99	18 36 53 / 71 88 106	4400	
14	8 11 14 16 / 23 27 31 / 35 41 / 47	8 12 / 16 25	16 25 / 33 41 47	10 19 30 / 39 48 58	14 27 / 34 41 / 48 54	14 29 43 / 57 72 86	17 33 50 / 66 83 99	18 36 54 / 71 89	23 45 68 / 90 113	24 48 72 / 97 121	4100	
16	8 12 17 22 / 25 29 33 37 / 42	8 12 17 / 21 31 41 / 52 62 72 82 / 90	23 47 71 / 79 98	19 48 / 39 58	19 30 / 39 48 58	19 38 56 / 75 94	22 43 65 / 86 108	23 47 70 / 93 117	30 59 88 / 118 148	32 63 94 / 126 158		
18	11 14 16 18 / 22 26 31 36 / 41 44 48 51	10 21 31 41 / 52 62 72 / 64 77 90	39 69 79 / 80 97 113	28 55 / 48 54 / 63 78 94	28 38 / 48 58	24 47 71 / 95 118	28 55 83 / 110 138	30 59 89 / 118 148	36 72 109 / 145	38 77 115 / 154	10000	
20	22 27 33 / 40 46 54 66 / 78	14 18 22 27 / 31 54 63 72	39 59 / 79 98	39 59 / 79 118 138	39 48 / 58 72 / 96 120	29 58 87 / 115	34 67 101 / 135 168	36 73 109 / 145	45 89 134 / 47 95 142	47 95 142	8300	
22	11 14 18 22 / 36 44 54 / 66 78	22 31 41 / 52 62 72 90	24 47 / 79 98	56 / 64	48 72 / 96	35 70 105 / 115 168	41 81 122 /	44 88 / 132	51 102 / 153	54 107 / 161	5200	
24	13 16 19 22 / 27 31 37 / 44 54 66 / 78	13 26 38 51 / 64 77 90	23 56 / 84 112	23 56 / 84	34 68 / 103	39 78 117 /	44 89 134 / 48 97 146	48 97 146 /	53 107 160 / 107 114 171	57 114 171	4400	
26	18	22 45 / 89	33 66 / 99	33 66 / 99	40 80 / 121	46 92 138 / 52 105 157	52 105 157	57 114	60 120	63 126		
28						33 66 99		60 120	60 120	63 126		

	BOARD FEET PER ACRE	CUT PER ACRE
	39,400	39,400

Note: See opposite page for instructions on the use of this form.

sample growth calculation which follows, the number of rings in the last inch of radial growth is used. Other growth prediction systems use measurement of the radial growth during the past ten or twenty years.

It is very desirable that sample trees be selected in proportion to the acreage and number of trees in various conditions in the forest. This is essential in order to eliminate bias in the sample. When various portions of a forest tract are sampled at different intensity or with recognized variability, the sample trees for each portion thus recognized should be segregated and computed separately. An alternative would be to weight the sample on the basis of the acreage or number of good growing stock trees found in each tract.

One rough method for calculating the average annual growth of a forest tract is to divide the total timber volume by the average age of the stand. This age can be determined either by counting the annual rings of a sample number of trees of representative sizes on stumps or by the use of an increment borer. For example, a stand with 8,000 b.f. per acre which averages 80 years old has grown at the rate of 100 b.f. per acre per year.

Although the most accurate growth estimate would be obtained through the remeasurement of individual trees or stands, only past growth is thus obtained. It is usually desirable to estimate future growth of the stand. A simplified system commonly used for such predictions follows.

Assume that, if in a fully stocked stand, the average for the several sample trees yielded the following information:

Instructions for Using Table 6–3

The figures on this volume tally are computed for a ⅕-acre plot (radius 52.7 feet). The figures are cumulative in each block, the first number representing the volume of one tree, the second number the volume of two trees, etc.

Tally trees in each "D.B.H. Merchantable Height" block by crossing out numbers in consecutive order, beginning from the first number in the block. The last number crossed out in each block indicates the combined volume of all trees in that "D.B.H. Merchantable Height" class. For each d.b.h. class add the volume in all blocks and enter this sum as a subtotal in the "Total" column. Total merchantable volume equals the sum of these subtotals.

Sawtimber Tally. Numbers in blocks represent hundreds of board feet (International ¼" Rule). They are already multiplied by 5, thus giving volume per acre directly from a ⅕-acre plot.

Legend. Different species or species groups are distinguished by using different symbols or colors in crossing out numbers in each block. Room is reserved in the "Legend" box to record the symbol or color used for each species. (Adapted by Tennessee Valley Authority from S. R. Gevorkiantz, Lake States Forest Experiment Station, St. Paul, Minnesota.)

Average tree (d.b.h. 12″ up)................................ 13.2 inches
Used height (merchantable)............................... 24 feet
Growth rate in rings per inch............................. 9 rings per inch
Number of near merchantable trees (10″ d.b.h.).......... 15 trees
Number of merchantable trees (12″ up d.b.h.)............ 50 trees

The growth calculation would then be as follows:

GROWTH ON GOOD GROWING STOCK	HEIGHT FACTORS	
	H	F
	16' — 1.20	
	24' — 1.07	
	32' — 1.00	
	40' — .95	

1. Average tree (d.b.h.12" up) ⎡d.b.h. _13.2_ inches [D] USED HEIGHT _24_ feet [H]→
⎣GROWTH RATE IN RINGS PER INCH __ [R]

2. GROWTH per year in average tree $\dfrac{[D]\ 13.2\ \times\ [H]\ 24\ \times\ [F]\ 1.07}{10\ \times\ [R]\ 9} = \underline{38}$ Board Feet [G]

3. INGROWTH per year from NEAR MERCHANTABLE trees (d.b.h. 10″) into MERCHANTABLE stand (d.b.h. 12″ up)

Number of trees per acre 10″ d.b.h. _15_ X $\dfrac{50}{[R]\ 9}$ board feet = _83_ board feet [K]

4. TOTAL GROWTH per year:
Number of trees per acre (d.b.h.12" up) _50_ X [G] _38_ = _190_ plus [K] _83_ = 273 board feet PER ACRE [L]

If there were twenty acres of such forest land then the growth on the entire tract would be:

[L] _273_ X _20_ acres = _5,460_ board feet TOTAL in Forest [M]

Stand tables show the number of trees in each diameter class on a per-acre basis and are constructed by averaging all plot data on tally sheets. They are used mainly for determining volumes and those trees which might logically be marked for cutting. Stock tables show the corresponding volumes by diameter classes. Growth data obtained from increment borings are added to stand tables to show what sizes and trees may be in the years ahead and so guide the forester in making management plans (Table 6–4).

Basal area, the number of square feet per acre represented in trees measured at d.b.h., is a useful method for determining proper stocking. By using optimum basal area tables for the species under consideration and comparing them with the stand being managed, a good measure of comparison is obtained. For example, foresters have found that when loblolly, slash, or shortleaf pine reach 120 sq. ft. of basal area per acre, they are too dense and are in need of thinning. If the thinning takes the stand down to about 80 ft. basal area, it will be in a thrifty condition for new, fast growth.

TABLE 6–4

Stand and Stock Table for Northern Hardwood and Hemlock Forest Type (Northeastern Wisconsin)

Average Acre—Merchantable Timber—Volumes in Board Feet—
Scribner Scale—Net Volume Old Growth Stand

| D.B.H. in In. | *Number of Trees* | | | | | |
	Hem-lock	*Sugar Maple*	*Yellow Birch*	*Bass-wood*	*Misc. Hdwds.*	*Total*
R	15.13	101.74	83.50	3.21	38.21	244.29
2	14.09	64.36	15.75	11.88	9.39	115.47
4	9.61	16.49	8.97	3.54	6.31	44.92
6	8.14	8.11	4.51	1.80	3.49	26.05
8	6.48	5.78	3.04	2.13	2.06	19.49
Total 2″+	38.32	93.74	32.27	18.35	23.25	205.93
10	6.08	3.96	1.33	0.88	0.75	13.00
12	4.90	3.77	1.28	0.54	0.83	11.32
14	3.90	3.29	1.44	0.59	0.58	9.80
16	2.86	2.32	1.33	0.50	0.50	7.51
18	2.38	2.33	1.04	0.36	0.30	6.41
20	1.59	1.64	0.90	0.26	0.32	4.71
22	1.27	1.06	0.54	0.15	0.14	3.16
24	0.88	0.86	0.39	0.11	0.03	2.27
26	0.61	0.40	0.12	0.07	0.01	1.21
28	0.32	0.23	0.18	0.03	. . .	0.76
30+	0.33	0.31	0.20	0.14	. . .	0.98
Total	25.12	20.17	8.75	3.63	3.46	61.13

| D.B.H. in In. | *Net Scribner Volume—Board Feet* | | | | | | *Basal Area Sq. Ft.* |
	Hem-lock	*Sugar Maple*	*Yellow Birch*	*Bass-wood*	*Misc. Hdwds.*	*Total*	
R							
2							
4			. . . Negligible . . .				
6							
8							
Total 2″+							
10	130.9	52.5	16.5	11.7	8.5	220.1	7.08
12	242.6	187.2	59.6	32.0	37.4	558.8	8.90
14	327.4	298.0	116.8	44.6	45.0	831.8	9.86
16	383.7	306.1	168.3	87.4	58.5	1,004.0	10.50
18	460.3	445.1	179.2	77.5	50.8	1,212.9	11.32
20	425.8	435.0	204.8	70.5	74.3	1,210.4	9.58
22	445.8	364.2	153.2	79.8	42.1	1,085.1	8.35
24	386.9	379.0	135.5	75.6	11.3	988.3	7.14
26	331.7	220.2	53.6	59.9	4.6	670.0	4.45
28	210.1	150.4	87.7	45.7	. . .	493.9	3.24
30+	299.7	245.2	118.6	144.4	. . .	807.9	4.80
Total	3,644.9	3,082.9	1,293.8	729.1	332.5	9,083.2	85.22

Source: Adapted from U. S. Forest Service-Forest Survey Stand Tables for Northeastern Wisconsin.

Yield tables also give a measure of the stocking density as well as the rate of stocked wood production of the stand. These have been constructed by measuring the volume of timber on a fully stocked forested acre according to site classifications, or site indexes. The student is referred to a text on forest mensuration for application of basal area or yield tables.

Timber Sales Procedures

On both public and private forest considerable preliminary work is necessary to prepare timber for sale. Most large forest-owning organizations have a manual containing full instructions as to how they proceed with a sale, so that the general principles will only be sketched here. Assume that the tract to be sold has already been estimated for volume and that it is part of a forest management plan (see Chapter 7) which shows that a quantity of certain species is ready for cutting. The forester assembles a timber marking crew under his direction to mark the trees for cutting and the boundaries of the cutting area. The choice of trees to be marked depends upon the size and species composition of the stand and upon the silvicultural system chosen (Chapter 5). Sufficient volume must usually be marked to make it profitable for the logger to operate.

The marked trees are recorded on tally sheets in small tracts, but on large ones the sampling methods used in timber cruising are usually followed. The total volumes for each species are recorded in cords and board feet. The values are determined by methods described in Chapter 7. Timber sale agreement forms are shown in Appendix D.

Boundary Marking

This is usually done by the compass and pacing method, following the previously prepared map of the area described earlier in this chapter. The compassman can often do this job working alone after he has developed proficiency. Where boundaries may be in dispute, a registered surveyor should be employed.

OTHER ASPECTS OF TIMBER CRUISING

The preceding discussion has included only the essential steps in determining volumes in timber stands and mapping out areas. There are many variations and several new systems which can speed up the work considerably. If the forest technician gets into timber estimating and mapping, he will probably learn these on the job if the decision has been made to use them. One new method which is gaining rapidly is called "point sampling," which uses a glass wedge prism or angle gauge. These are used to determine if a particular tree has been counted or not. The principles behind the method will not be gone into here in great detail. Greater emphasis will be placed upon field procedures.

Other new short cuts or methods for controlling accuracy may be found in the instruction books and government bulletins shown in the references for this chapter.* Time will tell how well they stand up in usage. In all methods there is no substitute for practical field application and experience.

Point sampling does not require that the plot diameters and tree diameters be measured. The cruiser counts the number of trees and the heights in bolts or logs whose diameter at breast height appears larger than the cross arm of the angle gauge or that do not appear to be detached from the stem when viewed through the prism wedge.

A simple angle gauge may be constructed by mounting a 1-in. cross arm on the end of a 33-in. stick. A peep sight is mounted on the other end. The end with the peep sight is held up to the eye and the instrument is sighted at the trees. Those trees that appear larger than the cross arm are counted. Those trees which just cover the cross are considered borderline and every tree is counted.

When using a wedge prism the sections of the tree covered by the prism appear to be displaced (Fig. 6–13). Those sections that do not appear to be completely displaced from the main trunk of the tree are counted. Those in which the opposite edges of the section covered by prism and the main trunk appear to line up are considered borderline and every other tree is counted. When the section covered by the prism appears to be completely displaced from the main stem the tree is not counted.

Care must be exercised when using either the angle gauge or the prism wedge to eliminate errors that may occur due to sloppy procedure.

Care must be taken to assure that the observation on a plot is taken directly over the plot center. When using the angle gauge the eye is the plot or point center. Be certain that the eye is maintained as the center when taking the tree count. Trees that lean toward or away from the center are treated as normal trees. Turn

* See Bibliography.

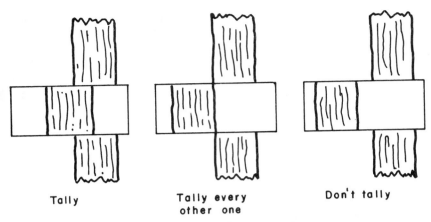

Tally   Tally every other one   Don't tally

Fig. 6–13. Use of prism wedge.

the cross arm until it is at right angles to main stem when sighting on trees that lean to the right or left. Slope correction factors are applied where the slope exceeds 15 per cent.

When sighting on trees that are hidden from view from the point center, care must be taken to maintain the same distance when moving off the point center.

When using the prism wedge, the prism is held over the point center. Again care must be taken to assure that observations are made from the point center. As with the angle gauge precautions should be taken to maintain the same distance when sighting on hidden trees.

Another precaution which applies to the wedge prism is to assure that it is held in a vertical position and at right angles to the line of sight. Tilting the prism away from or towards the observer can cause a larger displacement and can cause a tree to be omitted from the count. Any rotation of the prism in the vertical position will cause a smaller displacement thereby including trees that should be omitted.

In the point sampling method, cruising is commonly done by forest type. Types and acreages are usually determined from aerial photos and type maps.

A reconnaisance of the area is made to determine the variability of the stand and the number of points needed to give the level of accuracy.

Plot lines or point sample lines are laid out on the type map and a predetermined number of preliminary plots taken to obtain the

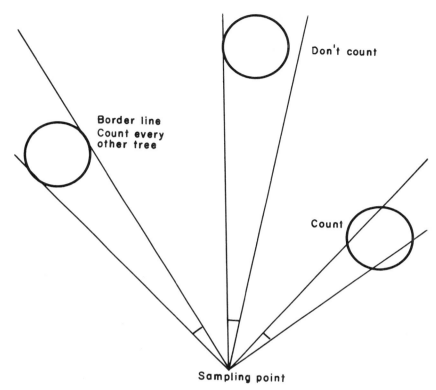

Fig. 6–14. Use of angle gauge.

necessary information to determine the variability of the stand between sample points. A count is taken of the "in" trees at each point. Each point is tallied separately. This information is used to determine the standard deviation of tree count and stand volume between sample points.

The standard deviation (SD) is determined by the following formula:

$$SD = \frac{Sum\ (x - x)^2}{n - 1}$$

where
n = number of sample points taken
x = number of trees counted per sampling point
x = mean = $\dfrac{\text{sum of } x}{n}$

The coefficient of variation $= \dfrac{\text{SD}}{\text{X}}$

The number of sample points needed for the area

$$N = \dfrac{(T)^2(CV)^2}{E^2 + \dfrac{(T)^2(CV)^2}{A}}$$

where:

$T = 1$ (representing a 68.3% level of probability), that is, the cruise will be accurate 68.3 times out of 100 times.

$E =$ desired accuracy of cruise within a stated limit, i.e., $\pm10\%$.

$A =$ population size $= S$ total area being sampled

                                 s sample size in acres usually obtained from chart based on basal area factors and average d.b.h. of trees on point.

When the number of sample points needed is determined cruise lines should be laid out on the type map or aerial photo for each type.

In placing the actual points on the ground, care must be taken to assure that they are on the same place as on the map or photo to insure against bias.

When the point is established the cruiser uses the angle gauge or wedge prism and calls out the species and height in bolts or logs. The tally man records the tree on a cumulative volume tally sheet or a prepared tally sheet using the dot count method. The tally man should be careful to tally each plot as it is measured.

The data is summarized into volume per acre and multiplied by number of acres in the tract to obtain the total volume. Other new shortcuts or methods for controlling accuracy may be found in the instruction books and government bulletins shown in the references for this chapter. Time will tell how well they stand up in usage. In all methods there is no substitute for practical field application and experience.

Continuous Forest Inventory

On large properties a system for keeping current records of timber volumes which is rapidly gaining in favor has been named the *Continuous Forest Inventory*. The "C.F.I." operates on the principle of regular remeasurement of a representative number of permanently located circular (fifth acre) plots. The plot locations are predetermined mechanically so as to include the proper proportions of each type and size class. Tree measurements are made with more than usual care; stand tables are constructed; detailed growth and mortality studies are made; and changes resulting from cutting are recorded. The C.F.I. system also keeps records of changes in size and quality of timber as well as species shifts. While it may not wholly replace regular reinventories, the C.F.I. system may reduce the necessity for making them at short intervals.

Computer Programming and Data Processing Systems

Industries and government agencies which have regular access to electronic computers put their forest data into a "programmed system" for data recovery. These remarkable machines will, for example, take stand table volumes and corresponding growth information and project expected timber yields for ten, twenty, or more years hence. Foresters can keep a very close watch on each portion of their forest without having to make repetitive field examinations. It is, of course, necessary to make periodic remeasurements, weigh the effects of windstorms, insects, and disease, and other causes of mortality. The computerized results are only as good as the data fed into the electronic brain itself.

Many other uses for the computer have been found by foresters. Land title records, logging cost data analysis, production and sales information, and nearly any part of the forest business which can be measured may be effectively computerized. Computer programmers need to be trained in forestry terms and practices, and foresters need to learn the basics of computer operation if the best results are to be obtained.

Individual project operating costs can be determined in advance by computer programming. Knowing slopes and topography, earth removal and paving unit costs, the total road cost per unit through a given area can be closely estimated. Similiar estimates of logging costs and profits can also be calculated from stand volume and logging data.

QUESTIONS

1. How many sections are there in a township?
2. What does T42N R11W mean?
3. Make a sketch of a section showing each forty and locate the NW-SW

with the number 1, the SW-NE with number 2 and the SE-SW with number 3.

4. How are distances usually measured in forest surveying?

5. When "sighting" a compass due South, what is the bearing and what is the azimuth reading?

6. How is the acreage of a forest type approximately determined from a type map?

7. How does one record seven trees on a standard tally sheet?

8. How many board feet (International Scale) are there in the following trees?   (a) 14″ d.b.h. and two logs.   (b) 18″ d.b.h. and three logs.

9. Using the composite volume tables for International Rule, what is the total volume of three trees 14″ d.b.h. with two logs plus two trees 12″ d.b.h. with 1½ logs?

10. Using the composite cordwood volume table, how much volume (in cords) is there in the following trees?   (a) 8″ d.b.h. and four bolts.   (b) 10″ d.b.h. and three bolts.

11. What are the tree measurements required to determine growth of a tree?

12. What factors influence rate of tree growth?

13. When using the prism wedge in point sampling the eye is the sampling point.   True (   )   False (   )

14. When using the angle gauge the eye is the sampling point.   True (   ) False (   )

15. When border line trees are encountered in point sampling: (a) count all such trees;   (b) do not count such trees;   (c) count every other tree;   (d) forget the plot and move on to the next plot.   (Underline one).

16. In cruising, all plots should be taken where the density is greater and the trees are larger to assure the greatest volume possible.   True (   ) False (   )

17. A Southern pine forest averages 40 cords per acre in a 25-year growth period: What has been the average annual growth rate?

18. A second-growth Douglas fir forest in the state of Washington has been growing at the rate of ¾ cord per ace for 60 years: What is its volume per acre?

EXERCISES

1. Locate one of the forest areas in your vicinity by section and township (if this system is used).

2. Check your own pacing and practice using a compass by measuring a known direction and distance through the woods.

3. Make a forest cover map of a small tract showing forest, other natural and man-made features. Use the proper symbols for each.

4. Demonstrate the use of the Biltmore stick, diameter tape, and other forestry instruments to which you may have access.

5. Estimate the volume of timber on a fifth-acre plot by tallying all the trees according to diameter classes and applying the proper volumes to each from the appropriate volume table.

6. Examine an aerial photograph of a forest area with which you are familiar and try to identify the forest types and other features.

7

Forest Management
and Finance

Filbert Roth, the famous teacher of forestry at the University of Michigan, once defined forest management as "setting up, putting in order, and keeping in order a forest business." Order can be maintained only by a well-designed and carefully kept set of records. Forest records mean financial accounting as well as data on timber volumes and growth, plus the necessary maps. Records are not kept for their own sake but to serve as a tool in management, both to assure profitable operation and continuous yields of timber crops.

The main objective of forestry practice is to obtain a sustained yield of forest products and other benefits without damaging the basic resources—land and growing stock. The methods of managing a forest to produce timber crops according to silvicultural principles have been set forth in earlier chapters. As a means of guiding these management techniques so as to obtain regular yields, it is necessary to develop plans which bring together all of the information gathered on the forest. The maps, the volume inventory data from timber cruises, the kinds of silvicultural methods, the products to be grown and marketed, plus the land records, protection plans, and any other data useful to the conduct of a forest business are all brought together into the forest management plan.

Under normal circumstances forest management plans are drawn up by professional foresters. Forest owners and forestry technicians often participate in obtaining the basic data and carry out the recommendations which the plan calls for. It is well, at this point, to develop the principal elements of a management plan and what items are included in order to give a better understanding of the recommended practices.

Prior to making the plan itself, several decisions of major importance must be made. A managed forest must be so handled as to have a regular output of timber products, which must come from growth. A forest with regular cuttings governed by the growth is considered to be under *sustained-yield management*. Growth studies underlie all sustained-yield forestry (Fig. 7–1).

Fig. 7–1. Measuring tree growth with an increment borer. The hollow borer produces a core which shows the annual rings of the tree. Growth studies are made by this procedure. (American Forest Products Industries, Inc.)

MANAGING FOR SUSTAINED YIELD

Sustained-yield forest growth should balance the losses in wood volume due to cutting and mortality in the whole forest, over a period of time, with management at a level high enough to produce maximum yields. This means, of course, that a growing stock of timber advancing on to merchantable age must be maintained at all times. Although a continuous forest business requires a steady output of forest products, the frequency and the amount of the cutting will depend on the market, on the size of the tract and its location, and especially on the rate of growth. These factors are included in the decisions on rotations and cutting cycles.

Forest yields vary greatly with type, site, length of growing season, and the intensity of management practiced. Under intensive management, annual growth may vary from more than 200 b.f. per acre in northern United States to as much as 1,000 or 1,500 b.f. in the Southern pines and on the Pacific Coast. Unfortunately, due to understocking, these high rates of growth are seldom reached over any large areas.

Regulation of the Cut

Sustained-yield management on even-aged forests differs considerably from that on all-aged stands. In both cases it is necessary to decide upon the rotation or the age at which mature timber will be harvested from the property. This decision depends upon such specifications for forest products as may be required by the markets.

A forest managed for sustained yield should be able to produce about the same quantity of products every year. This means that growing stock should have what foresters call "normal" distribution. Assuming uniform site, a "normal" forest composed of even-aged stands has an equal number of acres in trees which are one year apart in age for each year of its rotation. For example, an even-aged normal pine forest of 40 acres with a 40-year pulpwood rotation has 1 acre in each age class between 1 and 40 years (see Fig. 7–2). If this whole forest grows at the rate of 1 cord per acre per year, a volume of 40 cords can be cut each year from the acre which has gone through the full rotation. This would be done under a clearcutting and planting system.

A normal all-aged hardwood forest presents a different situation. Here trees of all sizes would be represented on each acre (see (Fig. 7–2). Assuming that this forest, too, was growing at the rate of 1 cord per acre per year, it would be necessary to cut 1 cord from each acre under the selection system every year. But as a practical matter this is not done. Instead, a cutting cycle is estab-

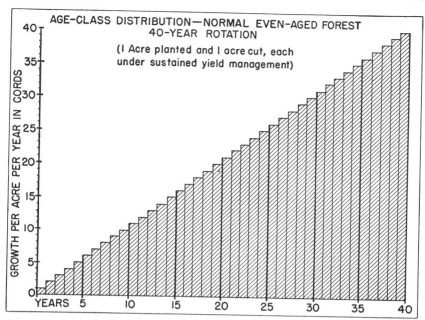

AGE-CLASS DISTRIBUTION—NORMAL EVEN-AGED FOREST
40-YEAR ROTATION

(I Acre planted and I acre cut, each
under sustained yield management)

Fig. 7–2. Age-class distribution in a normal even-aged forest. The actual growth rate would probably follow a curve, flatter for the slower growth at first and steepening toward the end of the rotation.

lished which in this case could be 5 years. Thus, instead of cutting off 40 cords from the whole 40 every year, it is possible to cut the 40 cords from 8 acres in each 5-year cutting cycle, or 5 cords per acre every 5 years.

It is more economical to cut a somewhat heavier volume at 5-year intervals from a small area under the cutting cycle plan than to make the cut over the whole property every year. Under this plan a different 8 acres is cut every year during the 5-year cutting cycle. The total cut must not exceed the total growth for the cutting cycle period, nor should the cut result in reducing the growing stock. If an increased cut is made in any year of high prices, it should come from surplus accumulated during years of low prices.

Although the annual cut should equal the annual growth, this applies literally only to normal forests in which trees of all ages—young, middle aged, and mature—are evenly distributed. Where most trees are mature or overmature, the annual growth is very small; but the annual cut, at first, could be heavy to avoid loss of wood through decay. On a small tract there would be a period during which no cuts could be made in order to allow for the establishment of the regrowth.

Another term used by foresters is "allowable cut." This is determined both from growth rates and from the amount of growing stock which either should be cut to put the stand in better condition or be withheld in order to build up the stand for the future. The allowable cut is usually calculated for periods of less than 20 years; it may exceed the annual growth of a forest with much overmature timber and may be below the growth of a young, developing forest.

FOREST MANAGEMENT PLANS

A great deal of planning is required to maintain a sustained yield of timber products. Forest management plans are based upon the types of field data obtained from inventorying timber, determining growth, and mapping the forest types and acreages. Protection data, logging methods, marketing, and other information set forth in the preceding chapters are all brought together into a forest management plan which can serve as a guide for some years into the future. A well-prepared plan should indicate which stands and species, amounts, and sizes of timber may be scheduled for cutting in the years ahead; where planting is needed, by number and kinds of trees; and what areas need timber stand improvement on specified dates. A management plan also deals with the forest fire protection system; with provisions for wildlife management by locations and practices; with the numbers of livestock to be permitted to graze in certain areas (if any); and with other important information required in the management of the area, including control of insects and diseases.

For convenience in management, forest properties are often divided into compartments which are frequently units of similar physical features bounded by roads or other natural boundaries such as lakes, streams, etc. Division into compartments makes for simplification of detailed record keeping.

Systematic record keeping of both finances and physical data is essential in a well-managed forest, just as it is in any other business. Tally sheets and summaries of timber cruises should be properly filed, as should all maps made of the area. Initial records of tree volumes are particularly important in order to make it possible to compare the development of the forest as management continues over a period of time. Forest type maps of the property should be made at ten-year intervals so that changes due to growth and cutting may be kept up to date.

A well-organized forest management plan ties together the specialized details which this book has considered into a unified whole for the operation of the forest business.

The following check list includes nearly all the essential items to be included in a forest management plan for a timber property. There is no set form to follow but the information shown below should be set forth as completely as possible. The plan should be preceded with a brief history of the property which brings out important forestry information.

Items To Be Included in a Forest Management Plan

1. Maps of area showing forest types and size classes, tabulation of acreages, and subdivision by compartments
2. Volume of each species present in each compartment area, and growth rate data showing volumes estimated to be available in a decade or so
3. On larger forests, an estimate of allowable cut by compartments during specified growth intervals
4. Forest management operating schedule:
   a. Harvest cutting areas for the next decade, showing the applicable silvicultural system
   b. Decisions as to applicable rotations and cutting cycles
   c. Stand improvement cutting areas for the next decade
   d. Forest planting areas showing species and acreages planned, by years
5. Lists of market outlets, historical price information, products which may be sold, and specifications of products
6. Logging plans, equipment inventory, labor requirements, facilities needed
7. Protection program: fire-fighting facilities and equipment owned and otherwise available, road and fire-lane system, detection program and system for suppression of fires
8. Insect and disease problems and methods for their control
9. Multiple-use management programs:
   a. Wildlife—practices and timing with other operations
   b. Fisheries and water
   c. Recreational land uses and facilities
   d. Agricultural and grazing uses
   e. Other uses
10. Cost accounting and bookkeeping system

A good management plan should provide for every aspect of forestry and other uses of the land area within the forest property. It should not be considered inflexible and unchangeable but as a useful guiding framework which will need to be adapted to changing conditions and to new information. As new scientific information comes out, markets for new products develop, or nature upsets plans with wind or fires, the plan will need to be brought up to date. A good forest manager adapts his planning to changing circumstances while remaining faithful to the principles of sound forest conservation.

Examples of two kinds of forest management plans for small timber tracts are set forth in Appendix C as an aid to the student and forest owner.

Compartment Records

In order to maintain accurate current records of various developments, including work accomplished in each area for the year in which it is done, simple compartment outline sketch maps have been found most practical. A sketch map such as the one shown in Fig. 7–3 can be used to record logging information, timber volumes standing and cut, trees planted, man days expended on each kind of job, silvicultural applications, etc., carried out during the year. Compartment sketch sheets are made only for the years when work is done, but over a period of time they will represent a continuous forest management and operating record, and form the basis for a case history of the compartment. This system has been successfully used in the Harvard Forest and elsewhere. The information recorded can provide the basis for revisions in the over-all forest management plan from time to time.

Seasonal Work Load Distribution

A growing forest, like a farm crop, goes through a series of seasonal cycles each year, but unlike a farmer a forester has more latitude of choice. He doesn't have to harvest his crop when it is ripe. But he can plant trees, control insects, and do many other operations only in season. Forestry must largely be tuned to the time of year when climatic and growth factors dictate. To illustrate this, the chart below, *"Forest Management Check List"* (Fig. 7–4), shows the way in which forestry operations can be distributed over the year to fit the natural cycle of forest growth. There is an added advantage in a chart such as this; it enables the

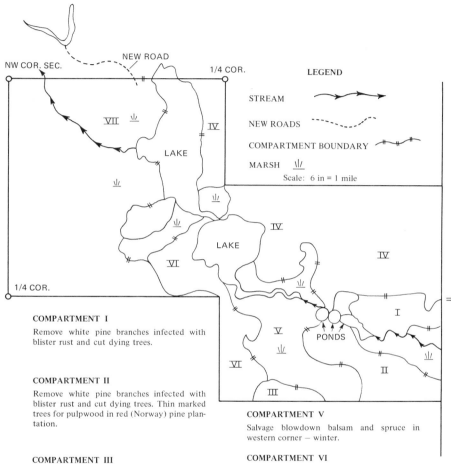

LEGEND

STREAM

NEW ROADS

COMPARTMENT BOUNDARY

MARSH

Scale: 6 in = 1 mile

COMPARTMENT I

Remove white pine branches infected with blister rust and cut dying trees.

COMPARTMENT II

Remove white pine branches infected with blister rust and cut dying trees. Thin marked trees for pulpwood in red (Norway) pine plantation.

COMPARTMENT III

Timber Sale – Using shelterwood system mark and cut 1/2 volume for preparatory cut (5,000 B.F.) – stumpage value $30/M.B.F.

COMPARTMENT IV

Blister rust control crew – one week early May – prune weevil on white pine; prune white pine, balsam fir, and red pine Christmas trees.

COMPARTMENT V

Salvage blowdown balsam and spruce in western corner – winter.

COMPARTMENT VI

Underplant aspen stand SW corner of lower lake with spruce stock from holding nursery.

COMPARTMENT VII

Plant spruce and Norway pine in openings; complete woods road to river with bulldozer.

(At end of season plot in locations of work, etc., and add map to records of past years.)

Fig. 7–3.   Compartment operations record map for one year. See also Fig. 6–6 and the management plan in Appendix C.

WHAT TO DO

PLANTING

ORDER SEEDLINGS _____

PREPARE PLANTING SITE _____

PLANT SEEDLINGS _____

PROTECTION

MAINTAIN FIREBREAKS _____

REPORT INSECTS AND DISEASES _____

MAINTAIN FENCES _____

TIMBER STAND IMPROVEMENT

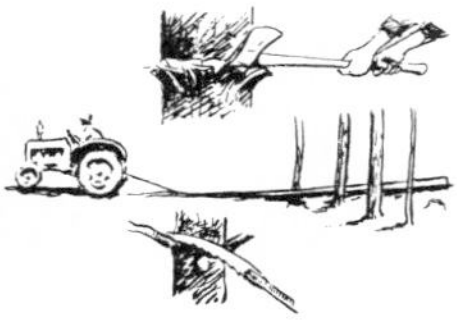

CONTROL WEED TREES _____

THIN CROWDED STANDS _____

PRUNE CROP TREES _____

RECREATION

MAINTAIN PICNIC AREAS _____

HARVESTING

CUT SAWLOGS, PULPWOOD, VENEER LOGS _____

CUT POLES, PILING AND OTHER PRODUCTS _____

Fig. 7–4. Seasonal forest management checklist and calendar. (American Forest Products Industries, Inc.)

WHEN TO DO IT

JAN	FEB	MAR	APR	MAY	JUNE	JULY	AUG	SEPT	OCT	NOV	DEC

Fig. 7—4. *(Continued)*

forest manager to keep his labor force fully occupied the year round.

MEASURING STUMPAGE VALUES

Determining the value of standing timber is a fairly complex process which is usually left to the specialist. Because a knowledge of the principles and the processes followed is useful, it is presented here to introduce the student to the subject. Forest owners seeking information on going prices of their own stumpage usually obtain local sales data from local forest industries, timber buyers, the State Extension foresters, or from local foresters with a knowledge of recent transactions.

Valuation of Timber

The primary objective is to determine the monetary value of timber when converted into various products such as lumber, pulpwood, railroad ties, etc. No attempt is made to estimate watershed, wildlife habitat, or other intangible (noncash) values. Essentially, standing timber values are the difference between production costs (of harvesting the logs and milling the products) and the selling prices of lumber or other products. A margin is also deducted for the profit and risk factors which must be accounted for. Thus stumpage is a residual value. Forest owners seeking information on going prices of their own stumpage usually obtain local sales data from public agencies or local foresters with a knowledge of recent transactions.

The methods of estimating timber value are fairly complex, involving the use of formulas which take into account the several variable factors influencing timber values. The first method used for smaller tracts which are cut over in short periods is called the "overturn method" and is the simplest to apply. From the sale values of the final products are subtracted the costs of logging, tranporting, and processing, leaving the stumpage, profit, and risk. Usually the latter two are determined from other logging and milling operations and subtracted from sales prices to give a net stumpage value.

The other method, called the "investment method," is used for large tracts of timber which may require a number of years to harvest. The formula used requires considerable data on plant and equipment investment, working capital, rates of depreciation, and other accounting information. The process also involves subtraction of total costs from values derived from the products carried through to the manufacturing stage.

The following is a simplified illustration of determining timber stumpage values by the overturn method:

Logging Cost per M.B.F.

Cutting	$ 4.00
Skidding	5.00
Hauling	8.00
Road building	2.00
Overhead	2.80
Total logging	$21.80

Milling

Sawing	$14.50
Handling	1.50
Piling	3.00
Overhead	1.90
Total milling	$20.90
Margin for risk	$ 2.00
Margin for profit	$ 4.00
Total of cost and margins	$48.70
Value of lumber per m.b.f.	$75.00
Value of stumpage per m.b.f. ($75.00 minus $48.70) =	$26.30

On large timber sales these calculations are made by a staff specialist familiar with the details as a result of several years of training and experience. The usual procedures for smaller timber owners and consulting foresters dealing with owners of tracts of a few hundred acres is to make inquiry on the going rate of stumpage sales in the vicinity during the recent months. Allowances are made for *accessibility,* for *quality of timber,* and for other factors which influence both the cost of logging and the value of the final product.

FOREST BUSINESS RECORDS

Systematic financial records are an essential part of any successful forest business. Although it is beyond the scope of this book to develop forest accounting in detail, an over-all review of the main features will be outlined briefly. Good accounting serves several important purposes: control over costs and income and hence profits, and for tax records. On smaller forests a *single-entry* accounting system may suffice, but on larger tracts under continuous management a *double-entry* system must be used. In setting up either system the advice of a professional accountant is recommended.

Single-Entry System (Small Forests)

The single-entry system is used mainly on smaller forest tracts or operations which have only seasonal production, and limited accounts are set up on separate sheets with the following suggested headings:

INCOME ACCOUNTS
Forest Products Income (Sales)
(Logs, lumber, pulpwood, other products)

Date	To Whom Sold	Quantity, Kind and Price (unit)	Amount Received
12/18/67	Art Nelson	24 m.b.f. rough pine lbr. @ $85	$2,040.00

Other Income

Date	Source	Kind	Amount Received
11/25/67	Wagner Scrap Co.	3 tons steel scrap @ $22	$ 66.00

Accounts Receivable

Date	From Whom	For (Products, Services, etc.)	Amount
12/31/67	Northland Pulpwood Co.	20 cords, spruce, pulpwood @ $24	$ 480.00

EXPENSE ACCOUNTS
Labor Hired (Logging, Decking, etc.)

Date	To Whom Paid	Hours Worked	Rate	Kind of Work	Amount Paid	Check No.
12/28/67	Ole Nordberg	40	$1.60/hr.	Skidding logs	$64.00	211

A separate sheet should be set up for each of the following:

Machine, Mill, and Truck Hire
Gasoline, Oil, and Fuel for Business
Water, Rent, Utilities for Business
Supplies Purchased
Cost of Repairs and Maintenance
Freight, Yardage, etc.
Taxes, Interest (incl. Social Security, Licenses, etc.)
Insurance Premiums
Other Expenses (Bad Debts, Losses, etc.)

The above should be set up with columns showing:

Date	To Whom Paid	For	Amount	Check No.
12/6/67	Superior Machinery Co.	Tractor Repair Parts	$24.37	162

Accounts payable should be provided for on separate sheets with appropriate headings.

In addition, a simple set of permanent accounts for the tract ownership should include:

1. Forest protection, management, planting, and improvements
2. Depreciation of equipment, machinery, and buildings
3. Capital account of initial land and timber investment, with provisions for additions through growth and subtraction through cutting
4. Depletion account to show reduction in timber capital
5. Inventory account showing logs and other forest products at the beginning and end of the year and interim changes

Double-Entry System (Medium and Large Forests)

The double-entry system is a more detailed and hence precise method of keeping business records. For large forest tracts and operations the double-entry method is recommended. It is suggested that the forest owner obtain the services of an accountant before setting up a double-entry accounting system.

The two basic records in a simple double-entry bookkeeping system are the *cash journal* and the *ledger*. The cash journal is usually in two parts, one for listing cash received and one for listing cash disbursed. Each day's cash receipts are listed, showing date, from whom received, the total received, and finally the nature of the receipt, e.g., sale of logs, sale of pulpwood and other forest products, etc. The first amount column (the total received) represents the increase in the bank account and is a *debit* item. The remaining columns describing the nature of the income are known as *credit* items. The cash disbursements are handled in a similar manner. Each check is listed by date, payee, number, the total amount, and the nature of the disbursement. The first amount column (the total amount of the check) represents the decrease in the bank account and is a credit item. The remaining columns, which describe the nature of the disbursement—which is either an expense or an increase in permanent additions to fixed capital— are known as debit items. Each month the cash journal is totaled and posted to the ledger.

The ledger consists of a separate sheet for each account, with a column for debit and credit postings. The accounts are usually grouped in the ledger in three sections—assets, liabilities, and net worth; income; and expense accounts. The net worth represents the initial investment plus or minus each year's profit or loss. The income and expense accounts are totaled each year and the totals transferred to the net worth account. Some of the major headings in the asset accounts include the following but can be expanded in detail as the enterprise grows:

Cash account
Capital accounts:
   Initial land and timber cost
   Permanent improvements:
     Roads
     Buildings
     Dams
     Other
   Forest development:
     Planting
     Protection improvement (fire lanes, towers, etc.)
   Other:
     Mechanical equipment
     Hand tools
   Reserve for depreciation and depletion
     (There is usually a separate reserve account for each category above, except land. These accounts have a credit balance representing a decrease in the value of the asset.)

Some of the more important headings in the current expense accounts will include logging, tree planting, machinery repair, building maintenance, road maintenance, utilities, insurance, taxes, wages paid (usually entered under the above items), depreciation and depletion, fire protection, and insect and disease control. Income accounts will include sale of logs, pulpwood, and other forest products, nursery stock sold (if any), and any other cash income received during the operating (fiscal) year. Two expense items which do not involve the outgo of cash are depreciation and depletion. An entry should be made in the ledger accounts each year debiting the expense account and crediting the reserve account for this expense. These two items should be handled with the assistance and advice of an accountant.

Forest Property Taxation

We would not think of including in the property tax assessment of farm lands the value of all crops raised up to today for we realize that farms could not operate with such a burden. And yet this is what we are doing in the case of woodlands when we annually assess the standing timber—taxing each year the accumulated timber crops of the past years' growth. But this is exactly what the general property tax does and it places an impossible burden on private forestry.

To alleviate the property tax burden on private owners many States have enacted special forest tax laws. These usually provide for a small basic tax on the land and a yield (income) tax on the timber stumpage when it is cut. State forestry departments are able to provide full information on the laws for each State—most of which differ considerably one from the other.

Income Taxes and Forests

The relationship of forest lands and forest production to Federal income tax laws is a highly complex one which can not be adequately treated in a paragraph. Forest owners who are keeping accurate records and accounts of expenditures and income by the accounting categories suggested previously, will be in the best position to deal with their income tax filing. The principal issues involved are whether expenditures made in the forest are production expenditures or capital expenditures related to long-term investment. Because Federal income tax laws change frequently, forest owners are advised to write to the Division of Forest Economics, Forest Service, U.S. Department of Agriculture, Washington, D.C., for the most recent bulletin dealing with this subject.

QUESTIONS

1. What is meant by sustained yield in forestry?
2. What is a cutting cycle?
3. What is a rotation?
4. Name five important items to be included in a forest management plan.
5. How does a sketch map aid in recording current forest operations?
6. Describe the method for determining stumpage values.
7. Describe the items included in production costs.
8. Name the two systems of accounting.

9. What are the two main account headings?

10. Give the two basic divisions used in the double-entry method of accounting.

11. Pine lumber is selling for $80 per m.b.f. rough, logging costs $20 per m delivered at the mill, sawing and piling costs $25, overhead $5. What is the stumpage value of a pine stand with 40 m.b.f.?

EXERCISES

1. Visit a large forest—national, industrial, or state—or an experimental research forest and examine the record system, maps, and forest management plan.

2. If you can locate a timber sale area in your locality, find out how stumpage values were determined.

3. Ask the owner of the stumpage what sort of contract he made with the buyer.

8

Logging and Measuring Forest Products

Logging has been described as the process of harvesting and hauling rough forest products from stump to the point of processing or sale. Felling trees, dividing them into the lengths desired, skidding, loading, and hauling them to market are all parts of the logging process. But before any logging is begun, many decisions must be made with regard to the layout of the logging operation, the equipment to be used, and the kinds of rough forest products which are to be cut. These decisions are dictated partly by the sizes and species of timber in the forest to be logged, partly by topography, and partly by the markets which are to be supplied.

Most forest products are sold as sawlogs, veneer logs, pulpwood, tie cuts (small sawlogs), bolts for a variety of uses (staves, shingles, excelsior, turnings, etc.), poles, posts, piling, and other products of more local importance (round mine timbers, charcoal wood, furnace poles, etc.). Sawlogs and pulpwood are our principal timber products. Specifications of some of the more important of these timber products are set forth at the end of this chapter.

Logging Methods and Equipment

Logging methods differ considerably between the Western mountain states and the states east of the Great Plains. Such factors as size of timber, topography, climate, type and skills of labor force, and transportation systems all influence equipment and systems to be used. Until World War I logging was largely man and animal labor with few mechanical devices to increase productivity. Trees were cut down with axe and cross cut saw, skidded with horses, mules, and oxen, loaded on wagons or sleighs by cross haul or gin poles, and finally put on railroad cars with animal-powered jammers (loaders). In the Western big timber, donkey engines with winches and steel cables were used to skid logs too large for animals.

Trucks for hauling and crawler tractors for skidding and road building were the major factors in improving logging efficiency during the years before World War II. Since then there has been a technological revolution in logging methods and equipment. Old time lumberjacks would find nothing familiar but the trees in modern logging operations.

Powered chain saws for small and large timber, crawler tractors for skidding, rubber-tired skidders, and loading winches are examples of the new equipment which has increased productivity in the woods so significantly in the Southern, Eastern, and Lake States forests.

In the great Douglas fir, spruce, and pine forests of the West crawler tractors are used for skidding in many situations, particularly on the steep slopes above the logging roads. Tractors can work downhill with the huge logs but not up. They cause a good deal of disturbance to young trees and to watershed soil mantle. However, the "skyline crane" and "high lead" methods are preferable because damage to residual stands and the soil is reduced. Skyline crane yarding of logs was introduced in North America in 1949 as a method of harvesting timber from steep, rugged topography where road construction is impractical or where soil disturbance would lead to excessive erosion and sedimentation. A skyline is normally suspended along the slope, with intermediate supports where needed to maintain adequate height above the ground. Logs are yarded laterally to the skyline, lifted free of the ground by the crane or carriage, and transported down the skyline to a landing which is usually in the canyon bottom. Distance to the landing may be as much as one mile.

With conventional "high-lead" yarding (Fig. 8–1), the main line is fed through a block high on a spar tree or steep crane to provide a lift or "high-lead" to the logs. This helps prevent the logs from gouging out soil as they move along and helps them ride up and over stumps and other obstructions. Logs drag on the ground

Fig. 8—1. High-Lead Logging uses spar tree to support cables and pulleys for moving logs from stump to central deck powered by stationary diesel unit and winches.

all the way to the landing, which is usually on a ridgetop. Maximum yarding distance seldom exceeds 1,000 feet, and the average is usually under 500. The longer yarding distances possible with skyline yarding permit a road density less than one-third that needed for conventional high-lead yarding, thereby reducing construction costs, soil disturbance, and area taken out of timber production.

Labor Force

The logging camp of yesterday is all but gone with good roads and easy access to the woods by car. Single men made up the logging work force in a logging camp. Today young married men living at home and driving to work have taken their places. The logger must be a skilled worker and machine operator who has had vocational instruction. Woods workers' wages and salaries have risen to levels comparable with other skills, but the forest industries have found they have had to operate training courses in order to attract and keep their labor force abreast of technological changes.

While the logging camp is restricted to only a few remote areas in the West and the Canadian timber country today, temporary housing is sometimes provided in difficult locations elsewhere with auto trailers or logging shacks which can be hauled from place to place.

Logging, Forestry Practices, and Watershed Management

Judicious harvesting of trees is a major part of forest management. Therefore, control over the use and type of machinery is a major element in success or failure in applied forestry. Of course, clear cutting systems require little care except to limit the size of the cuttings. Partial cuttings with marked trees require care in removal of product to avoid damage to residual stand and young trees. Not all modern, efficient equipment is efficient in applied silviculture. Thus, it will be important to choose carefully the machinery to be used as related to silvicultural objectives.

Because logging and logging roads on steep slopes concentrate water runoff, gully and sheet erosion may result unless special precautions are followed. Not only is there a loss of site quality but siltation of streams can seriously impair fish habitats. Foresters working with soil conservationists in the Redwood region of California have recommended a series of practices which are designed to minimize the damage:

(1) Leave buffer strips of timber along stream bottoms and small waterways to prevent slash and logging residue from entering streams. This practice has high aesthetic value and provides a seed tree source for nearby logged-over lands.

(2) Construct roads on lowest grades possible and prevent water concentration both by use of frequent water bars and dumping water into brushy areas not likely to gully.

(3) Avoid logging all areas over 50% slope—especially those likely to slide because of skidding disturbance.

(4) If clear cutting is followed on steep slopes, it should be in

small patches of 20 acres or less and immediately replanted to assure an early ground cover.

Preliminary Planning and Construction

Logging on large tracts of timber takes a great deal more advance planning and construction than in smaller woodland ownerships. Except where logs are taken out by water, there must be available both "feeder" logging roads and high standard trunk roads. Main trunk lines of railroads are still extensively used but logging spur lines are fast disappearing. Logging "drives" on Canadian rivers are still used for pulpwood in a few places, but elsewhere they have disappeared into the romantic past of this colorful industry.

Road building, then, must be the first step preceding actual logging of large forest tracts. Today most lumber companies use large trucks for the initial haul of logs from the woods. These require good roads, frequently graveled, and wide enough for two-way traffic. Construction of the truck road must be started well in advance of actual logging operations. It involves careful planning and execution. Roads in hilly country must follow gradual grades, and in laying them out, a topographic map with contours is extremely useful. Hand levels are used to determine the exact location on the ground. Grades should generally not exceed ten to twelve per cent (vertical rise of ten to twelve feet per 100 feet of distance). Anything steeper is dangerous and causes hard wear on trucks as well as greater erosion. Locating the road is an engineering job and requires considerable training, but the principles are fairly simple. A base map must be available, preferably topographic, on which the road may be plotted. Where the road travels along hillsides, it is cut on one side and filled over on the other (Fig. 8–2). Where roads cross hills and low spots. the hills are cut through and the lows are filled in with the material removed. Where sufficient "fill" material is not available from the cuts, a "borrow pit" is required.

Curves must be planned for safe travel of trucks, and so cannot be too sharp. Road surfaces in most cases must be graveled so that they will stand up under the extremely heavy wear and tear from logging and weather, and if heaving and chuck holes are to be avoided. Proper drainage is necessary to carry off excess water during rainy weather. In order to cross large streams and rivers, bridges must be constructed. Ordinarily, with plenty of timber

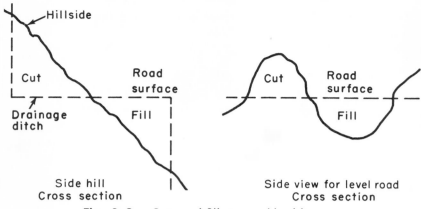

Fig. 8–2.   Cuts and fills in road building.

available for construction material, this can be done at relatively low cost, but the principles of good bridge construction engineering must be strictly adhered to if loads are to be carried safely across. Since these are engineering problems, the details will not be developed here. However, where small streams are to be crossed, wooden or steel culverts are often adequate and cheaper than bridge building, especially where length of service is a consideration. It is important that the culverts over streams be amply large to take care of flood waters.

PLANNING THE LOGGING JOB

Forest technicians should understand some of the important principles of getting logs out of the woods. Before considering them, it will be wise to establish the essential steps to be used in setting up a logging plan:

1. Prepare a good and accurate forest cover type map showing both variations in stand density and in the topography.
2. Lay out a permanent road system designed for frequent future use. Include log landings, main skidding trails, and turn-arounds, correcting the existing road system where necessary. Put roads on gradual slopes and avoid locations which will result in excessive runoff and erosion.
3. Relate the entire road system for accessibility to the nearest public road.
4. Make plans to insure that the trees will be cut up into the highest grade forest products possible so as to utilize the entire com-

mercial length of the tree. This means that the log sizes and specifications for the whole tree length should be set forth clearly to the labor force in advance of bucking, to obtain maximum quality.

5. Instruct log skidders to avoid breakage of young trees and to avoid gouging out skidding trails, which will cause erosion. Where such gouging is unavoidable, heal the scars immediately after logging by piling brush in the trail, or seeding with grass seed. Put in simple devices to carry off excess water on steep skid trails.

6. Check loggers as they cut to see that they log only marked trees. Absence of paint marks or blazes on the stumps means that unmarked timber has been cut.

PROCEDURES FOLLOWED IN LOGGING

Because most forestry-trained men work on large logging operations, more attention will be given to methods used on them. Essentially, the logging operation involves cutting down the tree (felling), sawing it up into proper lengths (bucking), dragging it over the ground (skidding) to a road where it is piled (decked) for loading onto a truck. Frequently, when small or moderate-sized timber is being cut, the full tree length is dragged to the landing by the road or water side, and bucking is done there. This makes possible more economical skidding with present-day equipment, and not only more economical but also more intelligent bucking. When bucking is concentrated at the landing, the crew can be better trained and supervised to obtain the maximum quality and quantity of the products desired. The processes by which these operations are accomplished vary widely, depending on the size of the timber, the topography, the machinery and equipment used, and the products produced. The reader is referred to the *Forestry Handbook** for information on the design and structures used in logging.

Pulpwood logging is the simplest. In pine woods the small trees are cut into 4- to 8-ft. lengths, depending on the specifications, and are carried out to a woods road where they are often loaded directly onto trucks by hand or with self-loaders mounted on trucks. Pine pulp sticks are often piled in "pens" in the South or decked in the North for partial drying and measurement. This is probably the simplest of all logging because pine forests are

* See Bibliography.

usually open and level. In heavy hardwoods or in conifer swamps in the North, teams or tractors generally skid out the pulpwood to a landing where it is piled and loaded. On "stumpwood" operations, where bucking is done in the woods, the cut sticks are brought out on "scoots" or drays to a landing where they are decked, or loaded directly on trucks. Haul roads must be built in advance and, where winters involve a lot of snow, provision must be made for snow plowing.

In bigger timber, where sawlogs are the primary product, cutting and transportation are more complex and require heavier equipment for handling. As recently as World War II, much timber in the eastern United States was cut and skidded by men and teams of horses. Tractors and trucks had made some headway, but mechanical self-loaders and chain saws were still largely experimental. These new developments have taken much of the sweat and back-breaking labor out of logging, but it still is a hard and hazardous business. In the Douglas fir and redwood regions, heavy wire cables powered with diesel-driven winches have been used for many years to skid logs over the ground or through the air (on skyline "high-lead" systems). In either case the logs are brought out to roads and decked, ready to be loaded onto trucks or railroad cars.

Each of the major steps in logging is carried out in the following order, with the equipment described:

1. The logging area is laid out with main haul roads and smaller skid roads, which are usually built in advance of cutting. In order to assign a specific parcel of timber to each logger, a cutting area with sufficient timber to last several weeks is laid out. The boundaries of these areas are marked either with paint or blazes.

2. *Felling*, *limbing*, and *bucking* are all part of the process of preparing logs. As a first step the tree is usually notched with an axe (power saw notches are now quite common) on the side toward which it is to be dropped (Fig. 8–3). The sawyer then takes his power saw and saws into the tree at a point on the opposite side of the tree stem from the undercut notch, so as to come out just above the bottom of the notch. Wedges are frequently used to keep the saw from pinching and to start the tree tipping in the direction desired. Careful loggers usually fell the tree into openings to avoid "hanging up" and to reduce damage to young trees as much as possible. Before it falls, they yell "T-I-M-B-E-R" to warn others out of the way.

Limbing the fallen tree is the next step. This may be done either

Fig. 8–3. Undercutting with a power saw. The sawyer is notching the big ponderosa pine on the side where he wants it to fall. (American Forest Products Industries, Inc.)

with the axe or saw, depending on the size of the limbs. In either case, they are cut off flush with the surface of the tree bole so that there will be no projections to retard skidding or cause accidents.

Bucking the fallen tree into log lengths may be done either in the woods or at the landing. In either case, decisions must be made by the logger in such a way as to make the best use of the full tree trunk. If the tree is perfectly straight, he can cut it up into uniform 16-ft. logs or into whatever other lengths the specifications may indicate. However, any small crooks, a defect, or a fork will dictate where the log should be cut, and lengths of 8, 10, 12, or 16 ft. may result. In big West Coast timber 32-ft. logs are commonly cut. To make an allowance for trimming boards squarely after they are sawn, loggers leave an additional 2 or 3 in. beyond these specified lengths. In sawing through the downed tree to make logs, the cut is usually made from the top side down through most of the trunk. At this point the tree may begin to pinch the saw, and either a wedge is driven in or the saw is removed so that the cut may be finished from underneath. Sometimes upside down bucking or "plunge cutting" (with a chain saw) from the middle down, and then up, is called for in the interest of safety or conservation of material.

3. The operation of skidding the logs or tree lengths may be accomplished by a number of different methods. In the Northern snow country where swamps are common, teams of horses are still used, after the ice has formed in the winter, but rubber-tired diesel equipment which can load and haul logs has all but replaced horse power even on small farmer-logger operations (Fig. 8–4).

Fig. 8–4. Mechanized, rubber-tired equipment with a self-loading clam hoist which can be maneuvered into nearly every kind of terrain is not only putting the last of the logging horses out of work but making it possible to harvest timber in summer from wet swamps. (Norfilm Service)

In the South larger softwood operators cut and skid tree lengths to a temporary deck, buck into lengths, debark, saw into lumber and chip slabs, edging and tops for shipment to pulp mills. In the West logging arches pulled by larger crawler tractors are used in ponderosa pine, whereas in the mountains "high-lead" cable systems are still common. The tractor has become a very popular skidding device all over the country because it is so adaptable, has tremendous power, and is highly maneuverable (Fig. 8–5). Power is hooked onto logs in a number of ways, but a chain or cable used as a choker loop or tongs which grip the log or tree length are usual. Skidding pans are sometimes used to lift the front ends of the logs off the ground and keep them from grinding in grit and gravel (which damage the saw). Logging arches or sulkies are even more common. Pulpwood is seldom skidded but is piled alongside narrow trails by the cutter. If the ground is suitable for trucking, it is loaded directly onto trucks. If not, it is loaded onto scoots with runners and pulled by tractors to decks.

Fig. 8–5. Skidding pine timber to log deck with crawler tractor and rubber-tired log lift. (American Forest Products Industries, Inc.)

4. Some pulpwood is peeled in the woods in the spring, when the sap is running. The use of a barking spud for peeling removes both outer and inner bark. Sodium arsenite has recently been employed successfully to prolong the peeling season. The chemical is applied to girdles around the trees some months in advance of logging, and the bark loosens so as to permit peeling at any time.

However, here again mechanical equipment has taken over from hand techniques. Mechanical log barkers are now extensively used at pulpwood landings and concentration points. These strip off the bark (and some wood) through rapidly rotating knives in a drum (Fig. 8–6). The advantages of this step are rapid drying out of moisture and, hence, lower freight costs, closer piling in shipment, and wood easily stored free from bark borers at the mill yard. Debarking of sawlogs is usually done at the sawmill. Slabs, formerly wasted or burned, are now converted into pulp chips.

Fig. 8–6. Machine peeling pulpwood in the woods. (U. S. Forest Service)

5. Tree length logging is also becoming more and more common. Instead of cutting logs into proper length in the woods, the full merchantable length is hauled to a log landing (thus requiring fewer units to be handled individually). The tree is then often sawed on a moving chain into sawlogs, pulpwood sticks, or other rough products. Debarking in a tree length often precedes this process.

6. Loading trucks with logs is the next step, and a variety of equipment and methods is used. The most common of these in the past has been the "gin pole" or "jammer." This is essentially moveable powered boom sticks which have cables for lifting the logs from the log deck onto the body of the truck. More recently, revolving boom power loaders on wheels or crawler tracks for big sawlogs, or tractors with fork lifts on the front, have been commonly used in smaller timber. Several types of "chain" loaders have been developed which are installed directly on the hauling trucks. Loaders vary greatly in size and design; they range from

the truck-mounted log "jammer" used by the small part-time logger to the cat-mounted crane used at mill sites or sidings. The small to medium hydraulic loader has proved the most economical for most eastern U. S. forest operations. The hydraulic-boom, clam-grapple type can be mounted on the hauling device or on the rear of a crawler tractor. The front-end, fork-grapple type can be mounted on a tracked or rubber-tired tractor. The type of loader to be used in any particular situation, of course, will depend on its planned use in the over-all harvesting operation.

7. To transport the logs, there are many different types of primary and secondary equipment. These include the extremes of 2- to 3-cord capacity, small, stake-body trucks and 12-cord semitrailers and the 35-cord gondolas used in rail transportation. Unit production costs vary with volume, weight, and size of the material, size of the truck trailer or rail car, road conditions, distance from market, delays, and stand-by time. Small volumes cannot be hauled economically for long distances. The secret to economic hauling for any distance is to minimize delay, loading, and stand-by time.

8. Some of the newly developing kinds of equipment for harvesting and transporting can be grouped into two general classifications, each descriptive of the work it does in the total job: combines or harvesters and processors.

Combines or Harvesters

Combines are relatively new in the logging industry. They can be used to very good advantage under moderate slope (5 to 10 per cent) conditions when clear-cutting timber. Each machine which performs more than one of the harvesting operations cuts, limbs, and skids tree lengths in consecutive steps (Fig. 8–7). This is especially adapted to forest plantations where trees grow in rows like corn. Mowing down a group of rows this forest combine piles tree-length logs on top of its steel cab and hauls them back to a log deck on a main road. Ground skidding is eliminated as well as costly handling of each piece of timber. At the log decks in the woods or at the mill, the tree length is bucked into appropriate products and then sorted out.

Processors

Processors have been designed to perform two or more parts of the harvesting operation. One type of processor barks, chips,

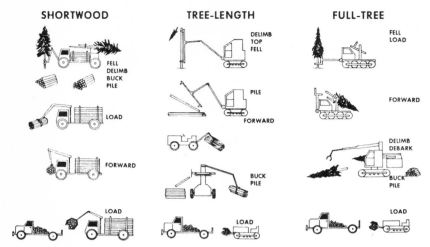

Fig. 8–7. Processing steps of three fully mechanized harvesting systems.

and loads, whereas others perform such operations as barking and slashing. Auxiliary logging equipment must be available to complement the operation of each processor. For example, some of the processors accomplish the loading operation while others do not. Many units are still in the experimental stage.

Logging in the Future

While the new kinds of equipment have wrought great changes in timber harvesting during the past decade even more amazing machinery is now being tested. To get into some of the more remote mountain forests, both helicopters and balloons are being used in place of high-lead spar logging. One revolutionary new method of logging utilizes a giant helium-filled balloon which acts as a "sky hook" to pull logs out of mountainous terrain. The U. S. Forest Service estimates that 26 million acres of inaccessible forest in the Pacific Northwest and Alaska would be opened to harvest by this method. These have the added advantages of reducing destruction of adjacent timber and eliminating all feeder roads. Watershed soils are left intact because ground skidding is all but eliminated. If these new developments can be perfected to commercial use, nearly a billion more board feet of timber could be harvested at a saving of 20% in the logging cost because road building would be greatly reduced.

Logging Equipment Operation and Maintenance

Logging operations, as well as nearly every other phase of forestry, require the use of many types of machinery, hand tools, and other types of equipment. One of the first jobs of the forest manager is to keep an accurate account of all types of machinery and tools, keep them in repair, and maintain them properly. A burned-out tractor or a fire because of an oil leak can mean the loss of lives and valuable timber. On a logging job, breakdowns due to worn-out and unrepaired parts can result in higher costs, lower production, and the loss of jobs. Such minor matters as cleaning out paint guns after marking timber, sharpening axes in spare time, checking the sprayers on back pumps for clogging and rust, and other minor but essential jobs of this sort should be no problem to a man with a sense of responsibility. Keeping up on these matters means observing how the equipment is working and when it needs attention. And it is wise to remember that tools can get lost much more easily than they can be found. A good record system will prevent such losses.

Safety Precautions in the Woods

Woods work is one of the most hazardous of occupations primarily because too many people forget elementary precautions and become careless. Trees dropped without warning, logs falling off poorly chained trucks, and logs carelessly skidded around corners are all common causes of accidents. Men who do not know how to use an axe or saw frequently end up with bad cuts. Many accidents are prevented by having safety meetings and by placing precaution signs in bunkhouses and other locations constantly to remind the workers against carelessness. One of the primary responsibilities of a forest manager on the job is to keep men from getting hurt. Preventing accidents saves times, pain, and trips to a doctor, and also saves money. The most dangerous operations and the safety precautions that should be followed to prevent accidents are:

1. Carrying tools. Carry an axe by grasping the handle near the head; never over the shoulder. When a power saw is carried in the woods, the motor should be turned off. Men unaccustomed to working in the woods are not as sure-footed as full-time lumberjacks. For this reason, it pays to give more than normal attention to one's footing and the path one is following (Fig. 8–8).

Fig. 8–8. Logging safety precautions. (1) Most satisfactory way of felling a straight tree: (a) undercut, (b) saw cut, (c) felling wedge. (2) Improper undercuts cause kickbacks. (3) The wrong way of carrying tools is shown at the left. If this man stumbles, he may injure himself with the axe. The right way to carry tools is shown at the right. (U. S. Forest Service)

2. Felling. In felling trees, the most important point is to make the undercut to a depth of at least one-fourth the diameter of the tree. Make felling cuts slightly above the undercut (Fig. 8–3). Clear the brush and any debris from the ground several feet in all directions from the tree so that when it falls workmen can move to safe positions without danger from tripping or falling. Tools when not in use should be kept at a safe distance from activity in order to avoid danger in tripping or falling over them. When the tree begins to fall, the workmen should move off to a safe distance at one side (not in back) of the tree both to avoid any falling debris or "kickback" of the butt.

3. Trimming. It is important that the cutter stand on the side of the tree opposite from which he is cutting the limbs. If it becomes necessary to trim up short lengths after they have been bucked, the axe should be grasped close to the head and short strokes used. Never grasp the axe close to the end of the handle when trimming short lengths.

4. Skidding. Skidding logs is dangerous, especially at the time the skidding chain is being fastened. Walk back of the load if possible; if not, watch for obstructions and change sides to avoid being sideswiped.

MEASURING FOREST PRODUCTS (SCALING)

One of the most common jobs on the logging operation, for a man with woods experience or training, is measuring cut logs and pulpwood. This is done so as to keep an accurate record of daily or weekly production, and, if the timber belongs to someone else, to make payments based on volume.

Scaling Sawlogs

There are four steps in scaling sawlogs (Fig. 8–9):

Fig. 8–9. Scaling decked pine logs. As the logs are scaled, the net reading is entered on the log scale tally sheet (Fig. 8–10) and the log marked with a crayon to prevent double counting. (U. S. Forest Service)

1. Measure the diameter in inches and the length in feet. The diameter of the log is measured at the small end, inside the bark. Since the end of the log is frequently not a perfect circle, two measurements are usually taken, one across the widest diameter of the circle and one across the narrowest diameter. Then the two measurements are averaged. The length of the log is measured in even feet after allowing about 3 in. at the end for trim. The volumes are entered on a log scale tally sheet (Fig. 8–10).

2. Deductions for defects are necessary to give correct net volumes. Logs with crook or sweep are reduced by sighting a line

LOCATION OF LANDING							DATE:		19
LOG NO.	SPECIES								
	SUGAR MAPLE	YELLOW BIRCH	BEECH	HEMLOCK	WHITE PINE	RED OAK	ELM	MISC. CONIFERS	MISC. HARDWOODS
	(Net scale in board feet)								
1									
2									
3									
4									
5									
6									
7									
8									
9									
0									
1									
2									
3									
4									
5									
6									
7									
8									
9									
0									
TOTALS									

Fig. 8–10.   Log scale tally sheet.

from center to center of the two ends of the log. Then take the number of inches this line deviates from the center of the log at the point of maximum sweep, subtract two, and divide the remainder by the diameter of the small end of the log. The result is the sweep deduction, from gross scale, in per cent. Interior defects such as rot, and exterior defects such as catfaces, are deducted by figuring the board footage to be lost and deducting this from gross scale. A handy alignment chart for figuring such deductions is given in Fig. 8–11. Kinds of defects are shown in Fig. 8–12.

Log grading has developed into an important quality measure in recent years. Log grades vary from region to region by species. The University of Wisconsin Extension Service has described the process of grading and general principles involved* (see Fig. 8–13).

3. Record the information called for, for each of the measured logs, on the log tally sheet. The record is made following the procedure for tree scale tally. Logs should be numbered with a crayon on the small end as they are tallied so they will not be counted again, and also so that a check scale can be made of the same logs should disagreement arise. The log volume tables shown in Table 8–1 are the basis for the figures used on a log rule.

4. Total the net scale volume for each species (which may be sold at a different price) and the grand total volume scaled.

Scaling Piled Pulpwood

Pulpwood is seldom scaled until it is piled in the woods or loaded on trucks or cars. Many operators and mills now use weight rather than gross stacked volume as a fairer unit of measurement. When stacked volume is used, all three dimensions of the pile are measured and then multiplied to obtain the gross cubic foot volume. This is then divided by 128 to give the number of cords. For example, a truck has a load 12 ft. long, 8 ft. wide, and 4 ft. high, a total of 384 cu. ft. Dividing this by 128 shows that the truck has a 3-cord load. A short cut is found in multiplying the length times the height, dividing by 16: $12 \times 4 = 48 \div 16 = 3$ cords.

---

* "Log Grades," Extension Service, College of Agriculture, University of Wisconsin, Special Circular 60; revised 1965; with the cooperation of the Northern Hardwood and Pine Manufacturers Association. The Scribner Decimal C Log Rule is used here as the standard log rule.

$$\text{Board feet} = \frac{W'' \times H'' \times L'}{16} \text{ or } \frac{(D'')^2 \, L'}{16} \text{ (for circular defect)}$$

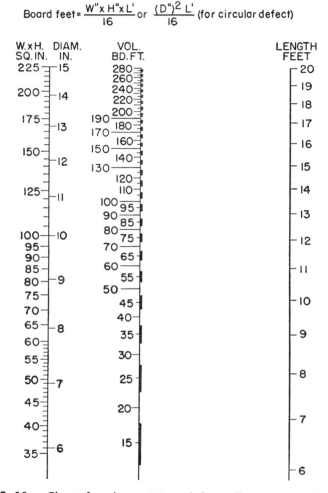

Fig. 8–11. Chart for determining defect allowance, with the International ¼" log rule. Instructions:

1. Measure width and height of defect, in inches. Add 1 in. to each defect to allow for waste.
2. Multiply width by height.
3. Measure or estimate length of defect.
4. Place a straightedge through product of $W \times H$ (left line) and length (right line).
5. Read deduction, to nearest 5 bd. ft. on center line.

Example: If a defect measured 7" × 8" × 10", the deduction would be determined by holding the straightedge through 72 on the left line

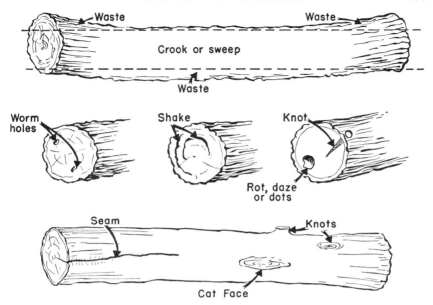

Fig. 8–12. Kinds of defects in sawlogs. (Redrawn from U. S. Soil Conservation Service)

Deductions are made for rot, undersized wood (usually less than 4 in. at the small end), abnormal voids, etc., by measuring the squared area and converting this into cubic volume.

In the South, pulpwood is piled in "pens" in the woods. Pens are layers of two sticks each, piled to form a hollow crib 6 ft. high. The number of such pens is sometimes used as a basis for paying piece workers. However, many mills are now buying pulpwood by weight; lengths may be odd.

The following tabulations are helpful in determining the number of sticks of 8-ft. pulpwood per cord. They clearly show that

---

(7″ + 1″) × (8″ + 1″) and 10 on the right line. The deduction, read from the center line, is 45 bd. ft.

The board foot deductions thus obtained can be used with the Scribner Scale. For the Doyle Rule, the following factors should be applied to the deductions:

Logs 8 in. to 11 in.: 0.6
       12 in. to 13 in.: 0.8
       14 in. to 20 in.: 0.9
       21 in. to 31 in.: none

Source: U. S. Forest Service, *National Forest Scaling Handbook.*

Hardwoods

Grade No. 1 or Veneer Grade

<u>Diameter:</u> All logs must be 12" or larger in average diameter, as measured from the small end inside the bark.

<u>Length:</u> Standard lengths are 8'6", 10'6", 12'4", 16'4" and 17'. Other lengths may be cut, optional with buyer. Note: 4" to 6" must be added to length for trimming allowance.

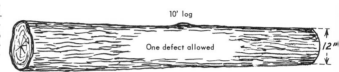

10' log

One defect allowed

12"

<u>Quality:</u> All logs must be cut from fresh, green timber. Diagrams indicate maximum number of standard defects allowed for various log lengths. Any number of defects located so that they can be cut out in one foot will be considered as only one defect.

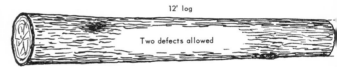

12' log

Two defects allowed

<u>Standard defects:</u> Worm holes, knots, bumps, shake, cat faces, dead and dozy spots, bird pecks, brown spots, pin holes or specified seams are standard defects. <u>Scale off one foot in length for each defect, except for center holes and seams allowed in this grade (see page 2).</u>

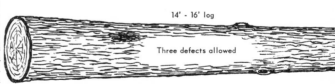

14' - 16' log

Three defects allowed

Select Veneer Grade

<u>Diameter:</u> Logs must be 14" or larger in average diameter at small end inside bark.

<u>Length:</u> Standard lengths include 7'6", 8'6", 10'6", 12'4", 16'4", and 17'. All lengths are optional with buyer.

<u>Quality:</u> Select Veneer Grade must be free of all defects, except as provided for center hole defects in Grade No. 1. Logs must straight. But, logs 14'4" over may have a slight sw provided one center cut make two straight bolts.

Fig. 8–13. Log grades and specifications. The Scribner Decimal C Log Rule is used here as the Standard log rule. (From "Log Grades," Extension Service, College of Agriculture, University of Wisconsin, with the cooperation of the Northern Hardwood and Pine Manufacturers Association.)

ter Rot or Hole: Logs 14" in average diameter may have a 3" hole, doze or shake in the heart; 15" in average diameter may have a 5" center defect, and 16" and over in diameter a 6" center defect. There is no deduction in scale for these defects. Logs 16" and over in diameter with center defects greater than allowable size are acceptable if such defects will be reduced to allowable size by deducting 2' from scaling length.

ms: No seam is allowed in logs 15" or smaller in diameter. Logs over 15" are allowed one tight, straight seam (such as caused by lightning or frost), not deviating more than 4" from a straight line stretched from end to end of log. An allowable seam counts as one defect with no deduction in scale.

ep: All logs must be reasonably straight. Sweep up to 1/6 of diameter of small end is allowed in logs 10'6" and shorter, when measured above the butt swell.

al Grain: Allowed in not more than 1" in 10" of log length. Excessively curly grain will not be accepted in any veneer grades.

Defects: Any defect in butt of log, such as fold, fluted bark, or shallow scar, not extending inside the diameter of the small end, will not be considered a grading defect. No scale deduction will be made. (Applies to all other grades.)

ches or Kinks: Crotches, crooks or kinks are to be scaled out when located so that a veneer log can be obtained.

Maple Stain: One half diameter of small end may be black heart or heavy mineral stain, with no deduction in scale.

CENTER ROT OR HOLE

SEAMS

STRAIGHT LINE

4"

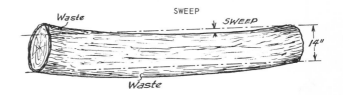

Waste

SWEEP

SWEEP

14"

Waste

SPIRAL GRAIN

1"

10"

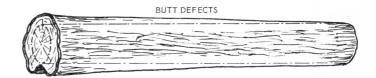

BUTT DEFECTS

CROTCHES OR KINKS

Fig. 8–13. *(Continued)*

179

Grade No. 2

Length: Standard lengths are 8'6",
10'6", and 12'6" or longer.
Proportion of 8'6" logs is optional with buyer. A trimming
allowance of 6" must be added
to standard lengths. No logs
are admitted with a net scale of
less than 50% of gross scale,
with a minimum of 30 board
feet for each log.

Diameter: All logs must be 10" or
larger in average diameter.
Logs 8'6" must be surface clear
butt logs (except basswood) with
a diameter of 10". Logs 8'6" to
10'6" must have a diameter 11"
or larger and 10" basswood or
larger. They must have 2/3 or
each of 3 faces clear in not
more than 2 cuttings per face
(cuttings 3' or longer). Logs
12'6" or longer must have a
diameter 11" or larger and 10"
basswood or larger with 2/3 of
each of 3 faces clear in not
more than 3 cuttings per face
(cuttings 3' or longer). A face
is a portion of log extending 1/4
of the circumference of the entire log length.

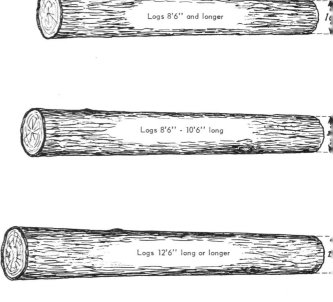

End Defects

Defects: End defects in Grade No.
2 logs may consist of black-
heart, mineral stain, heart rot
and shake. Defects on small
end must amount to less than
1/2 of average diameter for log
to be admitted to Grade No. 2.

If defect on small end of log 16"
or larger in diameter amounts
to less than 60% of average diameter of small end, log is
admitted to Grade No. 2.

Any defect in butt logs occurring outside diameter of small
end is not a grading defect.
These include shallow catfaces,
folds, fluted butt bark.

Sweep accompanied by end defects more than 1/4 of diameter
at small end, causing a gross
scale deduction of 20% or more,
is not admitted to Grade No. 2.

Logs 10" - 15" diameter

Logs 16" and over in diameter

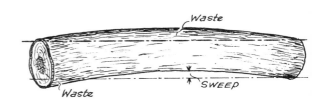

Fig. 8—13. *(Continued)*

Grade No. 3

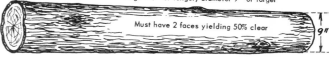

Logs 8'6" or longer, diameter 9" or larger

Must have 2 faces yielding 50% clear

9"

Diameter: All logs which do not qualify for Grade No. 2 must be 9" or larger in diameter to qualify for Grade No. 3. Logs under 14" are allowed with a net scale of less than 50% of gross scale, with a minimum of 30 board feet required in each log. Logs over 14" average diameter are permitted with a net scale of 33-1/3% gross scale.

Length: Logs which do not qualify for Grade No. 2 must be 8'6" or longer to qualify for Grade No. 3. The proportion of 8'6" logs allowed is optional with buyer.

Quality: Must have 2 faces yielding 50% clear.

Tie Cuts

Length: Lengths are 8' or 8'6" as specified. A 2" trimming allowance is required on all cuts.

Diameter: Minimum average diameter is 9" at the small end.

Quality: Tie cuts or bolts must be cut from sound, green timber, free from decay, split, shake, holes, large or numerous knots or other defects impairing strength or durability of railroad ties. If otherwise suitable, dead cedar and tamarack are acceptable.

Softwoods

White Pine

Veneer Grade: Logs must be 16" or larger in diameter and 10' or longer in length. They must be at least 75% clear on each of 3 faces. All knots outside clear cutting must be sound and not over 2-1/2" in diameter.

Grade No. 1. Logs must be 12" or larger and 10' or longer; at least 50% clear on each side of three faces or 75% clear on two faces. Logs must have a net scale after defect deduction of at least 50% gross log volume.

Grade No. 2: Logs must be 12" or over in diameter and 8' or longer in length with a net scale after reduction of at least 50% gross log volume.

Other Softwoods

Norway and jack pine, spruce, white cedar, tamarack, hemlock, balsam fir and aspen logs are included. White pine logs less than 12" in diameter also are included.

Logs must be 9" or over in diameter and 8' or longer in length and have a net scale after deduction for defects of at least 50% gross log volume. Minimum net log scale admitted is 20 board feet.

Ted Peterson
Extension Forester

Fig. 8–13. *(Continued)*

TABLE 8–1

Log Rules for Scaling Board Foot Content of Logs (Scribner, Doyle, and International Rules)

Diameter Inside Bark, Small End (inches)	Scribner°					Doyle					International†				
	8	10	12	14	16	8	10	12	14	16	8	10	12	14	16
6	5	10	12	14	18	–	–	–	–	–	10	10	15	15	20
7	10	10	18	24	28	–	–	–	–	–	10	15	20	25	30
8	10	20	24	28	32	8	10	12	14	16	15	20	25	35	40
9	20	30	30	35	40	13	16	19	22	25	20	30	35	45	50
10	30	30	40	45	50	18	23	27	32	36	30	35	45	55	65
11	30	40	50	55	65	25	31	37	43	49	35	45	55	70	80
12	40	50	59	69	79	32	40	48	56	64	45	55	70	85	95
13	50	60	73	85	97	41	51	61	71	81	55	70	85	100	115
14	60	70	86	100	114	50	63	75	88	100	65	80	100	115	135
15	70	90	107	125	142	61	76	91	106	121	75	95	115	135	160
16	80	100	119	139	159	72	90	108	126	144	85	110	130	155	180
17	90	120	139	162	185	85	106	127	148	169	95	125	150	180	205
18	110	130	160	187	213	98	123	147	172	196	110	140	170	200	230
19	120	150	180	210	240	113	141	169	197	225	125	155	190	225	260
20	140	170	210	245	280	128	160	192	224	256	135	175	210	250	290
21	150	190	228	266	304	145	181	217	253	289	155	195	235	280	320
22	170	210	251	292	334	162	203	243	284	324	170	215	260	305	355
23	190	230	283	330	377	181	226	271	316	361	185	235	285	335	390
24	210	250	303	353	404	200	250	300	350	400	205	255	310	370	425
25	230	290	344	401	459	221	276	331	386	441	220	280	340	400	460

Length of Log (in Feet)

° The Scribner Decimal C Rule drops the right-hand digit by rounding off the next digit to the nearest 10 bd. ft.

† Recognized as most accurate.

small sized wood requires many more trees to make a cord. It is better to let them grow larger before cutting.

Approximate Number of Trees per Cord		Number of Sticks of 8-ft. Pulpwood Required per Cord	
D.B.H.	Number of Trees	Top	Per Cord
5	91	3"	217
6	35	4"	125
7	21	5"	79
8	13	6"	54
9	9	7"	38
10	7	8"	31
11	6	9"	24
12	5	10"	20
13	4	11"	16
14	3	12"	14

Measuring Pulpwood by Weight

In recent years many pulp and paper mills have been buying pulpwood from producers on a weight (tonnage) basis. It is felt that this more accurately reflects actual cellulose content and further, that much odd length and crooked material now wasted will be utilized. Production costs are cut both in special efforts to size pulpwood and in scaling both in the woods and at the mill. The following table gives an approximate range of 128 cubic foot cord of pulpwood by species. The smaller figures are for wood which has been cut for a few months and lost some moisture.

Approximate Weight per Gross Cord of 8-ft. Pulpwood

Aspen:	
Rough	4,300–5,000
Peeled	3,000–3,200
Balsam fir:	
Rough	4,550–5,200
Peeled	3,300–3,600
Hemlock:	
Rough	4,550–4,900
Peeled	3,400–3,800
Jack pine:	
Rough	4,400–4,800
Peeled	3,100–3,400
Spruce:	
Rough	4,200–4,500
Peeled	3,100–3,400
Southern pine:	
Rough only	5,300–5,800

Measuring Other Forest Products

Railway ties, poles, posts, and many other products are measured by the piece, according to specifications established by buyers. These specifications are set forth in Table 8–2.

TABLE 8–2
Specifications of Forest Products

Kind and Measure	Principal Species Used	Lengths (feet)	Minimum Top Diameter (inches)	Other Specifications
Sawlogs (board feet)	Most hard-woods and softwoods	8, 10, 12 and 16; up to 32 in West	About 8 for softwoods; 10 for hard-woods	Logs may be graded as to size, knots, and defects*
Veneer logs (board feet)	Red gum, oak, yellow birch, basswood, walnut, maple, Douglas fir, white pine, yellow pop-lar, black cherry, etc.	6 to 16	12 in East; 24 in West	Same as above
Pulpwood (cords)	Nearly all con-ifers and aspen, birch, oak, and many other hardwoods	8′ or 100″ (Lake States); 4–6 (South); sawlog length in West	4 4	Varying with individual mills
Piling (piece)	All hard pines, spruce, Douglas fir, oaks, other hardwoods	30 to 90 and longer	10 to 6	Gradual taper, minimum sapwood, no rot, trimmed knots, little crook or sweep
Poles (piece)	Pines, cedars	20 to 75 in 5-ft. groups	4 to 9	Minimum spiral grain, no crook, sweep, or defect
Posts (piece)	Cedars, pines, and other durable species	6 to 14	3 to 8	Minimum sweep, defect

TABLE 8–2 (Continued)

Kind and Measure	Principal Species Used	Lengths (feet)	Minimum Top Diameter (inches)	Other Specifications
Railroad ties (piece by 5 size grades)	Cedars, pines, and most hardwoods	8, 8.5 and 9	6 by 8 7 by 8 7 by 9	Five size grades within specifications of railroad buyers
Mine timbers	Wide variation in lengths and diameters, depending on type of mining. Contact mine buyer for details before cutting.			
Charcoal wood	Dense hardwoods (birch, beech, maple, oak, hickory) preferred.	Variable. Often 52" (bolts) or 12"–15" (blocks)	2" minimum Larger pieces must be split so will go thru 10" ring. No minimum. Pieces over about 20" diam. must be split.	Deductions made for rot and excessive crook
Stave bolts (tight cooperage)	White oak	Variable. Usually 39" (staves) 24" (heading)	Round or split (quartered) from clear sections at least 20" in diameter	Soft textured (slow growth) with minimum of sapwood, clear
Furnace poles	All hardwoods	Full tree length	6 minimum; 30 maximum	Green hardwood cull unlimited

* Log grading according to size and quality enables the owner to obtain the maximum value present. Log grades form the basis of value scales in many areas. Ungraded logs are usually called "woodsrun."

Pocket Slide Calculators

Although log scale sticks from which one can read off the volume of logs directly are by far the most popular, the pocket slide calculator is a recent innovation. Essentially, this calculator is a light cardboard envelope open at one end, with a paper slide with the volume table printed on it which fits inside. Slots near the top of the envelope, one small one which shows diameters at the small end of the log and one longer one providing for log lengths, allow the user to read off the gross volume of his log by picking the proper dimensions in the slot holes. These slide calculators are made for each of the common log rules and are frequently given away by forest products dealers as advertisements.

SPECIFICATIONS OF PRINCIPAL FOREST PRODUCTS

We have already discussed specifications of sawlogs and pulp-wood to some extent in connection with measuring and scaling timber and forest products. There are, of course, many kinds of products taken from trees other than these two which form the greatest volume in terms of production. Some of these other products, such as veneer logs, stave bolts, and piling, may have a higher unit value in many localities than sawlogs. Others, like charcoal wood, may furnish markets for sections of trees that would otherwise have to be discarded as waste. Piling is used for docks, building foundations, and other similar construction. Posts made of wood separate most of our farm fields and poles hold up our telephone and electric lines. Railroad ties of wood "tie" our railway systems together. Specialized local uses of wood for excelsior, box bolts, stave bolts, and dozens of other products require certain kinds of wood preparation. The more important are summarized in Table 8–2, but producers should get more complete and specific information from local wood-using industries before cutting.

METHODS OF SECURING CLOSE UTILIZATION

During the last several decades American lumbermen have learned many ways of reducing the large amount of wasted timber which used to be found on the average logging job. Closer utilization of the whole tree has been made possible by a number of developments, higher values of timber being an important one. In the old days only the best parts of the best trees were taken. Today a market exists in many areas for lower quality material. For example, over wide areas of the East and South, the wide expansion of pulpwood markets has opened up outlets for thinnings and stand improvement cuttings, as well as for some of the larger material left in the tops.

New mechanical equipment, which has replaced much of the old man-and-horse logging, has resulted in lower unit logging costs and closer utilization. Power chain saws, for instance, make possible cutting lower stumps, thus saving one or more feet of the best material in the tree, which was formerly left in the woods. Men found it difficult to saw a low stump by hand because they had to get down on the ground to do it and thus lost leverage on the saw. The chain saw will cut the tree off right at the ground line. Chain saws have also made it economically possible to cut lower grade trees for the good logs they may obtain.

Formerly, material for corduroy roads, skidways, truck and car log stakes was cut from the most available, best, and straightest trees. Now much fine young timber is being saved for future growth by cutting tops, defective, and lower grade species for these purposes.

There have recently been experiments in chipping tops and limbs in the woods with portable wood chippers to prepare wood from waste material for pulp or other uses. This practice is just beginning to develop in a practical way. As this type of equipment is further perfected, the wood cellulose industries will come to depend more heavily upon woods-processed wood chips.

QUESTIONS

1. Before starting to log in any part of the country, what construction must be completed?

2. What are the first three steps in converting a tree into forest products?

3. When are "borrow pits" used?

4. What kinds of mechanized equipment have replaced logging railroads, horses, and river transportation?

5. Describe how to fell a tree in the direction you want it to drop.

6. When trimming branches from a tree with an axe, on which side do you stand?

7. What parts of the tree are measured in scaling cut sawlogs?

8. By each of the three log rules, how many board feet are there in a log which is 12 ft. long and has a top diameter of 12 in.?

9. A truck is loaded with pulpwood measuring 10 ft. long by 8 ft. wide by 5 ft. high. How many cords does it contain?

10. A "pen" of pulpwood cut in 4-ft. lengths is how many feet high?

11. Why is it necessary to place the scale stick in more than one position across the small end of the log to get a reasonably accurate diameter reading?

12. What are the reasons for knowing the market and products to be cut from a forest before beginning to log?

13. Name several advantages and disadvantages of mechanized logging equipment.

14. Calculate the volume of a defect 5 in. in diameter in a hollow log 15 in. in diameter (at the small end) and 16 ft. long. What is the net volume of the log? (Use International $\frac{1}{4}$-in. log rule.)

EXERCISES

1. Visit a logging operation in your locality and describe methods and equipment used in felling, skidding, loading, and transporting logs.

2. Measure the volumes of 12 sawlogs, using the volume tables shown in the text. Give the proper allowance for log defect.

3. Demonstrate that you know how to carry an axe and a saw properly in the woods.

4. Measure a truckload of pulpwood to determine the number of cords it contains.

9

Protecting Forests from Fire, Insects, and Diseases

PROTECTION FROM FIRE

Forest Fire Losses

From 1960 to the present, reported forest fires numbered from 100,000 to 160,000 per year in the United States—an encouraging reduction from the 500 per day reported in the decade before. Acreage burned varied from two to four million per year. This was a major drop from the more than 20 million acres burned over annually during the prior 15 years. This downward trend is attributed to accelerated efforts at prevention and an increasingly intensive fire control program employing modern equipment and techniques.

The great majority of forest fires, especially in the East and South, are *surface fires,* burning mostly in the duff or leaf litter on the forest floor. Promptly attacked with adequate manpower and equipment, such fires are fairly easy to control. But nearly every small forest fire is potentially a big one if a combination of dry weather and high winds occurs. A really bad forest fire fanned by high winds will destroy nearly everything in its path. The Peshtigo fire in Wisconsin in 1871 wiped out whole settlements and killed 1,500 persons; the great Idaho fires of 1910 wiped out several million acres of virgin timber in a few days. The Tillamook fire in

Oregon in 1933 killed as much timber as was cut in the entire United States the preceding year.

A surface fire will damage many of the larger trees and kill seedlings and small trees. Most fires start as surface fires but may develop into other types. Sometimes fires burn deep below the surface in the thick duff of decayed leaves or needles, or in dry peat soils, between surface outbreaks. Such "ground fires," common in northern bogs, may smolder for days or weeks before being discovered.

The crown fire, or a combined surface and crown fire, causes the greatest timber and property damage, and loss of human life. Starting as a surface fire and driven by a strong wind, it leaps into the treetops and sweeps through the timber, often jumping by sparks ahead of the main "smoke." Crown fires occur mostly in coniferous forests, for the green leaves of hardwoods are not easily ignited (Fig. 9–1).

Fig. 9–1. A crown fire. Forest fires destroy timber, wildlife, and watersheds. (U. S. Forest Service)

While losses of merchantable timber and property are direct and readily apparent, forest fires cause many damages not so easily recognized. As stated above, fire may kill the tiny young trees in a forest which would provide future timber crops. Fire in a forest in which valuable pines or spruces predominate may cause that forest to become mostly a scrubby growth of inferior species. Repeated fires have turned many millions of acres of forest land in the United States into unproductive wasteland.

But there are other damages. Surface fires may leave fire scars on the trunks of trees, where wood rots may enter. Fire-weakened trees may be attacked by insects, and are more easily felled by the wind. Storm runoff is greatly accelerated when fires burn the vegetation and surface litter on steep slopes. Fire is responsible for a vast amount of flood damage, for aggravated problems of water supply, and for the silting of reservoirs, stream channels, and harbors with millions of tons of sediment eroded from the land.

Forest fires kill many game animals and birds. Wood ashes washed into streams after a fire sometimes kill large numbers of fish. Destruction of the vegetation along streambanks may cause water temperatures to rise and make the stream unfit for trout. Sedimentation from fire-damaged watersheds has ruined many good fishing streams. And forest fires can hurt tourist and recreation business. Vacationers are not likely to visit areas where the scenery has been blackened by flames.

Losses such as these, and many other indirect and intangible losses caused by forest fires, are not easily measured in dollars. But in the aggregate they represent a huge drain on the resources and manpower of the nation.

In few parts of the world is the problem of keeping the forests from burning as complex and difficult as it is in the United States. In this country there are many regional variations in terrain, types of vegetation, and seasons of greatest fire danger. The normal fire seasons in the forests of the Eastern, Northern, and Central States are spring and fall. In early spring, soon after the snows have melted and before the deciduous trees have leaved out, a few days of sun and wind can dry out the forest litter and create a high fire hazard. After the leaves fall from the trees in autumn, the forest floor is again exposed to sun and wind, and the dry, new-fallen leaves are added fuel. The fire season may extend through the winter months in the Deep South. The dry summer months are normally the period of greatest forest fire danger. Prolonged droughts may bring periods of danger, and delayed snows may mean that the fire season extends into the winter. Even in normal fire seasons, forest fire danger fluctuates widely. A fire-control organization must be geared to meet any emergency situation. For example, large new areas of logging slash create very serious risks.

The forest fire hazard has increased in recent years throughout much of the West because epidemic attacks by insects have killed timber over large areas in Colorado, Montana, Idaho, and Wyoming. Increased industrial and recreational use of the forests means greater numbers of people in and near the forests who might start fires.

Causes of Forest Fires

Most forest fires are caused by human carelessness, negligence, or ignorance. Forest fire prevention, therefore, is mainly a problem of improving people's ways, of creating a better understanding of the importance of forests, an awareness of the danger of fire in the woods, and a sense of personal responsibility to safeguard the forests from damage. That is not an easy job. A city dweller used to paved streets, for example, does not easily change his smoking habits when he goes into the woods. A recent percentage allocation of the causes of fires reported on protected forest and watershed lands of the United States is as follows:

Cause	Per Cent
Incendiary	26
Smokers	17
Debris burning	23
Lightning	9
Railroads	5
Campers	3
Machinery	7
Miscellaneous or unknown	10

Incendiarism, the leading cause of forest fires, is a problem mainly in the South. Some 90 per cent of the forest fires of incendiary origin reported on protected lands are in the Southern states. Comparatively few man-caused forest fires are set maliciously, but these are often the most serious.

Annual woods-burning has long been a tradition in many rural sections of the South. The woods are fired every spring to "green up the grass," to get rid of underbrush, or because of mistaken notions that ticks or boll weevils can be eliminated by woods-burning. Ideas and customs of long standing will have to be changed by education, coupled with better fire laws and stricter law enforcement.

Debris burning causes many fires in farm woodlands and suburban areas. Too frequently, fires started by landowners to burn trash, get rid of brush, or to clear land get out of hand and spread to adjacent woods. A number of states still lack effective laws to foster safe practices in the burning of debris. Burning frequently destroys much organic matter that might better be returned to the soil.

Careless smokers are responsible for thousands of forest fires each year. They toss cigarette butts or matches while traveling in forested areas. Others are caused by careless hikers, hunters, fishermen, or woods workers. Many of the states now have laws against throwing lighted materials from automobiles.

Campers and picnickers who build campfires in unsafe places or who abandon their still-burning campfires are another cause of forest fires. Educational efforts to induce campers to douse their campfires thoroughly with water before they leave are reducing the number of fires from this cause.

Railroad and logging operations formerly caused many more forest fires than they have in recent years. Improved spark arresters and ashpans on locomotives, plus the conversion to electric and diesel locomotives, have reduced the danger from sparks. The percentage of fires resulting from logging operations is also lower than it was a few decades ago. Many timbermen provide intensive protection on their holdings. Most logging crews observe strict safety precautions, and when bad fires do occur, they are usually among the first reserves to be called.

Many *miscellaneous causes* of forest fires have been reported. All told, more than 90 per cent of all forest fires are man-caused and therefore preventable.

The only important natural and so far unpreventable cause is *lightning* (mainly in the West), which accounted for about 9 per cent of the reported fires on protected lands.

Beneficial Uses of Fire

Under certain circumstances, fire can be a useful tool in the forests, if carefully applied and controlled. Research has worked out practicable techniques for using fire to control sagebrush on certain types of western range where the topography is not too rough, and thus aid the natural comeback of desirable forage grasses or prepare the ground for artificial reseeding to grasses. In the southern pine region, foresters are using *prescribed burning* to aid the regeneration of longleaf pine when heavy growth of broomsedge or other ground cover interferes with natural reseeding. Fire, when properly timed, has been found to help control the brown-spot disease of longleaf pine. Prescribed burning can sometimes be used to get rid of undesired plants and trees on grazing areas, or to remove heavy accumulations of flammable ground cover and thus reduce the hazard of destructive wildfire. In the Northwest, broadcast burning at a safe season is sometimes used to get rid of accumulations of logging slash or debris. Such uses of fire, however, should never be attempted except under the direction of experts. In the South brushy areas are burned to prepare land for planting or direct seeding.

Organizing Forest Fire Control

The United States has developed a system of cooperative forest fire control in which the federal government (acting through the Forest Service) cooperates with the states in an organized effort to prevent, detect, and suppress forest fires. In some parts of the West, associations of private forest owners also cooperate in this program, and many industrial forests have their own fire fighting emergency equipment and crews.

The cooperative fire-control program gears together all of the control facilities of the several private and public agencies. Since the federal government recognizes that it has a responsibility for assisting the states and is responsible to our citizens in assuring future generations of adequate forests, it supplies both a part of the funds (about one-quarter) and the technical supervision and coordination of our nationwide forest fire control system. The sections which follow describe the operations of this integrated system. Forestry-trained men working with one agency often find themselves working with the others in this combined effort.

The protection of the forests from fire involves three general phases of activity—prevention, preparedness, and suppression.

Prevention. Foresters say that "the best way to stop a fire is never to let it start." Since more than nine-tenths of all forest fires are man-caused, and therefore preventable, the U. S. Forest Service, the state forestry departments, the forest industries, and various conservation organizations have for many years conducted educational programs aimed at fire prevention.

During periods of extreme drought and high fire danger, certain areas of state and private lands and national forests are sometimes closed to entry by the public. Hunting and fishing seasons may be suspended, and logging operations closed down, because of hazardous fire weather. Most states have a system for issuing burning permits which are given out only during safe burning periods such as during and immediately following a rain. This system warns the fire lookout that there will be a "smoke" at a certain location.

Spark arresters on railroad and logging equipment, "no-smoking-on-the-job" rules in logging operations, and other safety appliances and rules are prevention measures. Cleanup of logging slash, rubbish, and other flammable debris helps to reduce fire hazards.

Undoubtedly the Smokey Bear campaign of the Forest Service and the National Advertising Council and the Keep Green campaign of the forest industries were in no small measure responsible for the fact that the number of fires was drastically reduced during the postwar period from the years before World War II. The Civilian Conservation Corps also played a major role. This reduction occurred in spite of substantial increases in public use of forests and outdoor areas in the postwar years.

Preparedness. Preparedness calls for building up, placing, and training an effective fire-control organization. Adequate fire-control plans must cover *detection, communication, transportation,* and provision for the necessary *tools, equipment,* and *manpower.* Weather forecasting service, regular measurement of fire danger, and other technical services must be arranged under the "presuppression" program.

Presuppression Planning. Fire breaks or fire lanes cleared to a width of 30 or more feet along boundaries of large tracts, or cutting brush and trees along existing roads helps to confine fires inside limited areas.

Fire Danger Rating. Foresters have developed over the years a method for measuring the factors which influence the way a fire will burn. Wind velocity, air temperature, relative humidity, and time of day all strongly influence fire behavior. Wind velocity is measured by an anemometer, a set of four whirling cups which records wind velocity on a speedometer. Temperature is measured with a standard thermometer.

Relative humidity (the amount of moisture in the air) is a most important influence on rate of combustion. It is expressed on a per cent of the moisture present which the air can hold at a given temperature. Heavy fog is 100% humidity. Cold air holds less moisture than warm air as early morning fogs after warm days show. Air humidity is measured by a hygrometer; forest fuel moisture content is measured by comparing the weights of two sticks of exactly the same size and weight which have been located on the forest floor. One stick is dried in the oven and its weight compared with the undried stick. A delicate scale will show the difference in moisture content.

All of the measurements are carefully recorded at the same time of day—early morning, about noon, mid-afternoon, and early evening. They are then placed in a Forest Fire Danger Meter (Fig. 9–2) to obtain the Forest Fire Danger Rating and Burning Index as shown in Table 9–1.

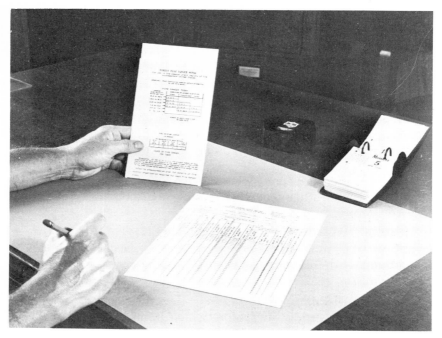

Fig. 9–2.   Forest fire danger meter. (U. S. Forest Service)

Locally the Fire Danger Rating includes the following factors which affect the start and spread of fires:

1. Fuels and fuel moisture quantity, size, and dispersion (logging slash, needles, dried grass, and heavy brush).
2. Topography and elevation.

TABLE 9–1
Fire Danger Rating and Burning Index

Burning Index	Degree of Danger	Description	Presuppression Planning
50%–up	7—Extreme	Explosive conditions. Fires start readily from sparks, burn fiercely, and tend to crown and spot generally.	Man all lookouts on 24-hour basis. Extra ground and air patrols. Regular and reserve personnel on 24-hour standby.
25–49%	6—Very high	Fires will start from a glowing cigarette butt or sparks, spread rapidly, and tend to crown generally. Spot fires common.	All equipment ready for immediate action. Issue emergency fire warnings—radio, TV, & press.
13–24%	5—High	Fires start readily from a match or glowing cinders, spread rapidly, and tend to crown in young conifers.	Man all lookouts. Full ground and emergency air patrol. All personnel at fire duty station, including weekends. Have road crews on standby. All fire-fighting equipment ready for immediate action. Fire danger warnings on radio & TV. No burning permits.
7–12%	4—Moderate	Fires start readily from a match, burn briskly, and tend to spread rapidly as they increase in size.	Man all lookouts. Full ground patrol. Key personnel within call from headquarters. Standby crew ready for immediate call. Burning permits early in morning and evening only.
4–6%	3—Low	Fires will start from a lighted match and spread (rapidly in dry grass and leaves) until extinguished.	Air patrol on regular schedule. Man primary towers only. Personnel same as (1—Safe) below. Burning permits.

TABLE 9–1 *(Continued)*

Burning Index	Degree of Danger	Description	Presuppression Planning
2–3%	2—Very low	Fires will start from an open flame but spread slowly and tend to go out.	Air patrol on regular schedule. Man primary towers only. Personnel same as (1—Safe) below. Burning permits
0–1%	1—Safe	Fires will not spread beyond the heat of a campfire or burning brush pile.	Air patrol only after lightning storms. Personnel used on repair and maintenance work. Burning permits.

SOURCE: Adapted from Bureau of Land Management, U.S. Department of the Interior.

3. Slope exposure to or away from sun and drying winds.
4. Type of timber and brush—pine and other conifers are much more inflammable than hardwoods.
5. Local risks and control factors such as access roads, use by recreation visitors, fire breaks, and water areas.
6. Wind velocity and direction.
7. Relative humidity.
8. Air temperature.
9. Normal regional fire season: Western states—June through September; Southern states—February to May and October to November; Eastern states—Spring and Fall months; Northern states—April, May, and October. (Drought years, of course, may radically change this pattern.)

The current Fire Danger Rating serves as a guide to the district forester-in-charge which warns him when to alert both his own forces, nearby private forestry operations, and the public-at-large. As will be noted, he can deploy his own and auxiliary forces as the danger increases. It is extremely useful in knowing when the safest time is for controlled or prescribed burning of brush areas planned for reforestation or game-habitat improvement.

Detection. Locating a fire in its early stages is of utmost importance to successful fire control. A good detection system usually consists of a network of permanently established lookout fire towers. During normal fire weather only the detection points that give the most complete observation coverage of the surrounding territory are manned.

Detection of fires from the air by regularly scheduled airplane patrols has proved feasible in several roadless timberland areas of the Northwest, the Lake States, and elsewhere. It is most successful where lightning-caused fires are the principal problem, and where a few key lookout stations are retained to supplement the air patrol and to act as radio communication hubs. In all forest regions of the country, airplane patrols are often used for supplemental or emergency detection when the danger of fires is unusually high or when haze or a smoke blanket from existing fires in the locality limits the visibility from ground lookouts.

A distinction should be made here between "fire" and "smoke." The term "smoke" is used until it is certain that a fire is spreading and cannot be controlled by the initial suppression crew. Smoke may originate at an unreported camp site, from rubbish burning, someone burning grass, etc., which may be under control or easily controlled by the initial suppression crew. The term "fire" is used only when it is apparent that the fire is spreading and that some time will be needed by the initial suppression crew to control it. Since it is desirable to have everyone alert when a fire does exist, indiscriminate use of the word "fire" could result in a reaction similar to that of the men when the boy cried "wolf!"

Lookout towers or stations are equipped with telephone communication and in some regions with shortwave radio as well. They also contain a *fire finder* for use in accurately locating a fire when smoke is visible. One fire finder, used at many stations, has a front sighting arm containing a cross-hair for accuracy in sighting a smoke column. It is mounted on a map table oriented so that the map directions agree with the compass direction on the ground. The rim of the map table is marked off in *azimuths* or the degrees of a circle, starting with 0 at the north and returning there at 360 degrees.

When the lookout man discovers smoke, he immediately sights his fire finder at it and records the azimuth and estimated distance from his station, together with other landmarks and location data which he can furnish from his map and his knowledge of the country. He telephones all of this information to the district ranger or central dispatcher. Upon receiving a lookout's report on a "smoke," the dispatcher obtains, if possible, azimuth readings on the fire from other lookout stations and then plots these on his map. The intersection of the plotted lines-of-sight gives the exact location of the fire on the map. This procedure is called "triangulation" (Fig. 9–3). The dispatcher, as soon as he has the necessary information from the tower (Fig. 9–4) regarding the location, size, and spread of the fire, and the fuel type in which it is burning, dispatches the initial suppression crew with proper instructions.

Fig. 9–3. Locating a forest fire by triangulation. When towermen sight a "smoke," each man calls the fire dispatcher's office, giving the azimuth from his tower. On the dispatcher's map, each tower is located at the center of a 360-degree circle. Using the pinned threads, the dispatcher lays out the reported azimuths, and the point where two or more threads cross is the location of the fire. (U. S. Forest Service)

New Detection Methods. The most highly developed and effective of the new remote sensing detection systems is an infrared system. Infrared is the name assigned to a "specific wave length region of the entire electromagnetic radiation spectrum." Its value is in its ability to detect fires by the energy emitted from the fire by wave lengths rather than by illumination. Thus problems of night detection would be eliminated as would the problem of

Fig. 9–4. Forest fire towers are always located at high points which command a good view of the terrain. (U. S. Forest Service)

discovering fires which went unobserved until the heavy smoke of a previous fire has been controlled. The infrared system also provides a method for measuring the size of the fire and for mapping its location to the extent that rivers, roads, and other landscape characteristics are shown. The fire's exact location is then determined and the best approach to the fire is revealed. The intensity and velocity of a fire can be calculated by this system. The infrared system is being used experimentally with aircraft; the system requires an unobstructed view of the sources of the energy or heat to be effective and thus a high observation point is essential.

Radar and sferics are two types of remote sensing being tested for use in tracking lightning storm situations. Radar is employed by the U. S. Weather Bureau to track "cumulo-nimbus cloud formations, normally associated with thunderstorm activity." The radar set operates by transmitting pulses of microwave energy in a narrow beam, detecting the energy reflected by a target such as a cloud formation. Radar is quite effective in determining the location of a possible storm but it cannot, as of now, distinguish between an actual storm and one that does not develop. It would thus be used primarily as a planning method in detection and as a study device to learn more about "the specific nature of fire-setting lightning storms." From such knowledge, techniques can be developed for early storm warnings and evaluations of wet or dry storms, fast or slow moving storms, and severe or moderate storms. Sferics is a method of tracking lightning by means of electromagnetic energy discharged by the lightning and carried in wave lengths of the radio wave spectrum. This travels along the curvature of the earth's surface, as well as in a straight line, giving the sferics device the ability to detect lightning from thousands of miles. This, in addition to a very low cost as compared to radar, makes the sferics equipment quite important. Television is also being considered. Although it has the same limitations as a human being, it has the added advantage of possible use in uninhabitable regions.

Factors Influencing Fire Intensity and Spread

The manner of burning, the shape of the burned area, and the speed and intensity of a fire depend on the kind, quantity, and moisture content of the forest fuels, and upon the wind velocity, topography, air temperature, and relative humidity. The rate of spread and severity of a fire depend upon its supply of litter, humus, fallen limbs and trees, underbrush, slash left after logging, and living trees. Except for conifers, green leaves and wood burn with difficulty even in prolonged dry periods, whereas dry fallen leaves, twigs, and punky wood may be easily ignited by a spark or burning object. Coniferous needles are much more flammable than hardwood litter. They produce a hotter fire and burn faster. At certain times of the year, grasses and other herbaceous vegetation become exceedingly dry.

The moisture content of forest vegetation is directly affected by the atmospheric moisture or relative humidity and rainfall. Fuels absorb moisture during periods of high relative humidity or rainfall and lose it during periods of low relative humidity. Where fuels are light and dry readily, it is important to measure and follow the atmospheric moisture and rainfall closely in order to forecast the probable moisture content of the forest fuels.

Before a forest fire will burn, fuel must be heated to a temperature of 600° to 800° F. When the fuel has a high moisture content, more heat is required because water must be evaporated before the fuel is ignited. Once a large volume of heat is created, the fire gains speed and progressively dries the fuel for its own advance. Slash-covered areas with a large accumulation of dry fuel are a menace to adjacent green timber. The severity of a fire is more directly dependent upon the amount of available fuel than is the rate of spread.

The direction and speed of the wind determine the direction and rate with which the head of a forest fire advances. Even a moderate wind increases the rate of speed of the fire and dries out the fuel ahead of the fire. Because hot air rises, fires create an upward draft or air current which may pick up and throw sparks forward 200 to 300 yards or even as much as half a mile to ignite new fires, called "spot fires."

The topography, i.e., direction of slope, degree of slope, and surface conditions, affects the spread and severity of a fire. In a rugged country with a varied terrain, the spread of a fire is irregular; a rolling topography favors a more uniform development of all sections of the fire. Fires burn rapidly up steep slopes, consuming all before them. Because the heat of the fire itself creates a draft, it intensifies the progress of the fire. Slopes facing south and west burn more severely than other slopes because they are warmer and drier from exposure to the sun.

FIRE-FIGHTING METHODS

Suppression begins only after a fire is discovered and reported. During the lapse of time from the first discovery to the arrival of the first control forces, each of the following steps take place:

1. *Discovery*—Estimated time when fire started to when it is first seen and located.
2. *Report*—Time from final discovery to receipt of report of location by control forces at headquarters station.
3. *Getaway*—Period required to dispatch forces after report of fire.
4. *Travel*—Time required to find and arrive at fire.

In suppressing forest fires, the following are of first importance: (1) quick arrival at the fire, (2) an adequate force, (3) proper equipment, (4) a thorough organization of the fighting crew, (5) skill in attacking and fighting the fire, and (6) mopping up and patrol to prevent new outbreaks. A small fire usually can be put out by a force of from one to five men. Large fires may require several hundred to a thousand or more men and take many days to control and mop up.

The three necessary requirements for a fire—heat, fuel and oxygen (or air)—can be illustrated by a triangle.

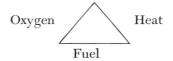

Oxygen   Heat

Fuel

Removal of any one of the three will extinguish a fire. Heat can be eliminated by use of water or use of mineral soil to "knock down" a fire. Fuel can be eliminated which is essentially what is done when constructing a fire break. Oxygen can be eliminated by burying in mineral soil.

No two forest fires are exactly alike. Fuel types, weather, slope, and exposure of terrain, accessibility, etc., vary so much that each fire presents an individual suppression problem. The suppression technique adopted by a fire boss on any fire will be based upon his experience and knowledge of fire behavior, but it will usually be an adaptation of one or more of the generally accepted methods of fire fighting. Two general suppression methods are known as "direct" and "indirect" attack on the various parts of a fire (Fig. 9–5).

Direct attack, or work directly on the burning edge of the fire may be used only on fires where the rate of spread is slow and the heat is not too great. While it is best to build a fire line down to the subsoil, shoveling, raking, or sweeping burning litter back into the fire is also effective. Beating out flames with wet sacks, with specially designed swatters, or even with green branches can re-

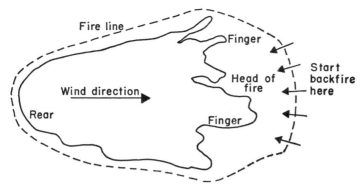

Fig. 9–5.   Parts of a forest fire.

tard small fires. Water pumped on the fire is often the most satisfactory if it is available.

Indirect attack involves work at some distance from the burning edge of the fire. It involves either the construction of fire lines
or the use of existing barriers as lines where the spread can be
stopped. It is used on hot, fast-spreading fires which require attack at a distance to provide the necessary workable conditions
and time to get a barrier around the fire.

Open land, roads, railroad grades, bare rock ledges, streams,
lakes, etc., may provide natural barriers to the spread of a fire,
or it may be necessary for the suppression crew, upon arrival at a
fire, to construct a special barrier called a fire line or control line
around the blaze, so as to confine the fire to the smallest possible
area. In constructing a control line, fire fighters cut away the
brush, logs, and small trees where the line is to be located, then
dig or scrape the burnable litter from a strip a foot or more in
width to prevent the spread of the fire on the ground. Any snags
or dead trees that might throw sparks across the line must be
felled. In soils with little rock, fire lines can be plowed with a
crawler tractor much faster and wider than men can dig them.

Whenever water is available it can also be used effectively with
indirect methods of fire suppression. Fire-control plans, however,
can seldom be based entirely on the use of water because in many
parts of the country water may be scarce or entirely lacking near
a fire. However, in sandy areas with shallow water tables, wells
have been driven in a few minutes to furnish water for fire
fighting.

Backfiring is an excellent fire control tool when used by a person of experience, but it can easily "backfire" on the inexperienced user, with disastrous results. Trained fire organizations use back-firing effectively, basing their operations on a control line cleared and dug well ahead of the fire (Fig. 9–6). A road, trail, stream, or

Fig. 9–6.   Backfiring from a plowed fire line. (Texas Forest Service)

other natural barrier also is often used. With a crew patrolling this line to prevent the fire from jumping it, a forestry foreman with judgment and experience sets fire along this line and the backfire is allowed to burn back to the main fire. This removes combustible fuels and widens the control line. When the oncoming fire ap-proaches the backfired control line, it will die from lack of fuel. Unburned corners inside the control line may also be burned out during mop-up work to prevent later flareups which might result in the fire getting across the control line.

Organizing fire-fighting crews is similar to organizing soldiers in a battle: the infantry (fire fighters) is deployed to the front lines (fire sectors) in platoons and companies (crews) under the local command of junior officers (sector and crew bosses). The general in charge is the *Fire Boss* with a *Line Boss, Service Chief,* and *Plans Chief* under his immediate command. The Service Chief has charge of supplies and services to the Line Bosses' crews. Records, communications, weather, and fire intelligence are the duties of the Plans Chief. A simplified diagram of a fire organization can be seen on the following page.

Rapid transportation and communication are of the utmost importance in fire suppression. To facilitate quick transportation of men and supplies, federal, state, and private fire-protection agencies have built roads, trails, and emergency airplane landing fields in many forested areas. But in some sections of the country there still remain vast roadless areas in which it is necessary for suppression crews to walk long distances to a fire, carrying necessary tools, equipment, and food on their backs. Therefore, forest protection agencies have in recent years used aircraft for the delivery of both men and equipment by parachute to remote areas.

Mopping-up and Patrol

Mopping-up after a fire has been controlled must be done or all the effort may be wasted. Without mop-up, fire can break out from smoldering coals the next windy day. Control means stopping the fire from any further spreading of the perimeter. Only when firebrands are no longer present on the edges can it be considered out.

Final mop-up, which is done after the fire is controlled, does not mean extinguishing every bit of burning material. Large fires may have smoldering material far back in the burn, but this is no threat to the flammable materials at the edge of the burned area. Smoldering snags or dead trees near unburned areas should be felled if they are within the maximum spark-throwing range of the fire line. All dead logs, limbs, roots, or anything else that extends into or across the fire line should be pulled back into the burned out area. Before leaving, the fire boss should go around the entire burned area to make certain no danger spots remain. Then a patrol should be stationed to give continued inspection of a mopped-up fire until it is completely safe.

New Fire-Fighting Techniques

In earlier days, fire fighters relied mainly on axes, shovels, and other hand tools for digging fire lines and throwing dirt on fires. Today gasoline and back pumps are used to bring water to forest fires. Although there is still need for much handwork, fire fighting

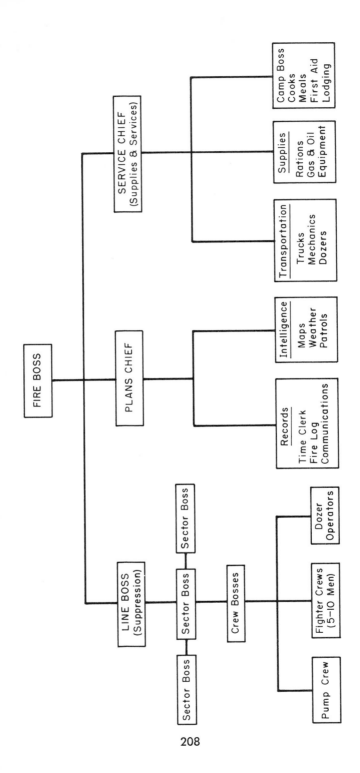

has become more mechanized with tractors plowing furrows for fire lines. Hand fire tools used by crews on direct attacks are shown in Fig. 9–7.

Fig. 9–7. Modern hand fire-fighting equipment. (U. S. Department of the Interior, Bureau of Land Management)

Transportation equipment has been vastly improved. Where once the mule string or pack train was the only means of moving equipment and supplies into remote forest areas, the airplane, helicopters, special trucks, "jeeps," and "trail scooters" now carry a large share of the load.

The use of aircraft has been a big help in implementing a "hit-'em-fast-and-hard" policy of forest fire suppression. Their first principal use was for reconnaissance of fires in progress and for detection of fires immediately after lightning storms. In a few instances they have replaced fire towers in otherwise inaccessible country. Now, emergency transportation of "smokejumper" fire fighters and supplies dropped by parachute have become two of the major roles of aircraft in fire control.

Specially equipped aircraft are used to drop water- or fire-retardant "slurry" to reduce the flammability of wood and wood-fiber materials (Fig. 9–8). In many cases the aerial application of retardant slurry has proved to be the tool that has made the difference between small fires and large fires by holding or retard-

Fig. 9–8. PBY Air Tanker dropping borate slurry at the head of a California fire. (U. S. Forest Service)

ing the spread until the arrival of suppression crews. Slurry, made up of chemicals (usually borate, diammonium phosphate, or bentonite clay) mixed with water, clings to fuels to reduce inflammability. When dropped at or near the advancing edge of a fire, a fire break is made and the fire suppressed. Water is often bombed directly on small fires in inaccessible places.

Since 1940, Forest Service smokejumper operations have been conducted every year by men carefully selected and thoroughly trained before the beginning of each fire season. Fires in remote areas can be attacked soon after discovery, whereas ground crews would require many hours to reach them. Hundreds of fires that otherwise would have spread to burn large areas and cause great damage have been quickly controlled by the parachuting fire fighters.

Mechanized Equipment. Groundwork in fire suppression is becoming increasingly mechanized. The Forest Service, state forestry departments, and forest industries are constantly working to improve their equipment and develop new items that will increase the speed and effectiveness of fire control. Water equipment used in fire control now includes efficient back-pack pumps, portable gasoline pumps of various sizes and capacities, and large tank trucks capable of good speed on roads. Crawler tractors with specially designed "breaker plows" (which cut deeper and wider than field plows) are able to rip wide, effective breaks in subsoil in minutes.

The Forest Service has special camp equipment for feeding, "sleeping," and otherwise caring for fire fighters. During a fire emergency, temporary camps must be set up quickly for dozens, and sometimes hundreds or thousands, of men. Compact camp cooking and other outfits designed for 1-man, 25-man, or larger camps are kept ready packed to go out on a moment's notice.

Communications. Speedy and reliable communications are one of the keys to successful forest fire suppression. Both telephone and radio systems have a part in the communications networks. Primary fire-detection stations are usually connected with headquarters by telephone lines, and many of them also act as radio relay or communication stations for contact with outlying stations and camps. Portable, mobile, and field radios are used by smoke-chasers and field crews for quickly setting up communications when fighting fires. A full line of equipment for use in a higher radio frequency band has been developed. Several state forestry agencies and private concerns have long been active in developing radio communication networks, and during the past few years the use of these mobile and portable radios has rapidly increased. Nearly all states are now using radio in forest protection, as well as for other services such as fish and game work and highway patrol. Special equipment has been installed in several states for tying together state and federal forest radio networks to provide for prompt interchange of fire-control information. New scientific research is developing new information on techniques of fire control. For example, cloud "seeding" is developing experimentally in such a way that lightning fires might be prevented, and artificially caused rain made to extinguish fires.

FOREST INSECTS AND THEIR CONTROL

Forest managers are often faced with the threat of insect infestation which may cause serious damage. It is therefore important to be able to identify the more important insects and to know what control methods may be applicable. While there are literally thousands of kinds of insects in the forest, many of which make their home in trees, only a relatively few species cause enough damage to require control. Nature in most cases provides for controls over outbreaks by insect parasites, insect-eating birds, and other natural predators.

Insects and diseases together have destroyed more timber in recent years than forest fires have destroyed, but because disease usually affects only a tree here and there, the damage is less dramatic. Occasionally a really serious insect outbreak will develop as in the case of the spruce budworm, the Engelmann spruce beetle, or the jack pine sawfly, where whole stands are seriously damaged or killed. Major control measures are needed in these cases to prevent widespread epidemics. From the time the seed is born until the logs are sawed into lumber, trees have a perpetual struggle to survive the attacks of insect enemies—and even the finished wood products are subject to attack. The study of forest insects is called *forest entomology*. It is a complex subject, but for purposes of the working forest manager or forest technician, it can be simplified into a few basic insect groups and control methods. An informed forest manager will be able to detect many of these attacks before they get out of hand and take measures for their control. However, a specialist in forest insects should always be consulted if an outbreak seems to be developing or if the kind of insect attacking is not known. Failure to do so may result in large losses of timber and time.

Control measures used to reduce forest damage from insect infestations are of two kinds: indirect control through properly applied forest management, and direct control, which is a counter-attack on the insect itself. Forests subject to insect damage often have numbers of overmature or decadent trees, nearly at the end of their life cycle. They are, therefore, in a weakened condition and more subject to attack by certain diseases and insects. Forest management which removes these trees and maintains healthy, thrifty stands contributes importantly to keeping them "bug proof." Strong, fast-growing trees are infrequently damaged although some insects, especially during outbreaks, will attack all trees in their path, regardless of growth conditions. Where conditions are such that it is impractical to apply indirect control measures, direct control measures may often be required. It is important for the forest technician to be able to recognize the activities of the more damaging forest insects and eventually to learn to identify each kind in the forests of his locality.

Classes of Forest Insects

Because insects attack different parts of the tree and have different habits as well as appearance, entomologists have classed them into groups just as other forms of life are scientifically classified by biologists. But for forestry purposes, seven main classes, based on the way insects attack trees, are adequate:

1. *Bark Beetles.* Insects that work under the bark and in the wood surface, causing damage to the cambium layer and death of the tree through girdling or introduction of destructive fungi.
2. *Wood Borers.* Insects which bore into the sapwood and heartwood, rendering the wood useless for commercial purposes. They also destroy cut logs.
3. *Leaf Eaters* (Defoliators). These insects suck juices from, or eat, the needles or leaves and thus destroy the foliage, slowing down the growth rate or killing the tree by defoliation. (Larvae do the damage in most cases.)
4. *Sucking Insects.* Insects which feed by sucking the sap from trees (aphids and scales).
5. *Tip Feeders.* Insects which eat the terminal growth of trees or the tip buds and thus cause deforming damage.
6. *Gall Makers.* Insects that cause abnormal growths on twigs, limbs, trunks, or leaves of trees but do not usually kill or damage the wood.
7. *Seed Feeders.* Insects that destroy the fruit, nuts, or seed of trees and thus spoil them as a source of new seedlings.

The first five of the above groups are of major concern to foresters and forest managers because they include the principal destructive insects. But before discussing them in detail, it is appropriate to consider insect infestation as it may look in the forest. Much of the damage comes during the growing season, usually early or in the middle of the summer. Most of the above groups of insects go through a life cycle beginning with the egg stage. Eggs hatch into larvae ("worms" and caterpillars) that feed on the tree. When full grown, the larvae enter a resting stage where they are transformed into pupae (usually cocoons). After spending some time in the pupal stage, the insects change and emerge as adults. Insects spend the winter either as eggs, larvae, pupae, or adults.

The forest in which an insect attack is under way frequently presents a brownish, unnatural appearance at a distance, particularly where defoliators are at work. Sometimes ground droppings in quantity are an indicator. In the case of boring insects, fine wood powder at the base of the tree tells the tale. Sometimes the indicator is drops of pitch on the ground. In tip weevil damage, the new growing leaders may bend and shrivel up or turn red and die. Any of these indications are a cause for alarm.

Control of Forest Insects

The injurious insects are, with few exceptions, native and have been around for many years. It is virtually impossible to completely eradicate either these, or the well-established foreign pests. Under forest conditions, a certain number of insects occur normally and natural control factors maintain the populations at endemic levels. When conditions become especially favorable for a particular insect pest, its numbers rapidly increase and an outbreak occurs, requiring artificial controls.

Natural Control Factors. Insect activity is limited at temperatures above or below an optimum. At temperatures above 120° F., only few insects survive, and this makes possible the control of many species of bark and wood boring insects by exposing infested logs to direct sunlight. Low winter temperatures, or severe late frosts (occurring after new growth of the trees has begun in the spring) also kills many insect pests.

Moisture has both a direct effect on the insects and an indirect effect through its influence on the pests' hosts. Inadequate precipitation may lower the trees' resistance to bark beetle attack; flooding or excessive soil moisture also may weaken the trees.

Severe rainstorms have provided excellent control by knocking defoliating larvae from foliage. Windstorms, however, may provide additional breeding sites for bark and wood inhabiting insects that are dependent on the dead wood of broken tops and branches.

Insects, like other living things, have natural enemies which prey upon them and hold them in check. Such birds as nuthatches, chickadees, creepers, warblers, kinglets, and many others destroy countless numbers of defoliating and wood-inhabiting insects each year. The meadow mouse, white footed mouse, moles, shrews, voles, chipmunks, and squirrels play important roles in the destruction of forest insects which spend part of their life in the soil. Although little is known about the real importance of parasitic nematodes, certain species attack bark beetles, wood borers, soil inhabiting grubs, lepidopterous larvae, and grasshoppers.

Many species of insects and mites are distinctly beneficial in that they feed on harmful species. Most native forest insects, with the possible exception of borers and other forms which feed inside the host plant, are attacked by insect parasites. All stages of an insect from egg to adult may be attacked, although as a rule, the larvae and pupae are most heavily parasitized. Unfortunately, many of the beneficial forms are themselves parasitized. This hyperparasitism may be occasionally carried to the second or third degree making the host parasite relationship extremely complex. The effectiveness of parasites and predators is difficult to measure. Their success is influenced by factors such as the character and habits of the host insect, the population density of the host, the presence of alternate hosts, the degree of hyperparasitism, the conditions affecting hibernation, etc.

Silvicultural Control of Forest Pests. Under virgin forest conditions, no checks were placed on the activities of destructive agents other than those imposed by nature herself. Fires, as well as insect and disease outbreaks, developed, spread, and eventually ran their course. The whole process, although wasteful, seldom resulted in the permanent destruction of the forests over large areas. Natural checks were imposed and regenerative processes came into play.

With more intensive forest management and the development of control methods, attention was turned to preventive control of forest insects and diseases. In a managed forest, the principal objectives of pest control are to regulate conditions for maintaining natural balance between the destructive insect population and their natural enemies, between the insects and their food supply, and between disease and disease-caused tree mortality or degradation. These objectives may be attained more fully in the future through application of silvicultural practices in growing stands where conditions unfavorable for insect development are maintained and greater resistance to insect and disease attacks is achieved. This would involve such measures as (1) the removal of susceptible trees and the regulation of density and composition by means of periodic salvage or improvement cuts and thinnings; (2) the regulation of environmental factors through drainage and density; (3) the selection of insect or disease resistant varieties and species of trees; (4) careful seed selection; (5) site selection; (6) adjustment of cutting cycles and methods; and (7) rotation of crops.

Chemical Control. Direct controls with chemicals are employed when other methods of control fail. Forest pest epidemics often appear suddenly in a localized area rendering preventive control measures useless. It then becomes necessary to suppress the destructive pest population with a chemical before severe damage results.

Insecticides used against forest insects are of two main types: contact poisons which kill insects upon contact with their integument; and ingested poisons which cause death following ingestion and absorption in the insect's digestive tract. Ingested poisons are used against insects with chewing mouthparts. They swallow the poison while feeding on their natural food to which the insecticide has been applied. Chewing insects include the large group of forest defoliators. Insects with sucking mouthparts which feed on internal juices of their hosts must be controlled with contact sprays. Sucking insects include the aphids and spittlebugs which feed on juices of leaves, needles, or twigs. Often an insecticide will have both properties and may be used in combating a variety of pests.

Methods of Direct Control. *Bark beetles (Dendroctinus* and *Ips)* are mainly serious in the South and West, where they attack pines, fir, and spruce (Fig. 9–9). Much damage to Douglas fir, Engelmann spruce, Western white pine, sugar pine, lodgepole pine, and several Southern pines has also been reported. Large areas of forest have been laid waste by these beetles. They become active in the spring and continue their activity until cold weather, sometimes hatching out five or six generations in a season in the South. One beetle can have 100,000 descendants in one summer! As the attack proceeds, the tree's needles change to a reddish-brown color and the bark is loosened as the result of the numerous channels where the insects have been boring (Fig. 9–10).

Direct control methods are accomplished by spraying with insecticides or by removal of the brood trees. (Brood trees may be identified by the above indications.) If the trees are still green, the insect can be prevented from spreading by felling and removing from the stand all infested brood trees from which the young adults will soon emerge. If this is not practical or possible, such trees should be sprayed immediately over the entire length of the trunk, until it drips. A mixture of 2.5 lb. of gamma isomer benzene hexachloride with 50 gal. of No. 2 diesel oil is recommended. These materials are usually put on with hand-pumped, pressure-operated sprayers. Where the trees are already dead or dying from a general infestation, rapid logging of the whole infested stand is the only way in which loss can be prevented.

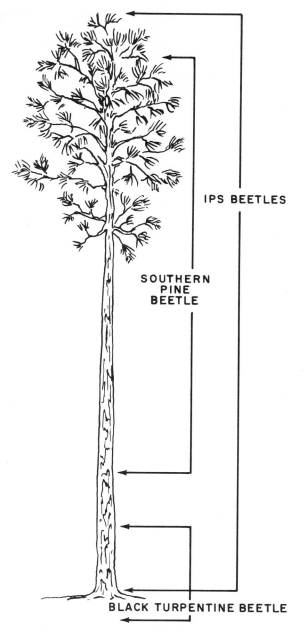

Fig. 9–9.   Where pine beetles attack.

Fig. 9–10.   How bark beetles kill pine trees. (U. S. Forest Service)

Wood borers usually attack logs and pulpwood decked in the forest or in wood yards and can cause tremendous amounts of direct damage by wormholes in the wood and through introduction of the blue stain fungus. Prevention of this damage can often be accomplished by storing logs in the water, by peeling them before warm weather, or by quick utilization. Large piles of logs are often protected by insecticide sprays. When these wood borers are at work on a pile of logs in hot weather, one can actually hear them grinding their way through the logs!

Leaf eaters or defoliators include a large group of insects which attack both conifers and broadleaved trees. Usually they do not kill the trees the first year, but repeated attacks over several years will starve the tree to death by eliminating the food-making functions of the leaves and needles. While there are many different types of defoliators, they all eat the needles or leaves in the caterpillar stage. Sometimes the only sign of feeding may be a brownish cast at the needle tips. Mature and overmature timber is more subject to serious losses from epidemic infestations. There is great variation in the types and extent of damage from year to year and between different species of insects. Most of the damage is done in the larval stage. The more important defoliators, their victims, and control methods are listed in Table 9–2.

Some of the standard sprays such as lead arsenate and nicotine sulfate which are contact sprays kill the insect larvae as they feed upon leaves and needles. There are a number of newer sprays like Malathion, which work well in many cases; the use of DDT is now nearly prohibited because it has been found to kill birds and fish. Research in finding new, non-spreading insecticides is progressing rapidly to the testing stage. Chemical control of defoliating insects in the forest is usually by direct spray or aerial application of an insecticide spray at the time of or just before the insects are feeding. Since this is a highly specialized operation in each case, trained entomologists must plan, direct, and execute control operations (Fig. 9–11).

Fig. 9–11. Aerial spraying of insecticide by helicopter in conifers. Because helicopters can spray more slowly than planes and blow the chemical directly down to the needles, they are considered more efficient. (American Forest Products Industries, Inc.)

Tip feeders attack the buds and new growing shoots of conifers in the early part of the summer by drilling into the wood tissue and destroying the cambium layer. In effect the tip is girdled and the shoot dies. Two of the most serious tip feeders are the *white pine weevil,* which attacks eastern white pine, jack pine, and Norway spruce, and *European pine shoot moth,* which attacks the

TABLE 9–2

Common Forest Tree Insects—Damage and Control

Name	Principal Species Affected	Type of Damage	Prevention	Direct Control	Control Season
				Control Method	
Gypsy moth	Oaks, birch, aspen	Defoliation		Spraying insecticide	May–June
Bark beetles	Ponderosa pine	Girdles tree by killing cambium layer under bark	Salvage green, blown-down timber	Fell, peel, and burn bark; salvage infested logs; burn slabs	Spring, summer, fall
Red turpentine beetles	Hard pines—South (esp. turpentined trees)	Bores holes, reduces strength, making subject to blowdown	Remove infested trees	Cut and remove infested and suspected trees	All seasons
Sawflies	Eastern & Southern pines and tamarack	Reduces growth by defoliation; epidemics kill stands	Cut mature and over-mature stands	Aerial insecticide spray	Early summer at period of greatest activity
Spruce budworm	True firs, Douglas fir	Reduces growth by defoliation; kills older trees extensively	Cut mature and over-mature stands	Aerial insecticide spray	Early summer as insects emerge
White pine weevil	Eastern White pine, Norway spruce	Kills leaders, causes forked and crooked boles	Maintain shade where possible to 20 feet	Hand spray upper stem and new growth with sodium arsenate or cut and burn infected tip—leave only best side branch on first lower whorl	Early summer as insects emerge

Tent caterpillar	Broadleaved trees (esp. Northern hardwoods and aspen)	Defoliates; kills older and weaker trees	Remove tents by hand or burn	Aerial spray of insecticide as insect larvae emerge	Spring
Scales & Aphids (also Spittle bugs)	All trees	Sucking insects reduce growth	—	Insecticide spray or remove infested trees	All seasons
Hemlock looper	Western hemlock	Defoliation; kills oldest trees	—	Aerial insecticide spray	June–July
Tussock moth	True firs, Douglas fir	Defoliation, all sizes	—	Aerial insecticide spray	June–July
White grubs	Conifer seedlings	Destroys roots and kills trees	—	Force insecticide into soil	Summer
Pales weevil	Pine seedlings and saplings	Girdles bark of seedlings and defoliates saplings	—	Spray insecticide over seedlings	Spring
European pine shoot moth	Pines and spruces (sapling stage)	Deforms trees	Plant only where temperature falls below 10° F.	Prune infested shoots and burn them	Fall–late spring

tips and new leaders of red pine, Scotch pine, and Austrian pine. Damage by the white pine weevil can be prevented by spraying the growing tips and buds and previous year's growth with common garden insecticides in mid- to late June before the eggs hatch into the larval stage when they begin their work. A better way which assures future straight timber from weeviled trees is to remove by pruning all growth above the most recent year's whorl (rows of branches from which the tip arises) and all but the best one of the branches in the whorl. This branch will then become the new leader. It is essential that all infested material be carried away and burned or drowned in water. Smaller stands of young pine may be sprayed with a mixture of insecticide that is directed to the tip and the bud about to start growing. Aerial spraying at low heights, especially with a helicopter, has been found to be an effective and cheap way to control infestations of the weevil in large areas of young pines. However, if pines have an overstory of broadleaved trees which keep down the temperature by shading, weevil damage is not serious. Stand improvement which removes the overstory should be delayed until trees reach a height of 20 ft. or more, after which they are fairly resistant to weevil infestation.

Gall makers may damage individual trees, but they usually do not ruin whole stands. Therefore control measures are not usually undertaken. If they should reach epidemic proportions, a forest entomologist should be consulted.

In conclusion, it is important to realize that insect damage can result in great losses to standing timber and that if this is to be prevented, immediate detection is imperative. While we have not attempted to cover the field of forest entomology in any detail, the important aspects have been set forth and should be mastered by the forest manager.

FOREST DISEASES AND THEIR CONTROL

Like mankind, trees are subject to many kinds of diseases. Some attack the leaves, others the main woody trunk, and still others the roots. Although there are hundreds of tree diseases, most of them do not attack healthy forest trees but take advantage of weak old trees or young seedlings struggling for establishment. Leaf spots, rusts, wilts, blights, cankers, and decays are examples of diseases which either weaken or kill forest trees. Fortunately for the forest manager, relatively few diseases are really serious enough to require direct control. Here again a healthy forest, well managed and thrifty, is as nearly resistant to disease as nature will allow. The study of tree diseases is called *forest pathology*.

Important Forest Diseases and Methods of Control

Some of the more destructive tree diseases are white pine blister rust, chestnut blight, oak wilt, Dutch elm disease, brown spot needle blight on longleaf pine seedlings, little-leaf disease on shortleaf pine, the heart rots, and dwarf mistletoe on western conifers. Most tree diseases are caused by fungi, a form of plant life carried from tree to tree by spores, which are the "seeds" of the parasites. Other diseases are caused by viruses, bacteria, nematodes, and dwarf mistletoes. Most native forest diseases are so well established and so widely distributed that their complete eradication would be impossible. However, the more serious pests can be controlled. It is sometimes possible and feasible to wipe out a newly introduced pest that is still confined to a limited area.

In the long run, good forest management is the best defense against many insects and diseases. Some insect and disease losses can be greatly reduced by harvesting trees before they reach the most susceptible age. Some diseases attack vigorous as well as weakened trees, while some others can be held to a minimum by removing diseased and weakened trees. Although losses from some diseases can be reduced by good forest management, direct control measures are needed for highly contagious diseases, such as white pine blister rust and oak wilt.

Fungi attack the forest in many ways. They kill some trees outright, they reduce the growth rate of many more, and they destroy the heartwood in living trees, making it unfit for use. Their total effect on the productivity of the forest exceeds that of all other enemies.

Chestnut blight and *white pine blister rust* are well-known examples of killing diseases. Chestnut blight is caused by a parasitic fungus that was introduced from Asia on nursery plants before this country had enacted quarantine laws to reduce the international spread of diseases. It produces tiny spores, comparable with seed in higher plants, that float through the air, settle on the bark of healthy trees, grow through it, and eventually kill the tree. As yet, no practical means of controlling chestnut blight has been found, but the search for chestnut trees resistant to the disease is continuing, and eventually chestnut may be restored to our forest.

White pine blister rust has unusual life habits. The fungus

causing it must live alternately on the pine and on currant or gooseberry plants (genus *Ribes*). It also was introduced from abroad on nursery seedlings. The fungus enters the pines through the needles and grows into the bark, where it causes diseased areas known as cankers. About three years after a tree becomes infected, orange-yellow blisters form on the cankers. In the spring millions of spores from these blisters are released into the air and scattered by the wind for many miles. These spores can infect only the leaves of currants or gooseberries. There the fungus grows and forms brownish yellow spots, on which spores capable of infecting pines are produced. These are delicate and short lived and can spread only a few hundred yards.

Work in developing strains of white pine resistant or immune to blister rust is showing encouraging results, and we may soon have resistant planting stock available for reforestation. Loss of white pines from blister rust can be prevented by destroying the wild and cultivated *Ribes* bushes (currants and gooseberries) growing within infecting distance of the trees and by preventing the establishment of new bushes.

Ribes bushes are removed from pine areas by trained workers who systematically locate and destroy the bushes on hundreds of thousands of acres annually (Fig. 9–12). They are generally uprooted by hand or dug with a tool. In some situations it is best to kill them with chemical sprays (2,4,5-T Esterons). In others, dry chemical mixtures or concentrated liquids are applied to the stubs after the tops have been cut off flush with the ground. One thorough working of an area gives protection for a few years. However, some small bushes may be overlooked, seeds in the soil may germinate and produce new plants, and sprouts may develop from bushes incompletely destroyed. Any of these conditions may result in restocking an area with *Ribes*, which in time can become a new menace to the pines. This can be prevented by reworking treated areas and destroying the *Ribes* plants where they have become re-established.

Heart rot fungi seldom kill trees, but they change the sound wood of the trunks into a useless, rotten mass. They require a wound to gain entrance to trees. Any broken branch or injury to the bark or roots opens the way. Once the fungus enters the tree, it usually continues to grow until the tree is a hollow shell or is so weakened that it breaks over in the wind. The presence of advanced stages of heart rot is made evident by the appearance of

Fig. 9–12. Blister rust control using herbicides to eliminate alternate host and *Ribes* plants. (U. S. Forest Service)

shelf fruiting bodies or conks which resemble brittle mushrooms. Young vigorous trees are generally free of heart rot. Losses may be reduced by protecting trees from injuries and by harvesting them before the fungi can destroy the wood in the trunks.

In recent years forest managers all over the world have been increasingly concerned by the spread of *Pine root rot* which can cause extremely high mortality in pine plantations caused by the red heart fungus, *Fomes annosus.* The spores are airborne and infect fresh stumps during thinning operations and pass through the roots to nearby trees. Entire plantations have been threatened.

A crash research program of industry in cooperation with the U. S. Forest Service and with forestry schools and other agencies discovered a definitive answer to *annosus* root rot. They found that application of borax, a harmless household chemical, to a stump immediately after a tree is felled prevents the spread of the fungus. The treatment is simple to apply in the field, inexpensive, and positive in action.

But there was a second problem. Evidence indicated that the soil, once infested with root rot, retained the infection potential for several years. This could mean further loss of revenue for idle land. Research on the problem discovered further that several common plants, including even the familiar marigold, can help to check the disease organism.

Oak wilt has spread rapidly in the Midwestern states during the past few years and has been found recently in states in the East and Southeast also. It attacks all native oaks in states where it has been found, but develops most rapidly on red and black oaks, which quickly die. The U. S. Department of Agriculture and many states are carrying on research to find an effective method of control through sanitation and prevention of spread.

Dutch elm disease is attacking both the shade and forest trees in many Eastern and Middle Western cities, causing great losses. The most effective means of control is by cutting and burning the diseased trees and pruning dead and dying branches from uninfected trees. It is an impractical method in forest stands, however, because of the expense involved. Elms in the forest which are diseased should be salvaged as soon as possible to prevent local spread of the disease.

In the South, *brown spot needle blight* attacks longleaf pine seedlings and retards their growth by killing the needles. Continued attacks may kill many of the little trees. Carefully planned burning of infected plantations or areas of natural reproduction helps control the disease in young seedlings. This is an example of how fire can be used to good advantage in forestry. Longleaf pine, which produces both lumber and naval stores (rosin and turpentine are called naval stores) is one of the most important forest trees in the South.

An enemy of the shortleaf pine, another of the South's important forest trees, is the *little-leaf disease*. Trees with this disease show shortened, yellowish foliage and slow growth, and infected trees die after a few years. The disease is caused by a fungus that kills fine roots of trees growing in poorly drained soils. Shortleaf pines highly resistant to little-leaf disease have been developed.

Dwarf mistletoes are serious pests of western coniferous forests. They are plant parasites that grow on the branches and stems of trees. The dwarf mistletoes are related to the Christmas mistletoe, but should not be confused with it. They slow the growth of infected trees and kill many of them, stunting and deforming those not killed.

When dwarf mistletoe seeds ripen, they are shot out of the casings with explosive force for as much as 60 feet. The seeds are sticky and if they strike branches of the same or other susceptible trees, they may cling to them and start new plants. Dwarf mistletoes tend to spread steadily to other trees in the forest and can only be controlled by removing infected trees or branches in harvest or stand improvement operations. Other means of control are being investigated.

A strong forward step in providing better control of forest pests was taken in 1947 when Congress passed the Forest Pest Control Act. This Act recognizes federal responsibility for controlling diseases and insects on federal lands, extends federal aid to control projects on nonfederal lands in cooperation with states and private owners, provides for systematic detection to locate and evaluate pest outbreaks on all forest lands, and offers leadership and funds for planning and carrying out control operations.

The more important tree diseases and their control methods are set forth in Table 9–3.

OTHER DAMAGE TO THE FOREST

Hail, windstorms, and glaze ice all cause serious local damage which can result in large losses. In one instance a June hailstorm in northern Wisconsin stripped young hardwoods completely of their leaves and so damaged the cambium layer under the bark as to kill a majority of the trees over an area of 10 miles long and 2 miles wide! Ice damage in the wintertime, especially in the Central states, often causes a great deal of limb breakage and exposes trees to diseases. During the winter of 1967 one glaze ice storm cut a swath through 15 Piedmont counties of Virginia 10–20 miles wide and 200 miles long. Salvage operations continued for more than a year. But wind is probably the greatest natural force over which man has absolutely no control; it can lay flat huge areas of timberland. Hardwoods resist wind damage when their leaves are off, but conifers are vulnerable at all times. While the downed timber can usually be salvaged, it is more costly for loggers to get around broken off and half-down trees. If the trees are not salvaged, they frequently favor the build-up of many kinds of damaging insects, which can spread to standing timber.

TABLE 9-3

Principal Forest Tree Diseases—Damage and Control

Common Name	Host	Symptoms	Cause	Control
Eutypella canker	Sugar maple, red maple	Lesions on trunk around branch stubs, with concentric callus rings.	*Eutypella parasitica*	Remove cankered trees in improvement cuttings.
Hypoxylon canker	Aspen	Yellowish to reddish-brown sunken areas centered around a wound, developing into elongated cankers delimited by vertical cracks in the bark; trees commonly break at cankers.	*Hypoxylon pruinatum*	Remove infected trees in thinnings.
Fusiform rust	Slash pine, loblolly pine, occasionally longleaf pine	Spindle-shaped swellings on stem and branches, often causing distortion and breakage; orange spores produced in spring on swellings in blister-like pustules.	*Cronartium fusiforme*	Encourage early natural pruning by maintaining high density in stands. Prune infected branches, particularly after occasional year of heavy infection.
White pine blister rust	Five-needle pines of eastern and western U.S.	Yellow to orange lesions develop on bark at base of needle about 2 years after infection; in the third or fourth year these become girdling bark cankers which in spring and summer bear blisters containing orange spores; these infect leaves of currants and gooseberries; cankers grow down branch to stem and kill by girdling.	*Cronartium ribicola*	Eradication of all currants and gooseberries (*Ribes*) within the stand and in a protective border of variable width up to 900 ft. around the stand; European black currants should be eradicated for a distance of one mile.

Disease	Host	Symptoms	Cause	Control
Root rot	Conifers	Death of affected trees; soft, stringy rot in roots and butt. In ponderosa pine, light-brown striations under bark at root collar; decay confined to single root.	*Fomes annosus*	Put borax or creosote on freshly cut stumps to prevent spreading.
Root and Butt rot	Species of pine, mature stands, also plantations 15–25 years old	Decline in vigor, needles short, becoming yellow then dying; cones appear prematurely; fruiting bodies at base of tree or one ground surface arising from roots.	*Polyporus schweinitzii*	Avoid planting white or red pine on poorly drained or high pH soils.
Little-leaf	Shortleaf pine, loblolly pine	Progressive decrease in terminal growth accompanied by yellowing and reduction in needle length; root systems defective, with many roots dead; affected trees die in 3–10 years.	Soil fungus *Phytophthora cinnamomi* associated with diseased roots on soils with poor internal drainage	Salvage cuttings in infected stands.
Leaf and Twig blight; also Anthracnose	Hardwoods	Leaves and tips of twigs turn brown and die in the spring, resembling late frost injury.	*Gnomonia veneta*	No control for forest trees. For shade trees spray with 4.
Rot or decay	Mature trees of all species	Presence of conks of wood-rotting fungi; large open wounds with softened wood; large branch wounds and top injuries; swellings and cankers on trunk.	Various fungi, especially species of *Fomes* and *Polyporus*	Prevent wounds, such as those caused by fires and logging; avoid pruning wounds over 3 in. in diameter.

TABLE 9–3 (Continued)

Common Name	Host	Symptoms	Cause	Control
Butt rot	Young sprout stands of oak species	Large, unhealed stump wounds or dead companion stems.	Species of heart-rotting fungi	Remove unwanted companion sprouts before they reach 3 in. in diameter at base and before stands are 20 years of age; in older stands remove companion stems only if they form a low union and leave a wound over 3 in. in diameter.
Western red rot	Ponderosa pine	None, except presence of decay and red discoloration in heartwood.	*Polyporus anceps*	Periodic pruning of dead branches on crop trees.
Dutch elm disease, associated with attacks by Scolytid beetles	American elm	Progressive dwarfing and yellowing of leaves, accompanied by various degrees of defoliation; followed by death of branches or entire tree.	*Ceratostomella ulmi* carried by *Scolytus multistriatus* and *Hylurgopinus rufipes*	Mainly through destruction of infected trees and protection against bark beetles by insecticidal sprays and maintenance of tree vigor by appropriate pruning and feeding practices.

Disease	Host	Symptoms	Causal organism	Control
Oak wilt	Oak species, particularly those of the black oak group	Leaves crinkle and become pale green, later turning brown or bronze; mature leaves shed at any symptom stage; lower branches affected last; trees usually die after the summer symptoms appear.	*Chalara quercina*	Some promise of control has been obtained by cutting or poisoning healthy oaks for 50–100 ft. around spot infections.
Maple wilt	Maple	Sudden dying of single branch, followed by others; eventual death of tree.	*Verticillium, spp.*	None.
Brown spot	Longleaf pine	Small spots on needles causing needle dieback; retards growth of seedlings.	*Scirrhia aricola*	Controlled burning in third year of seedling's life or spray with prescribed chemicals.

Wildlife and Livestock Damage

Over-grazing by cattle, sheep, and browsing game animals can also be damaging to the forest. Where elk are over-stocked in the West, serious loss of young trees takes place. In the northern Lake States young white cedar has become almost extinct in some localities due to over-browsing by deer. Cattle and sheep grazing in farm areas has eliminated young hardwood reproduction; in some Southern and Western forests trampling by livestock has taken out whole generations of seedling reproduction.

Girdling of small trees by rabbits and other rodents takes a heavy toll when these species become too numerous. Bears have caused great damage in Douglas fir by scratching off bark.

Whether it be domestic livestock or wild animals, over-production can cause abnormal damage. Livestock numbers can be controlled and must be kept in line with carrying capacity of the forage resource so they are not forced into forest browsing. Wild game numbers can be controlled by harvesting during hunting seasons if bag limits are related to animal numbers.

QUESTIONS

1. Name five important causes of forest fires.

2. Describe the three main types of activity in forest fire protection.

3. The process of locating a forest fire on the map in a dispatcher's office is accomplished when towermen call in two bearings or azimuths. What is it called?

4. Name the three factors causing a forest fire to spread.

5. Give the two general methods used in fighting forest fires.

6. Name two parts of a forest fire.

7. Describe some of the recently developed mechanized fire-fighting equipment.

8. Is it true that insects and diseases usually attack old and overmature trees before they attack healthy trees?

9. Name three important insects which seriously damage forest trees and give the kinds of trees each attacks.

10. Name two important tree diseases and the trees attacked by each.

11. Why is DDT an undesirable chemical to use for insect control?

12. Describe one control method used for a tree disease affecting Southern pine forests.

EXERCISES

1. Visit a forest fire tower and discuss with the towerman how he sights and reports a "smoke."

2. Go to a central forest fire control headquarters and study the system used to report and locate fires and dispatch fire-fighting crews.

3. Examine different kinds of hand and mechanical fire-fighting equipment.

4. Write your state forester for information on any outbreaks of forest insects or diseases in your area, and go into the field to identify these at the proper season.

10

Processing and Marketing Forest Products

Forest managers, who are primarily interested in producing as much raw material as the forest can be made to yield economically, must have a general knowledge of the processing of rough forest products and the ultimate finished products manufactured. American forest industries include large and small sawmills which produce lumber, pulp and paper mills which manufacture a wide variety of paper products, veneer mills which supply plywoods and veneers, and dozens of other smaller specialized industries which produce everything from toothpicks to laminated timbers (Fig. 10–1). Most of these manufacturing plants, which use rough wood in the form of small and larger logs, are located in communities near the forest. This is because it costs more to transport raw material than it does to transport the finished products. Many smaller communities could not exist were it not for the paper mill or sawmill which is their principal industry.

ECONOMIC IMPORTANCE TO THE NATION

Taken together, employment in the woods on logging jobs, in wood-processing plants, and in timber-connected activities provides jobs for more than three and a half million people, or about 5 per cent of the nation's total labor force. In terms of value of product, the forest industry annually contributes about 35 billion dollars, which is about 5 per cent of the gross national product. Thus the forest products industries are a highly important part of our national economy and are particularly strategic in that they are decentralized and are the principal industry in hundreds of our smaller communities. The economic importance of each major group of forest industries on the basis of the number of people employed is shown in Table 10–1.

TABLE 10–1
Employment Attributed to Timber in the United States

Kinds of Timber-Based Economic Activity	Employment	
	1,000 Employees	Per cent
Forest management	82	3%
Harvesting	342	10
Primary manufacturing	489	15
Secondary manufacturing	793	24
Construction	840	25
Transportation and marketing	776	23
Total	3,322	100%

SOURCE: U.S. Department of Agriculture, Forest Service, *The Economic Importance of Timber in the United States*, Miscellaneous Publication 941 (Washington: U. S. Government Printing Office, 1963).

Approximately 40,000 sawmills, pulp mills, and other processing plants in the United States depend upon wood for raw material. In recent years nearly 10 billion cu. ft. of timber (excluding fuel wood), including almost 50 billion b.f. of sawtimber, was cut to supply the wood used by these plants and by other wood consumers. About 58 per cent of the timber cut for commercial use went into sawlogs, which were used chiefly in building construction, shipping, and manufactured products. Twenty-eight per cent of the cut went into wood pulp for various forms of paper, board, rayon, and other cellulose products. Nine per cent of the timber harvested went into veneer and plywood for furniture, containers, and similar laminated products. Five per cent was utilized for a variety of miscellaneous wood products such as poles, piling, mine timbers, barrel staves, and posts.

THE LUMBER INDUSTRY

As an industry, sawmilling had its beginning in Colonial times. White pine and oak lumber were produced by the colonists for export to England and other countries in order to buy manufactured goods. Good white pine boards sawed from New England forests were welcomed in the Old World, which was finding it increasingly difficult to feed a growing population without clearing more and more forest land. Until about 1900 the United States produced more and more lumber from its forests each year until the record cut of more than 46 billion board feet in 1906 was reached.

Although lumbering first began in New England, it moved on to New York and Pennsylvania, then to the Lake States pineries, to

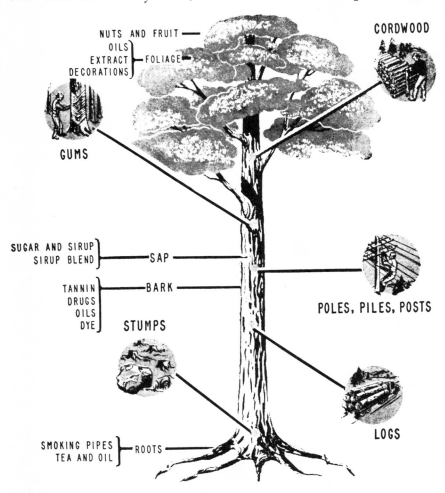

Fig. 10–1. What we get from trees. (U. S. Forest Service)

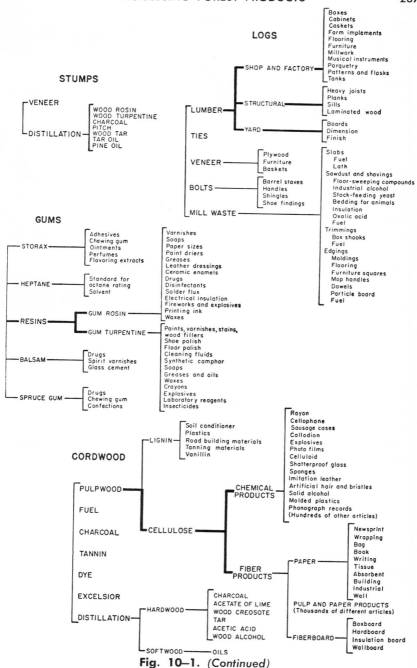

Fig. 10–1. *(Continued)*

the South, and finally to the Pacific Northwest, where it is still the
most important industry (Table 10–2). Following logging, mil-

TABLE 10–2
Lumber and Pulpwood Production by Geographical Regions, 1965

Region	Billions of Board Feet	Pulpwood MM Cords
Pacific (Oregon, Washington, California)	17,376	10.2
Western & Mountain (inclusive)	4,085	1.2
Southern	11,894	29.4
North Central (Lake States— (Michigan, Minnesota, Wisconsin)	1,131	3.7
Central Middle West	612	.6
Northeastern	1,528	4.6
Total	36,626	49.7

lions of acres were burned over in huge forest fires which destroyed or set back new forests for many generations. The development of fire control and other forestry programs during the past
quarter of a century has made possible a regrowth which is forming a solid raw-material base for an expanded forest industry.
Meanwhile, the still extensive forests of Douglas fir and other
West Coast species produce the most important source of lumber
today. Oregon has led all other states in production since 1938.
The sawmills of the Pacific Northwest are still large and medium-
sized mills, producing millions of board feet per year, whereas in
the other parts of the country most of the mills are small. They
saw smaller logs and produce considerably less per year. Many of
these small mills are portable and are moved from location to
location ("setting") where sufficient logs are accumulated for the
duration of the sawing job. In 1964, approximately 33,000 sawmills (Fig. 10–2) located in the principal lumber-producing states
sawed out 36.6 billion board feet. The amounts cut of the different
species involved are given in Table 10–3.

Milling Logs Into Lumber

The logging process, described in Chapter 8, prepares logs for
delivery to the mill by rail or truck from the woods. In days gone
by, log driving down the river systems was the principal form of
transportation, but with the removal of timber close to the rivers
and the development of modern logging equipment and truck

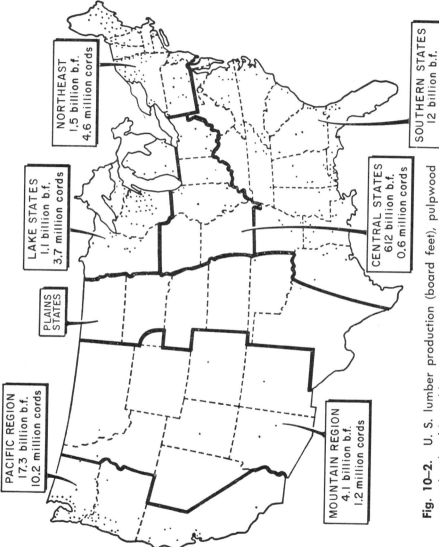

Fig. 10–2. U. S. lumber production (board feet), pulpwood consumption (cords), and location of paper mills, by regions, in a recent representative year.

NORTHEAST
1.5 billion b.f.
4.6 million cords

SOUTHERN STATES
12 billion b.f.
29.4 million cords

LAKE STATES
1.1 billion b.f.
3.7 million cords

CENTRAL STATES
612 billion b.f.
0.6 million cords

PLAINS STATES

PACIFIC REGION
17.3 billion b.f.
10.2 million cords

MOUNTAIN REGION
4.1 billion b.f.
1.2 million cords

TABLE 10–3

Lumber Production by Important Species, 1964

	Billion Board Feet
Douglas fir	8.9
Southern pines	6.4
Ponderosa pine	3.7
Redwood	1.2
Western true firs	2.5
Hemlock	2.5
All other softwoods	4.1
Oak	3.4
All other hardwoods (maple, gum, yellow poplar, birch, etc.)	3.9
Total	36.6

Source: *Current Industrial Reports: Lumber Production and Mill Stocks,* 1964. Bureau of Census, U. S. Department of Commerce.

hauling, pulpwood is the only timber in the United States moved by log driving today. At larger mills logs are still dumped into log ponds for storage before they are moved up the "jack ladder" (an endless chain conveyor) into the mill (Fig. 10–3). At smaller mills, logs are decked on rollways where they are rolled by men with cant hooks up to the sawmill carriage.

Unloading of logs and pulpwood from rail cars on trucks onto decks or into log ponds requires men with skill in handling timber. Logging experience is a valuable preliminary training. Sorting, grading, and measuring the logs as they are received requires a knowledge of log grades and scaling methods, an ability to identify different species, and facility in the use of equipment such as scale rules, cant hooks, and peavies. Since timber is measured as it is received, wood yardmen must be able to make entries on tally forms, to add up volumes, and be conversant with volume calculations as set forth in Chapter 8. A knowledge of forestry is becoming increasingly important in wood yard operation.

Larger sawmills operate with several types of saws—*circular* and *band* saws being the most common, although *gang saws* are used to some extent in larger mills. Logs are rolled by hand or tossed by steam piston onto the moving carriage which holds them in place with steel "dogs." The sawyer is the key man in this operation and it is his judgment that determines how the log shall be cut up (Fig. 10–4). He regulates the width of the board to be cut by moving the log on the carriage toward the saw. Then he speeds the log on the carriage into the saw and the boards drop

Fig. 10–3. Sawmill in Maine showing jack ladder with eastern white pine logs on the way to the band saw. (American Forest Products Industries, Inc.)

off onto a *roller conveyor* which carries them to the edger or trimmer, or to the resaw for further sawing.

Until quite recently a substantial portion of the round log was wasted when it was squared into lumber. This waste—slabs, edgings, and trimmings plus bark—if it was not burned to make steam for power, was conveyed into a "slab burner" (a round silo-like steel structure). Today, in most larger and many small mills bark is removed by jet streams of water or by mechanical means and the slabs and other wood waste ground into chips for conversion to paper pulp, particle board, and even plastics.

In larger mills the boards which still have the bark and irregular edges left move to an *edger*, which squares them on the two

Fig. 10—4. Squaring a log prior to further processing. The sawyer regulates the width of the debarking cut by the bandsaw. (American Forest Products Industries, Inc.)

sides. From the edger they move along to a *trimmer,* where odd lengths are cut off and the ends are then squared. After this, the boards are conveyed out on the "green chain" where graders pick off boards of different quality and grade and place them onto piles which are moved off on fork lift trucks. They are then piled in the yards for several months of air drying, or into *dry kilns* where they can be dried to specification in a few days. Hardwoods, which are difficult to dry evenly in air, are most commonly put through the dry kiln. Following drying, the boards are put through a planing mill to surface them before shipment.

Measuring the lumber as it is cut is frequently a job which forestry-trained men learn at sawmills. This is done with a tally sheet on which each board is shown by length, width, thickness, and grade. Each board has a definite number of board feet, as shown in the board volume table (Table 10–4). The boards are tallied by size class on a tally sheet (Fig. 10–5), totaled at the end of the shift, multiplied by the number of board feet for each class,

TABLE 10–4

Board Foot Contents of Sawn Lumber
(Commonly used dimensions)

Size in Inches	Length in Feet				
	8	10	12	14	16
1 × 4	2⅔	3⅓	4	4⅔	5⅓
1 × 6	4	5	6	7	8
1 × 8	5⅓	6⅔	8	9⅓	10⅔
1 × 10	6⅔	8⅓	10	11⅔	13⅓
1 × 12	8	10	12	14	16
2 × 4	5⅓	6⅔	8	9	11
2 × 6	8	10	12	14	16
2 × 8	10⅔	13⅓	16	19	21
2 × 10	13⅓	16⅔	20	23	27
2 × 12	16	20	24	28	32
4 × 4	10⅔	13⅓	16	19	21
4 × 6	16	20	24	28	32
6 × 6	24	30	36	42	48

and a total added up. With a little practice, the lumber scaler soon learns to distinguish an 8-ft. from a 10-ft. 2″ × 4″, and a 1″ × 6″ × 8′ board from a 1″ × 5″ × 10′ (Table 10–4).

Lumber is also graded according to quality. The number and size of knots, defects, and other imperfections are the determining factors in lumber grades. Considerable skill, acquired through study and practice, is needed to become a proficient lumber grader.

Although sawmills have not changed radically in layout, design, and processing flow for many years, the movement of logs to the mill and products from it have been greatly affected by fork-lift and other mechanical handling equipment. Automated sawmill operations have been built which give promise for rapid development in the years ahead.

The timber industry has organized itself into trade associations for each major forest region and has established a national association called the National Forest Products Association. These organizations supply the individual companies with technical information, report on market developments, promote lumber uses, and represent the industry on legislative matters.

Smaller and Portable Mills. The removal of our larger forest tracts and their replacement by second-growth forests has turned the attention of the lumber industry in the eastern part of the

DATE 3/4/58				CAR NO. 500 47823						NO. SHEETS 18				
FROM *Chittamo Landing*										CAP. ——				
TO *Libertyville, Ill.*										TARE ——				
INSPECTED AT SHIPPING PT. ✓ DESTINATION				STARTED 3/3		FINISHED 3/4				INSPECTOR P.C.S.				
KIND & GRADE *-Norway Pine, No.2 Com. S/4/s*										ORDER NO. 482-A				
SIZE	LGTH.	1	2	3	4	5	6	7	8	9	10	11	12	PCS.	FEET
1 X 6	12	THL	THL	THL										15	90
1 X 8	12	THL	THL	THL	THL									20	160
1 X 10	12	THL	THL	THL	THL	THL	III							28	280
1 X 6	16	THL	THL	II										12	96
1 X 8	16	THL	THL	THL										15	160
1 X 10	16	THL	THL	THL	II									17	227
2 X 4	8	THL	THL											10	53
2 X 4	16	THL	THL	II										12	132

Fig. 10–5. Lumber scale tally sheet. One sheet is used for each grade in each species. "S/4/S" means "surfaced (planed) on 4 sides." (Redrawn from National Agricultural Supply Co.)

country to smaller bodies of timber such as farm woodlands and other small private holdings that cannot support large sawmill operations and big logging jobs.

As a result of this development, small portable sawmills have sprung up over much of our eastern forested area. Often as little as 25 thousand board feet are enough to attract a portable sawmill operator. These sawmills can be moved from setting to setting. Although they usually turn out only 3 to 10 thousand feet per day, there are so many of them that their total production is an important part of our national output. Ordinarily they employ only four to ten men, producing lumber and railroad ties as their principal product.

THE PULP AND PAPER INDUSTRY

From the forest also comes the raw material—pulpwood—used in the manufacture of paper and numerous other wood-pulp products. The basis of paper is pulp made from fibers of wood or other kinds of cellulose, that remarkable material which forms the cell walls of plants. Wood is the most abundant source of commercially used cellulose from the plant world. More than one half of its substance is cellulose fiber.

The United States uses more paper than all the rest of the world combined. Soaring demand has increased the use of paper in the United States from about 300 pounds per person in 1946 to more than 500 pounds in the middle 1960's. Our annual production of pulpwood, the principal constituent of paper, has climbed from 2 million cords in 1900 to 50 million in a recent peak year. By the year 2000 it is projected to be more than double this figure. In addition, this country imports large quantities of paper from Canada in the form of newsprint.

While most of the pulpwood cut is from conifers, new processes are making possible the utilization of larger proportions of hardwoods. However, conifers still account for a majority of the wood used by the pulp mills. Pines make up half of this total, with spruce, balsam fir, and hemlock contributing most of the balance. Aspen, birch, oak, and gum are the major hardwood species used in making pulp. Great quantities of pulpwood are still stored at mill yards (Fig. 10–6), but more and more mills are moving logs directly into the mill without yard storage to save handling and losses or are shipping them in as chips.

The paper industry includes nearly 800 paper mills and 330 pulp mills located in 37 states (see Fig. 10–2). Pulp mills convert wood into pulp which the paper mills process into finished paper. The industry was first established in the Northeast and is still an important industry in that region. From there, however, the industry has spread to the Lake States, the Central States, the Pacific Coast, and in recent years throughout the South, from Virginia to Texas. Cutting pulpwood has become an important source of rural income in most forest areas. Over one million people are employed in the manufacture of paper and paper products. It is the fifth ranking industry in the United States in value of products. The American Paper and Pulp Association and the American Pulpwood Association, as well as several technical organizations, keep the individual company members informed of developments af-

Fig. 10–6. Unloading pulpwood at paper mill storage yard. The pulpmill is seen in the background. (American Forest Products Industries, Inc.)

fecting the industry in much the same manner as the lumber trade associations.

Paper Manufacturing

Wood is reduced to a fibrous form suitable for paper making by five commercial chemical and mechanical pulping processes. In the *mechanical* or *groundwood* process, fibers are produced by pressing bolts of wood against the rough surface of a rotating grindstone made of sandstone or synthetic abrasive material. A shower of water is provided to cool the stone and convey the pulp away. In the chemical pulping processes, the wood fibers are separated by dissolving the lignin and other binding material from wood chips. Solution of the lignin cementing material is accomplished by heating the chips in cooking "liquor" at high temperatures and pressures in large pressure vessels called digesters. The three chemical processes commonly used for pulping are the *sulfate* or *kraft,* the *soda,* and the *sulfite.* The sulfate and soda processes employ alkaline liquors and the sulfite process uses an acid liquor. A newer process is making possible the use of short-fibred hardwoods for newsprint and related products.

Modern processes which employ both chemical and mechanical

action are called *semichemical* processes and are beginning to be used extensively. In these processes, the chips are first given a mild softening treatment with steam or a chemical cooking liquor in a digester, after which they are reduced to fibrous pulp by mechanical treatment in an attrition mill or a "beater."

After the soft pulp is thoroughly washed, it looks quite similar to wet cotton fibers and may have dye for coloring, fine clay, rosin, and other matter added in the beater. The purpose of these additives is to give the finished paper color a shiny finish, or other surface qualities. The pulp is then flowed out onto a vibrating screen, over which it spreads evenly to drain off some of the water and form a wet sheet. The first wet sheet leaves the screen to go around a series of heated press rollers (the "Fourdrinier" machine) traveling at high speed. These rollers dry the sheet, which finally comes out at the end as a huge roll of paper. The paper is then either shipped in this form for direct use or remanufactured into hundreds of other paper items for consumer use.

Another product of wood pulp is rayon, a soft, silky fiber which is widely used for clothing and automobile tire-cord material. It is made from some form of plant cellulose, preferably cotton or wood, and at present more than 80 per cent of the rayon produced comes from wood cellulose. In the manufacture of rayon, the cellulose is dissolved by various chemicals (which differ with the process employed), and the thick, syrupy solution is forced through minute apertures corresponding to the spinnerets of the silkworm. The fine threads, or filaments, coming through these openings are coagulated either in a fixing bath or by a process of evaporation, and several of them formed simultaneously are twisted into a strand for spinning.

Wood Fiber Board

Production of wall boards by the use of wood fiber in rougher form than needed for paper has become an increasingly important building industry material. Under most processes unrefined wood fibers are formed with a binder into thick sheets and pressed into soft wall board. Hard board variations of this product are made either by compressing wood chips with a resin binder or by exploding chips into fibers (after cooking under steam pressure and releasing) which are then passed through steel presses. These processes form a hard board which can be substituted for lumber in roof sheathing and for plywood in home building. Some predictions have been made that re-formed wood fiber products will soon constitute the principal forest product.

OTHER PRODUCTS FROM THE FOREST

Vast quantities of logs are consumed in the veneer industry to produce thin sheets of wood used in the making of plywood and baskets, berry boxes, and other containers. Douglas fir plywood, which constitutes by far the largest proportion of plywood, is largely used in building and other construction. High-grade hardwood veneers are used extensively in the manufacture of furniture. Maple, oak, gum, and birch veneers are highly prized for furniture.

The Douglas fir plywood and veneer industry is located in the Pacific Northwest, where "peeler logs" are still available in quantity. Hardwood veneers are manufactured in the South where red gum and oak grow, and in the northern hardwood areas of the Lake States and the Northeast, where maple, yellow birch, basswood, and other hardwoods are found. The large-sized quality material demanded by the veneer industry is becoming increasingly scarce and has forced log buyers to search over wide areas for suitable raw material. The high value of veneer logs permits long-distance freight hauling.

The cooperage industry annually consumes large quantities of logs and bolts in the manufacture of staves and headings for barrels, kegs, and buckets. White oak is prized for "tight" cooperage because of its ability to prevent passage of liquids. Vast quantities of wood are also used for fuel, piling, poles, posts, railroad ties, and mine timbers, and for other miscellaneous products. Although wood as a fuel has declined rapidly in importance since World War II, it still is one of the major uses, in terms of volume. Most of the other products are treated with wood preservatives in order to extend their usable life.

After wood, the most important forest products are perhaps turpentine and rosin. They are obtained by the distillation of the gum that exudes from the longleaf and slash pines of the South. The gum is bled from the trees into small cups. Later it is carried to a still, where it is cooked in closed iron retorts. Another source of resin is obtained from the distillation of chipped wood from old stumps. The turpentine is given off in the form of a vapor, which is collected in a condensing coil. The rosin is the part of the gum left after the turpentine has been distilled. The name "naval stores" was originally given to these products because for many years they were used chiefly in shipbuilding. Naval stores are now used in the manufacture of paints and varnishes.

Maple Syrup and Sugar

From New England to Minnesota and down the Appalachians to West Virginia, maple sap is collected in the early spring when days warm up and nights are cold. On the old-time farm, the maples in the "sugar bush" were tapped with bored holes, spouts inserted, and buckets hung. Full sap buckets were emptied into a horse-drawn tank sleigh which transported the sap to the sugar house where it was evaporated in pans heated by firewood (Fig. 10–7).

Fig. 10–7. This traditional method of tapping maple trees and collecting sap is giving way to the use of plastic tubes leading directly to the boiling pans in the sugar house. (U. S. Forest Service)

Today modern techniques—power drills for tapping, plastic tubing to transport the sap, and oil- or gas-heated evaporators—have taken over on the larger production units. The discovery that even at low temperatures, bacteria can cut the flow of sap has led to more sanitary processing at each stage.

In addition to developing new production techniques, research in tree selection is increasing the sugar content of maple trees by selecting stock for planting from trees with higher than average sugar yields. Although standards of quality vary from state to state, maple products enjoy a wide market and the demand, even at high prices, exceeds the supply. As a steady source of income to owners of northern hardwoods, maple syrup has no equal.

There are also many specialized forest products of importance in certain localities. The bark blisters of balsam fir produce a resin which, when refined, has a limited market. In spite of all the work and skill of chemists, wood and bark remain the chief sources of tannins; and dyes from various trees, such as black oak and Osage orange, are still to be found in trade channels. Many kinds of edible nuts, fruits, and crude drugs are important sources of income to some rural communities.

Christmas Trees

Christmas trees and greens for wreaths and roping have been an important source of seasonal income to residents of coniferous forested areas for many years. Until quite recently, however, wild-grown trees from young natural forests have been the source of most of the material harvested and marketed. But with the development of new forest plantations into Christmas-tree size, forest landowners are finding this market an important outlet for thinnings and prunings. Northern and mountain-grown balsam fir, Douglas fir, and spruce are finding increasing competition from Norway (red) and Scotch pine produced from plantations of private landowners and public forests. Consumers in many cities are showing a liking for these species, which hold their needles well and are usually well rounded and symmetrical. Nearly 40 million trees are cut annually for Christmas trees (Fig. 10–8).

Another development has been the small table spruce treated with a solution for holding needles, sprayed with a paint, and mounted on a stand. These little trees—produced entirely from northern Minnesota stunted black spruce—are particularly popular with apartment dwellers.

Christmas-tree growers have been organizing into associations in recent years in an effort to keep better informed on market conditions and prices, and to reduce marketing waste. Much information has been developed by Extension Foresters on the special techniques needed for shaping trees in order to obtain the best prices. Because closely planted stands are just right for thinning when they reach Christmas-tree size, this market is a highly beneficial one for intensive forestry. However, competition from artificial trees is having a severe impact in many urban areas.

Fig. 10–8. Harvesting Christmas trees in Minnesota. (American Forest Products Industries, Inc.)

MARKETING FOREST PRODUCTS

Individual owners of forest lands who have no direct connection with the forest industry face marketing problems very similar to those of farmers with crops to sell. Some landowners prefer to sell timber standing; others do the logging, or hire contractors, and offer cut products for sale to industry buyers. Larger lots of timber or forest products are usually contracted for in advance and bring better prices than smaller quantities.

The forest products industries obtain much of their raw material through direct purchases from forest owners and logging operators. Some pulpwood, for example, is produced on company lands, while more comes from company operations on stumpage purchased from federal, state, or individual private owners. A location close to a paper mill, sawmill, or other timber industry is a distinct advantage to the owner (because of lower hauling costs), although good quality and sizes of timber can be sold in almost every section of the United States. Material which is of lower quality or small size is frequently difficult to sell at any price.

Marketing Methods

Buying and selling of forest products is accomplished through individual transactions rather than through central marketing exchanges, as is the case with many other important farm commodities. Most larger wood-processing industries have log buyers whose business it is to know the timber and the timber producers in their territory. Local loggers and sawmill men usually can direct forest owners in getting in touch with these buyers. Market and price information, including lists of wood-buying industries, are being compiled and published by some state Extension Foresters. Most foresters are familiar with prices and market conditions in their locality and are able to furnish this information if published material is unavailable.

Prior to cutting any timber, the forest owner should make certain of having a written contract with a buyer at a firm price. Otherwise, it is possible that a slow market would force him to leave a considerable amount of cut timber on hand; such timber would be ruined by wood borers and rot.

Before selling merchantable standing timber, the forest manager must decide whether to sell standing trees or to conduct his own logging operation. The first system relieves the owner of detailed supervision, financing, and other tasks connected with logging; but in selling stumpage, the owner loses the opportunity to make an operating profit. In either case he should definitely make a volume estimate of the timber and make sure that proper silvicultural methods are followed by marking only those trees which are to be cut.

One recent study showed that owners who sold their timber on volume scaled or estimated received $9.00 more per m.b.f. than those who sold without any measurement of volume, either standing or cut! Most sellers took the offered price of the buyer, but they would have found that it pays to shop around for the best price.

In preparing to sell standing timber which has been estimated and marked for cutting, an advertisement stating the amount, minimum acceptable price, and the location is placed in local papers and regional trade journals. Bidders are asked to visit the tract, cruise it if they wish, and submit their bids. The successful bidder is asked to sign a timber sale agreement which binds him to the conditions it sets forth, including proper cutting of marked trees (see Appendix D). The advice of an experienced forester is suggested in assisting the owner with the first sale or two until he becomes thoroughly familiar with the process.

Where the seller decides to conduct a logging operation of his own and to offer cut products for sale on the market, a considerably different procedure is required. After the timber has been estimated and the merchantable volume marked, a written contract with a buyer should be obtained to record the details of the agreement. This contract states the total volume, the specifications of each product by species, the point of delivery, unit of measure and method of scaling, price per unit, and the period during which delivery can be made (see Appendix D). With this in hand, the forest manager makes his plans for logging—either by hiring and operating his own crew and equipment or by contracting with a logging operator who agrees to deliver the cut products at so much per m.b.f. or cord. (See Appendix D for logging contract form.) Chapter 12 supplies several important kinds of information to forest owners wishing to obtain the assistance of forestry agencies and industry groups in working out problems connected with each of the steps suggested above.

QUESTIONS

1. More than half of all the timber cut goes into the manufacture of lumber. What is the next largest use for timber?

2. Name the two most important lumber-producing regions in the United States today.

3. The largest volume of lumber is sawed from Douglas fir trees. What group of species makes up the second largest volume, and in which region does the production take place?

4. Name three important methods for converting pulpwood into pulp and paper.

5. Give four other important products from trees besides lumber and paper.

6. How important are the forest products industries to our national economy?

7. Why is it important to provide for the sale of forest products before they are cut rather than after?

8. Before selling standing timber (stumpage), what should an owner know about his timber?

9. What are the advantages of a written agreement or contract to the forest owner?

10. How many board feet are in an 8-ft. 2 × 4? In a 12-ft. 2 × 6? In a 16-ft. 2 × 8?

EXERCISES

1. Visit the nearest sawmill operation in your area.

2. Locate any other wood-using industry and find out required specifications for rough forest products.

3. Find out how forest products are marketed in your locality.

4. Visit any local Christmas-tree, naval stores, or maple syrup operation in your area.

11

Managing Forest Lands for Other Purposes

Although forest products are the most tangible commodities derived for human consumption from forest lands, many other "products" are important in their own way. Most of these cannot be measured in concrete ways nor can we put an exact dollar value on them, but they might be considered forest by-products and services. Included in this broad group are wildlife, watershed protection, recreational uses such as hunting, fishing, camping, and forage for grazing livestock—mainly cattle and sheep.

Many of these forest by-products will develop whether we consciously plan for them or not—if we manage the forest well for timber alone. But by including certain additional practices for improving the environment for game and fish, for providing recreational facilities, for preventing erosion on logging jobs, and other practices described in the following pages, the forests can be made to serve us far better. This chapter describes some of the more important methods by which these additional forest values can be obtained.

Forests exert a number of influences on the land which are important to note or review at this point. The leaves and needles of the tree crowns break up and lessen the impact of raindrops, with the result that they fall more gently to the ground so that more rain soaks into the soil and less of it runs off quickly. Forest soils are a deep accumulation of dead leaves and rotten wood which filters moisture into the soil much more rapidly and in larger amounts than is possible under other types of cover. The temperature of the air in a forest is usually cooler in the summer,

255

due to the shade and transpiration; and the air contains a higher relative humidity. Wind velocities are usually much lower in the forest than out in the open (in either summer or winter), due to the protective influence of the trees. These are some of the reasons why the forest produces values that are important to the public at large even though the owner does not actually obtain any income from them. Let us see how they affect forest management practices.

WATERSHED PROTECTION AND MANAGEMENT

In addition to providing crops of timber, wildlife, and forage for grazing animals, forest lands have important influences on rainfall retardation and subsurface water flow. Well-managed forested watersheds have less erosion of the soil and hence contribute very little silt to streams, reservoirs, and harbors. Many communities protect the watersheds around their water supplies from fire, grazing, and logging so as to protect their sources of water—a resource more valuable than any other forest product. Good management of the forest, however, can produce both timber and water, as well as wildlife.

Here is how the forest acts to protect watersheds. As we have said, the tree crowns of different heights, together with the mass of shrubs below them, intercept the rainfall on its way to the ground. By breaking up large drops into smaller ones, the vegetation "feeds" the porous forest soil which is covered by the loose litter and duff of decomposing leaves and twigs. Fallen leaves on the ground act further to break up large raindrops. The action of bacteria, earthworms, fungi, insect larvae, and other minute forms of plant and animal life keeps the soil porous and spongy—ideal for holding, storing, and filtering large quantities of water. Tiny drops of rain are thus fed into this spongy mass instead of running off the surface, as much more of it does in a plowed field, for example.

Below the organic surface soil is the subsoil layer which contains more mineral content. It is not as porous as the surface soil but has many openings and channels made by roots and animal burrowings that allow water to penetrate to greater depths. Later on, some of the water returns to the surface in the form of springs. Thus the speed and volume of water movement into the soil depend upon the structure and number of pore spaces formed by plant and animal activity. When rain falls on a forest, a part of it clings to the leaves and needles of trees and other plants, where it gradually evaporates. Some trickles down the trunks and plant stems into the soil. In long, hard rainfalls the spongy forest floor will become soaked to the point where surface runoff will begin to take place. Thus it is possible for floods to develop in forested areas, but they are usually slower in coming and the water contains much less silt than the runoff from farming or burned-over areas (Fig. 11–1).

Part of the rainfall which soaks into the ground is used by trees and other plants for their growth. Some evaporates from the plants, some is soaked up by the spongy forest soil, and, as we have seen, some goes deep down into the water table. After all these things have happened, surface runoff will begin. But that requires long, hard rains. Some forest soils in good condition can absorb 50 per cent of their total volume in water before this happens.

Forest cover has a strong influence on snowfall. It protects snow from the sun and wind, enabling it to stay on the forest floor weeks after it has melted off open ground. Frequently the forest will prevent the soil from freezing and thus keep it receptive for infiltration when the snow melts in the spring.

Over-grazing, careless logging which tears up the forest soil in skidding, and forest fires are the sources of greatest damage to watersheds. Over-grazing destroys much ground cover, compacts the soil, and causes water to run off rather than soak into the ground. Skidding rips up the soil and starts eroding gullies which carry off water and silt unless great care is exercised.

A well-managed watershed shows up sharply in contrast to a poor one. The plant cover is thick—both the understory of small trees and plants as well as the overstory of trees—and the soil is porous and spongy. Clear streams and flowing springs—even in dry seasons—are another sign of a good watershed. Streambanks are well covered with vegetation—not caving in or cluttered with logging debris, and the cool, clear streams usually have plenty of fish.

Watershed Conservation Practices

Forest management plans which take into consideration watershed values (and in all cases they should) include special provisions for grazing, logging, and road building. Grazing animals are limited in numbers and are moved from place to place so that

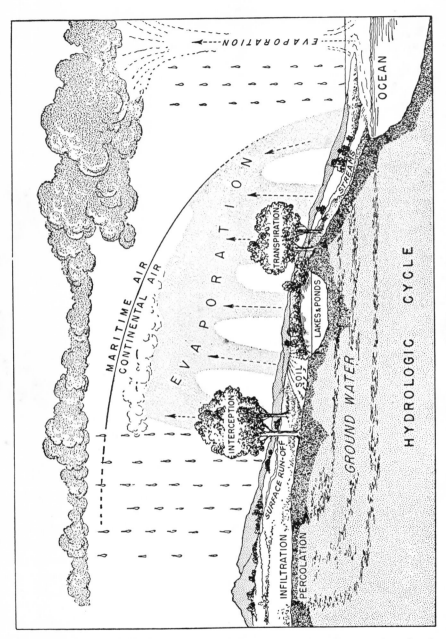

Fig. 11–1. The hydrologic cycle. (From *Forestry Handbook*, edited by Reginald D. Forbes and Arthur B. Meyer for the Society of American Foresters. Copyright, 1955, by The Ronald Press Company, New York)

258

they will not over-graze plant cover nor compact the soil. Recreational uses are so located that fire danger will be kept to a minimum and pollution of streams will be prevented by proper sanitation facilities.

Well-designed management plans will locate roads so as to cross streams and rivers infrequently, thus keeping raw silt from entering the streams. Instead, roads will parallel waterways some distance back from them so that silt will be filtered out through the forest before reaching the streams. Raw roadbanks and any raw streambanks will be sloped and planted to vegetation to stabilize the soil which has been disturbed in construction.

Where feasible, "high lead" cable systems can be substituted for ground skidding in steep areas so as to disturb the soil as little as possible. Where ground skidding is unavoidable, skidways should be planted to grass, and water diversion bars should be constructed immediately upon completion of use. Logging debris and other slash should be kept out of stream channels by felling the trees away from streams. Reserving a strip of untouched timber along waterways will not only prevent damage to the stream but preserve esthetic values as well.

And finally, any open lands with insufficient ground cover should either be reseeded to grass (if in Western grazing country) or planted to trees as soon as funds become available. If these measures are followed—and in most cases they simply require some foresight and direction—adequate protection of the watershed will result even though multiple use management is made of the area.

Some of the soil erosion control techniques for range conservation are applicable in watershed protection. One of the most important protective measures which will reduce siltation and retard runoff is fencing forest land so as to exclude livestock. Allowing undergrowth and tree reproduction to develop, and preventing compaction of the soil by animal hoofs will markedly improve the infiltration capacity of forest soils.

A series of new techniques, still in the experimental stage, is being developed to increase water yields from mountain areas with a water deficiency. It has been found that snow intercepted and held on the crowns of conifers is lost in direct evaporation and sublimation into the atmosphere. By partial cuttings and other techniques which reduce crown densities, and by replacing conifers with hardwoods, increased water can be made available to water-shortage areas without damaging the watershed. This practice is limited in application. Fig. 11–2 shows a station for measuring stream flow.

Fig. 11–2. A stream gaging station on a North Carolina watershed. This weir makes it possible to maintain a continuous record of the stream flow, using an automatic recorder located in the small building. (U. S. Forest Service)

WILDLIFE MANAGEMENT IN FORESTRY

Previously, the relationship of plants and animals to each other and their environment was discussed as the study of ecology. Wildlife is the product of the land. Forests provide a home, or habitat, for many kinds of wildlife—game animals, songbirds, and many forms of tiny insects and animal life. Hundreds of kinds of plants make their home under the forest canopy and could not exist without it. The important elements of a wildlife habitat are food, cover, and water, and the combination and balance of these factors determines the kinds of wildlife to be found in any forest area. Most game fish, for instance, prefer clear, cool streams in forested watersheds.

Some of the well-known game animals and birds found mainly in forested areas are deer, elk, bear, moose, squirrel, turkey, ruffed grouse, wood duck, woodcock, and raccoon. There are also many songbirds and other small mammals which are essential to a well-balanced forest community. The shade of dense old-growth forests is often too great to provide the shrubs and herbs needed for food by birds and animals, but a well-managed forest with openings can produce abundant supplies. Weeds and shrubs which produce edible seeds spring up along with grasses and tree seedlings when the sun's rays can reach the ground. Well-planned forest management will create small openings such as these and leave a few hollow old wolf trees for animal dens, bird nests, and for the nuts or acorns they may produce. Wildlife tends to work along the edges between the woods and the openings because food lies on one side and escape cover on the other.

The forest manager can do much to improve the area under his control as a wildlife habitat. In addition to creating openings and leaving den trees, he can assist nature by supplemental plantings. For example, plantings of pines or spruces in or near hardwood forests make good winter escape cover from both enemies and snowstorms. Many shrubs which bear persistent seeds make good food and cover when planted along the edge of plantations or openings in the forest. These measures will tend to increase the numbers of wildlife present in the area, and this will usually be beneficial. More songbirds and game birds mean better protection against insect outbreaks.

Water is essential to all forms of wildlife, and its scarcity or abundance influences their numbers and distribution. Beavers, ducks, and fish require it for their homes. As a protector of watershed, the forest yields steady supplies of water for these species from springs and retarded runoff into lakes, streams, and swamps.

Destructive cutting over wide areas, like fire, greatly alters the habitat for wildlife and it may be years before balanced conditions are restored. Sometimes wildlife-forest relationships get out of balance, due to man's interference. Cutover areas spring up with millions of hardwood seedlings which provide excellent deer food. The deer population increases greatly, but the trees soon grow out of their reach, thus forcing them to eat any form of vegetation (Fig. 11–3). Sometimes this results in great damage to young conifers such as hemlock and white cedar. Unfortunately, man has largely eliminated wolves, which are predators of deer; in many areas the number of human hunters is not large enough to keep the deer population in balance.

National and state forests are usually open to hunting and fishing, subject in both cases to the state game laws. The forest manager must acquaint himself with the laws and with the habits

Fig. 11–3. Deer reaching for forage in overbrowsed habitat. (U. S. Forest Service)

of the hunter and fisherman, both for purposes of wildlife management and to protect his forest against carelessness with fire. On private forests more control over hunters and fishermen is exercised, but recently several large owners have found that it is not only good public relations but also good management to allow hunters and fishermen to use their lands. Proper sites for camping sportsmen are often supplied in forests in order to encourage concentration of use in a few areas.

By using care in constructing roads, in reserving trees along streams, and in keeping logging slash out of streams, the forest manager can maintain healthy water for game fish.

Some Forest-Wildlife Management Practices

With little additional work, but with intelligent advance planning, many practices to improve the forest for wildlife can be developed. Sometimes it is merely a matter of timing; in other cases simply leaving a few den trees in logging will bring results. While wildlife management is a field which requires special training, just as forestry does, the forest manager can master a few techniques which will improve the wildlife habitat in his forest. A few important ones are listed, but it is suggested that the student do additional reading on the subject (see the Bibliography), particularly if his work requires him to do extensive wildlife work. Keeping in mind that birds and animals all need food, water, nesting sites, and escape cover, the following practices have been found to fit in well with forestry programs:

1. In the heavy deer country of the North, winter logging, stand improvement, or thinning, if done in mid- or late winter, will make available browse from tops and limbs just at the time the deer need food the most.

2. In mountainous, hilly, or dry country with long distances between water courses, it has been found beneficial to build small ponds to hold back seepage or runoff water on the slopes. This has the effect of spreading out wildlife over the forest and may reduce damage to young trees from deer browsing. Larger ponds may be used by waterfowl, especially wood ducks if houses are provided (see Fig. 11–4).

Fig. 11–4. This pond supplies water, slows runoff, attracts waterfowl, and provides fishing. (U. S. Forest Service)

3. To improve ruffed grouse habitat, it has been found that the planting of clover along logging roads will increase the food supply and improve hunting. In acid soils this planting of clover must be accompanied with lime.

4. In badly burned Northern forest areas, where second-growth forests have few fallen logs, distribution of a few old hollow logs near low spots has been found a useful means of encourag-

ing ruffed grouse to spread out during the "drumming" period at mating time.

5. Clearing out small openings in the forest during logging and planting them to berry-bearing shrubs (if none are present) will increase the food supply of many birds and small animals.

6. Building of houses for wood ducks and placing them along waterways will increase the population of these rare and beautiful waterfowl.

7. Planting of coniferous stands in hardwood forest areas or in open farming country will provide the best kind of protection for wildlife from winter snowstorms and high winds.

8. Placing rock or log deflectors in small streams permits the current to cut out pools deeper than the normal streambed and thus makes better fish habitats. The proper handling of forests to assure steady streamflow, however, is the most important contribution which can be made for fish conservation. While special practices may be carried out, they usually require considerable advance planning by fisheries biologists.

9. Quail habitats in the South can be greatly improved along the edges of the forest and in small openings by planting lespedeza, leaving brushy edges between the forest and adjoining fields and excluding grazing animals where grazing is too intensive.

10. Fencing farm woods to exclude livestock will encourage brush and young trees for wildlife food and cover.

Field observation and the study of wildlife management methods will suggest other practices when one is actually practicing forestry. The assistance of a wildlife specialist is suggested in planning the details of technical applications.

MANAGING FOREST LANDS FOR GRAZING

Grazing on forest lands, if not controlled, can do more harm to the basic resource than the income which it may yield. This has been especially true of the hardwood forest areas in the Central states and the East, where dairy cattle have done extensive over-grazing (see Fig. 11–5). Elimination of reproduction and compaction of forest soils are all too common results from over-grazing on farm woodlands. Studies by forest experiment stations have clearly shown that forage yields in farm woods are very low and runoff of water is greatly accelerated, due to soil compaction from over-grazing. On the other hand, light grazing for very short periods

Fig. 11–5. Without frequent herding, livestock quickly over-graze forest areas, causing damage to the watershed by compacting the soil and reducing vegetative cover. (U. S. Soil Conservation Service)

may occasionally be beneficial. During drought emergencies, when pastures dry up, farm woodlands can be a useful source of forage. Generally, however, farmers must make a choice between pasture and timber. Steeper slopes should be retained in trees; on level lands economic needs will probably dictate that grazing should prevail.

Both in the Southern states and in the West, cattle grazing is an important auxiliary forest use. Handled properly, the forest can produce a moderate amount of forage, but the number of grazing animals must be kept in line with the growth of forage. This is essentially sustained-yield management of the grass!

Range management is the science and art of planning and directing the use of the range so as to obtain maximum production of forage for livestock and wildlife without damage to the forest and watershed. Here again is a specialized field of work which requires additional study. The forest technician should familiarize himself with some of the essentials of range management because grazing can be a source of additional income to the forest owner.

In the South there are many fields and openings in the pine

forests and some in the hardwoods, both of which produce varying amounts of forage. For many generations people believed that
burning off the old accumulation of dead grass and shrubs improved spring grazing. Sometimes it did, in certain situations, but
it was done too often and too indiscriminately. Thus many valuable plant nutrients such as nitrate and phosphate were lost into
the air. Damage to timber and destruction of seedlings are of
course serious at best and completely destructive at worst.

In managing the Southern forested areas it is vitally important
both to the trees and to the cattle that only such grazing be permitted as will support an optimum number of cattle adequately
without damage to reproduction. As in the West, the number of
livestock permitted to graze should depend upon the kind and
abundance of forage available—the "carrying capacity." This is
determined by range surveys and made by range experts familiar
with the species of grass and other palatable forage plants. There
are, however, several rules-of-thumb which an observant forest
manager can follow in detecting over-grazing: If grasses are
closely cropped, if unpalatable weeds are abundant, if brush and
small trees are nipped and the lower leaves cropped off of larger
shrubs and trees, if erosion is found near cattle trails or streambanks, it is time to suspect over-grazing. The carrying capacity of
a forest range depends largely upon the number of openings in
which grasses can get established. Most well-managed forests in
the South do not have much open land; but if a combination of
livestock and timber production is desired, management plans
will provide for open fields. Intensive livestock production will
require that these fields be sowed to good perennial pasture
grasses for management of forage. Over large areas of open land
in the South, five acres with good soil will supply forage for one
head for a year. Mixed forest and open land will require anywhere
from ten to forty acres per head.

Although Western forest ranges are usually in the mountains,
whereas those in the South vary all the way from coastal plains to
Appalachian highland, most of the principles are very similar.
Western forest ranges do not ordinarily support as many head of
livestock for a given area because the forage production is lower
—owing to lesser rainfall. Greater care must be taken against
over-grazing in the West because regrowth of damaged range
grasses takes a long time.

Fortunately, most of the forest range land in the West is under
public control—national forests and federal grazing districts—and

grazing is more closely regulated than on the private lands of the South. Range management specialists try to keep a close check on the progress of grazing and to limit livestock when over-grazing seems imminent. In some cases this has led to political pressure from stockmen to open up the lands to more intensive grazing. Only when the public agencies have been able to resist this pressure has improved range cover resulted.

Range Conservation Practices

A number of successful measures have increased the amount of forage on range lands and reduced possible damage from live-stock. Prior to undertaking them, the range manager made an estimate of the carrying capacity of the area based on an inventory and classification of the grasses according to palatability. The most important and generally used range conservation practices are as follows:

1. Fencing off the tract into several "pastures" allows for rotating grazing from area to area and thus permits development of grasses until an area is ready for grazing.
2. Water impoundments, windmill pumps, stock tanks, and other sources of water can be developed at scattered points so as to provide adequate water in many places for small groups of animals.
3. Salt licks are placed away from water holes so as to keep the animals from concentrating their grazing and to keep them moving.
4. Killing of brush and weeds which occupy good grazing land is usually done by spraying chemicals and following up with a seeding of grass.
5. Large areas are also disked and reseeded to palatable grasses after the poorer grasses and brush are removed, especially areas where sagebrush, cheat grass, or other poor forage plants have moved in and replaced better grasses following over-grazing.
6. Firebreaks which are kept open by occasional disking, espe-cially in the South, can be seeded to forage grasses and made to yield livestock feed. Grazing keeps these breaks clear so that they still serve their primary purpose.
7. Small gullies which have cut through the soil because of rapid runoff of water resulting from over-grazing can often be con-trolled with brush and log dams if the watersheds above them

have been reseeded. Larger gullies require substantial engineering and earth moving; building dams to make water impoundments at the upper ends of gullies is usually quite successful.

8. Water-spreading devices of several types can be constructed to make the maximum use of flash floodwaters and thus increase forage production in the areas immediately below the water spreaders. These include diversion terraces, check dams, and contour furrows.

9. In the South some prescribed (controlled) burning has been found to be beneficial to eliminate certain types of unpalatable encroaching vegetation. This must be executed by people completely familiar with the forest and range situation. Burning should never be done in hardwoods and only under expert planning in piney woods.

10. Complete exclusion of livestock from over-grazed rangeland should be maintained until recovery of native grasses restores watershed porosity.

RECREATIONAL USES OF THE FOREST

Since World War II there has been an explosion in the demand for outdoor recreation. For such activities as family camping, hiking, fishing, sight-seeing, skiing, boating, and canoeing, and for summer camps and cottages, forest areas near lakes or rivers have the greatest attraction. To the natural features must be added visitor-use facilities such as campgrounds, trails, access roads, overlooks, ski runs, boat docks, and supporting developments.

This great increase in outdoor recreational demands is evidenced by some recent forecasts from the Bureau of Outdoor Recreation:

	(Millions of Occasions)		
Activity	1965	1980	2000
Picnicking	451	668	1,022
Fishing	332	422	574
Camping	97	173	328
Sight-seeing	457	705	1,169
Hiking	167	262	433

The impact of this greatly increased use of outdoor recreation areas will be felt most heavily in public forested areas: National and State Parks, National and State Forests, Wildlife Refuges, and in private industrial forests (larger tree farms). The task of the forest manager is to manage this recreational use so as to provide the greatest opportunities to the recreationist and the least damage to the ecology of the forest. This means careful planning of roads, camp grounds, service buildings, sight-seeing overlooks, etc., and such planning is as much of a specialty as forestry itself.

Some areas such as our nearly 30 million acres of National Parks and Monuments and National Forest Wilderness Areas are not managed for multiple use but are frankly kept as nature preserves. Evidence of overuse by recreationists is already present in such popular areas as Yellowstone and Yosemite Parks and others where visitors tend to concentrate. Damage to the soil and plant life becomes so serious that camping and other facilities must be moved frequently to maintain the natural environment. The National Forest Wilderness Areas have been given additional protection in recent years by the Wilderness Act of 1964. It provides for recreational use by people but no construction or commodity production, the lands are to be "kept forever wild." These specially zoned areas are highly valuable for scientific research and ecological studies. Additions to Wilderness Areas are provided in the law after hearings and congressional action.

On National and State Forests and Industrial Forests where multiple-use management is the goal, an even more difficult job of coordinating visitor use with timber production, grazing, mining, and other commodity production faces the forester. Actually there are few serious conflicts between recreational uses of the forests and other uses. People do not ordinarily camp out in the middle of a freshly logged area. They do like to locate their camps near water; for this reason, areas with both forests and water attract the largest numbers. The greatest number of people go into the woods in the summertime, with the result that fire becomes a serious danger from campers and smokers. These, then, are some of the considerations in forest recreation (Fig. 11–6).

Types of Recreational Areas

Our public forests and parks, state and national, attract the largest numbers of people. Since every area differs from every other in its combination of forest types, topography, water, and other natural factors, classification for recreational use can be only

Fig. 11–6. Most people prefer to camp in wooded areas adjacent to lake or stream. (U. S. Forest Service)

approximate at best. There are two major groupings of areas on which outdoor recreation is carried on: intensively used occupancy tracts, and extensive general areas. These are divided in the following manner:

Intensively Used Occupancy Areas. These areas include the following types:

1. *Forest Camps.* Usually 10 or more acres in tents, trailer sites, or seasonal buildings, with essential parking and minimum facilities such as water, sanitation, tables, and fireplaces. These are usually publicly developed areas.
2. *Picnic and Roadside Areas.* Small acreage for day use only with-

out provision for overnight stays but with other minimum facilities, including parking areas and playing fields. (Public development predominantly.)

3. *Group or Organization Camps.* These require from 25 to 100 acres, depending on the number of people (usually 1 acre per person); the average capacity of a large camp is about 80 persons. Used by such groups as Boy Scouts, church organizations, welfare agencies, etc., facilities should include water, sanitation, lodging, boat houses and docks, playing field, etc. Development either by a public agency or by the group using the area.

4. *Resort and Service Areas.* These require from 25 to 100 acres for lodges, guest cabins, stores, boat and bath houses, water and sanitation, dock and beach development, playground facilities, power, etc. These areas are usually privately developed on private lands or on publicly licensed concessions.

5. *Summer Home Areas.* Private developments usually located adjacent to a lake or stream. There is no established acreage size, but the optimum seems to be 10 to 30 acres or more for single-family summer cottages or cabins. Smaller tracts are considered less desirable.

6. *Winter Sports Areas.* These usually include several hundred acres with ski hills and service areas in concentrated use. Usual facilities include lodging, sanitation, parking areas, ski runs, etc. Development is usually by private owners or concessionaires on public lands.

7. *All Other Special Use Recreational Areas.* Such uses would include (a) hunters' and fishermen's overnight camps, (b) trails and portages maintained mostly for recreational use, and (c) waterfront developments (beaches, docks, boat landings, public access strips to lakes and beaches, etc.).

Extensive Recreational Areas. Nearly all other kinds of forest areas may be used in some manner for recreational purposes. Hunting, fishing, camping, mountain climbing, pack and canoe trips attract the greatest number (Fig. 11–7). There is considerable variation in the sort of attraction offered in different areas, and people tend to go to those with outstanding scenic and other attractions.

1. *Areas Dedicated Primarily to Recreational and Other Noncommodity Uses.* These include all of our National Parks, National Monuments, Wilderness Areas, Roadless Areas, many primitive areas of the National Forests, most National Wildlife Refuges

Fig. 11–7. Girl Scouts canoe along the shore of the Niobrara River near Valentine, Nebraska. (U. S. Department of the Interior, Bureau of Outdoor Recreation)

(hunting excluded except on Public Hunting Grounds and camping restricted to designated campsites), most State Parks, and private preserves from which the public is excluded.

2. *Areas on Which Recreational Uses Coexist with Other Land Uses.* These areas include most national and state forest lands, private woodlands of both large and small owners (where permission is given for public use) upon which logging, grazing, and other commodity uses may be carried on but which are otherwise available for picnicking, hunting, fishing, camping, etc.

3. *Areas Excluded from Recreational Use.* Military lands, certain natural and experimental scientific areas which would be disturbed by human use, danger areas around logging and mining operations, and lands dedicated to the preservation of endangered species of wildlife are among those areas excluded from recreational use. This group is small in the total of available forest land.

These types of recreational land uses may be outlined on the forest cover map or indicated on aerial photographs. Symbols depicting each of them are a useful method for quick identification. The forest or park management plan will denote the location and acreage of each area by classification and all recreational facilities should be concentrated on them.

Planning Intensively Used Recreational Facilities

To take care of people in forest areas requires an advance estimate of the number of people and the type of use to be expected. Because recreational uses are expected to be so much greater in the next few years, plans and developments for campgrounds will be executed on a scale much greater than anything known heretofore. These estimates are usually made by the planning staff of the forestry or park administration which has access to such information as past uses and demands on similar areas and the amount of space needed for a tent camp, picnic ground, summer home development, or other group uses. Once these decisions are made, a recreational management plan can be developed. Preparations of plans for buildings, outdoor fireplaces, water systems or individual pumps, toilets, and waste disposal areas are usually handled by the staff planners. A map of the area is drawn up with the location of each of the above facilities shown on it. Designs for each type of facility, e.g., fireplaces, toilets, picnic tables, etc., are prepared by engineering staffs. Many designs of recreational improvements are set forth in the *Forestry Handbook*.

Prior to actual construction of facilities, preparation of the campsites and surrounding areas involves considerable careful work. It is essential that the attractiveness of the forested surroundings be preserved, but it is also essential that fire hazards be reduced to a minimum (a fire lane around the camp is often needed) and that dangerous dead trees be removed. Mosquito control is often needed in areas where these pests persist. The facilities which are provided should be fitted into the woods so as to reduce the need for cutting trees to a minimum. Most trees should be preserved except for those on tent sites or on space needed for buildings. Open playing fields for baseball and other games are frequently provided. Brush, in and close to the camping areas, often constitutes an undesirable obstacle except where small patches of interesting shrubs are reserved for landscaping values, or where they are needed for screening between campsites.

If the campsite is on a river or lake front, easy access should be provided for people to back in their boat trailers. Swimming and boat dock facilities usually are found in such areas. Running water and electricity are luxuries not found in the more inaccessible areas but are often necessary where large numbers of people congregate. If electricity is available, the placing of outlets near tent sites is frequently done. Running water, of course, can make for better sanitary facilities, although a plumbing system will cost considerable money. Septic tanks for sewage disposal are also essential. Other features such as picnic tables, rustic log chairs, etc., are often made available to campsite users. More and more forest products concerns are providing excellent visitor facilities on their tree farms, partly to encourage user concentration and forest protection. Landowners need to know what kinds of recreational activities to provide facilities for and how to protect the basic resources. While a system for charging for camping and other visitor facilities is developing satisfactorily on some private, federal, and state lands, private landowners have not yet found a practical means for obtaining revenues from the use of their lands for hunting, fishing, and other extensive visitor uses.

One final word should be said of the need for campsite conservation. Heavy visitor use through trampling, camping, driving vehicles, etc., usually compacts the soil and causes not only damage to the land but also a change in the plant composition. Large old trees will succumb when their environment is drastically changed. Campside rotation is a way to reduce this kind of pressure and to use nature's recuperative powers. By moving to different locations every ten or so years, it is possible to restore the natural vegetation of heavily used sites.

Forestry and Natural Scenic Beauty

During the surge of conservation activity in the 1960's, public attention and interest has been focussed on the appearance of America's countryside. Views of hillsides ruined by billboard advertising, junk car yards, attractive woods roads littered with beer cans, and destructive lumbering have been given public scrutiny and criticism.

People unfamiliar with forest growing and harvesting have been critical of logging generally. In addition to public education to show that all logging is not bad, it is important for forest managers to give attention to the aesthetic aspects of their forestry measures. We have already mentioned the desirability and even necessity of leaving timber strips along streambanks. Roadside strips of uncut timber several hundred feet wide are as important as belts around recreational facility areas to preserve the forest scene. Removing of fallen, defective, and some overmature trees will not harm the scenic effect of these strips if tops and limbs left from logging slash are cut up and lopped to the ground.

The following forestry practices are suggested by the Massachusetts Extension Forester:

1. Utilizing all material possible from harvesting operations.
2. Performing light harvest cutting operations which leave the forest intact.
3. Favoring trees of special interest as to foliage coloration, form, and branching habit.
4. Enhancing aesthetic qualities of the landscape by developing vistas and emphasizing desirable topographic features of the area by either creating or utilizing existing openings in the forest.
5. Protecting woodlands from uncontrolled fires.
6. Protecting uncut trees, seedlings, and shrubs by careful felling, skidding, and hauling practices.
7. Replacing cut trees, if needed, by (a) planting seedlings, (b) utilizing natural seedings, (c) releasing desirable understory stems already established.

8. Protecting the site against erosion by proper extractive procedures including well-planned skid and haul road layout, adequate water drainage facilities.
9. Cleaning up afterwards such unsightly things as refuse, tin cans, discarded equipment and parts.
10. Cutting up logging slash and severely damaged trees to lie close to the ground after a harvesting operation.

Where clearcutting in patches is required by silvicultural prescription, areas of less than ten acres, and preferably smaller, scattered throughout the forest, are the least offensive to the landscape. If edges of corner cuttings are rounded and conform to the contour of the land rather than sharp lines and corners, scenic values may actually be enhanced by variety and contrast. Likewise, forest tree plantings established to fit contours and composed of mixed species are less offensive scenicly than straight lines of the same species marching up and down the hill like Prussian soldiers. It makes doubly good sense to plant trees along contour furrows to save moisture and reduce soil erosion.

Other Aspects of Recreational Land Use

Management of the extensive recreational areas is usually carried on as part of the total land management job on the forest. Wildlife habitat management practices described earlier are the job of specialists in this field and are quite different from the management of camping and other areas used intensively by people. Road and trail maintenance is also part of the over-all forest administration job, even though the tourists and other recreation seekers may use them. If heavy recreational use is made of these transportation facilities, special provision must be included in construction and maintenance operations.

Visitor concentration and overcrowding at the attractive and highly scenic areas, such as Yellowstone Falls and Yosemite Valley, is forcing a new system of park planning. Location of visitor facilities away from these scenic attractions is becoming more and more necessary. For smaller parks it may be that outside visitor accommodations will be the only choice. These visitors can use and view the scenic wonders in their natural, untrampled form. Good roads and access trails will of course be needed if overnight accommodations are moved elsewhere.

Administration and Maintenance of Recreational Areas

On most publicly owned forest and park areas, the resident forest administrator-ranger or superintendent is in general charge of all recreational facilities. Under his supervision all construction of improvements and facilities takes place with such assistance as he may have from staff specialists—engineers, wildlife and fisheries technicians, etc. In addition, many larger publicly and privately owned recreational areas have resident managers whose duties include all of the maintenance tasks required to keep the grounds and facilities in serviceable condition. As recreational uses continue to expand rapidly in the future and more and more camping and other areas are developed for use by larger numbers of people, employment opportunities for men with a basic knowledge of recreational area supervision will show marked increases.

Some of the main types of activities which recreational area managers are responsible for are as follows:

1. *General Annual Spring Maintenance.* Repairs and renovation of buildings, facilities, and equipment, as well as any new construction needed, are done in the early spring before seasonal use begins. Water systems are checked and repaired if necessary, garbage pits are dug and other sanitation improvements checked, wood supplies laid in, signs repainted, footbridges around camp areas repaired, posts replaced or painted, buildings refinished, tables and fireplaces repaired, general cleanup of winter debris, etc.

2. *Daily or Weekly Maintenance.* These activities vary considerably according to the type of recreational area and its intensity of use. Debris cleanup is usually of most importance. Regular check-up of all essential facilities to see that they are in operation (water system, sanitation, and garbage, etc.), burning out garbage pits, filling in chug holes and making general road repairs, cutting grass and weeds, checking signs, controlling mosquitoes, and collecting revenue if charges are made. A full-time forest recreational area manager is always available in emergencies.

QUESTIONS

1. Name three important uses of the forest besides timber production.
2. How does a forested watershed reduce the runoff of water?

3. How do grazing and improper logging act to increase water runoff?

4. Name four important game animals or birds which are found primarily in forested areas.

5. What are the three important things that make up a wildlife habitat?

6. Why is burning land for grazing a poor practice?

7. What damage does livestock do to a forest?

8. What is the most desirable type of forest recreational area, from the user's viewpoint?

9. Why should an expansion in available recreational facilities be provided in the near future?

10. Should any recreational improvements and facilities be provided in wilderness or natural areas?

EXERCISES

1. Find out whether any soil conservation or watershed projects are being carried on in your area.

2. Visit with a state conservation department or with wildlife management specialists and examine several field projects which they may have under way in wildlife habitat improvement.

3. Go to a state or other park area where camping facilities are provided and describe the improvements made available.

4. Determine whether grazing on forest lands in your area is damaging the forest or if it is well managed.

12

Organization and Administration of Forestry Programs

All of the various activities connected with managing a forest area must be organized into units convenient for proper administration. Nearly all of the larger forest areas, both public and private, provide consistent and continuous management. Some smaller owners manage their lands themselves, with the help and advice of a forester, or put it in his hands to manage. But since most of these forestry lands are still inadequately managed, they constitute one of forestry's greatest challenges. Because the methods of handling forestry programs differ considerably by kinds of organizations, they will be described separately and in detail.

In addition to the actual management of forest lands, there are many other forestry programs directed toward forestry problems but not necessarily connected with one or another type of ownership. Such programs as fire prevention and control, insect and disease control, administration of forest tax laws, provision for technical assistance to private owners, and many other programs cross ownership lines. Research in forestry is a major activity of the federal Forest Service and is becoming increasingly important in several universities and in private industry.

Forestry programs are included in two departments of the federal government—the Department of Agriculture, which has both the Forest Service and Soil Conservation Service; and the Department of Interior, which has the Bureau of Land Management, the Bureau of Indian Affairs, the Fish and Wildlife Service, and the National Park Service.

The basic laws establishing the programs administered by these agencies were set forth in Chapter 2. Many have been expanded and developed as the forestry needs of the country have increased. The organization charts in this chapter show how these bureaus are organized. On the state level, more than forty states have regular forestry divisions within their conservation departments or as separate agencies (see Appendix E). Large private holdings are usually managed by the lumber or paper company which owns them. Because most state and many large private forestry agencies are organized along lines similar to those of the Forest Service, the operational situations and functions of this large federal agency will be given in detail.

FEDERAL FOREST LANDS AND PROGRAMS

U. S. Department of Agriculture

Forest Service. Forestry programs of the federal government are centered in the Forest Service, a bureau in the Department of Agriculture (Fig. 12–1). Its principal activities, which are highly decentralized, include the administration of 153 national forests and the operation of a research program centering around 9 regional Forest Experiment Stations and the Forest Products Laboratory at Madison, Wisconsin. In addition, the Forest Service supervises cooperative federal-state programs dealing with forest protection, technical assistance to private owners, and various other cooperative activities with the states, private owners, and the general public. Probably the Smokey Bear program is the one with which the public comes most closely in contact. Another important activity is the general dissemination of information on forestry and conservation.

The policy of the Forest Service has been to make the national forests serve the greatest number of people—consistent with proper resource management. The principle of multiple use is a primary objective. All the resources of the national forests—timber, forage, minerals, hunting and fishing privileges, recreational facilities, and other resources—are available for public use under regulations designed to assure their long-term conservation.

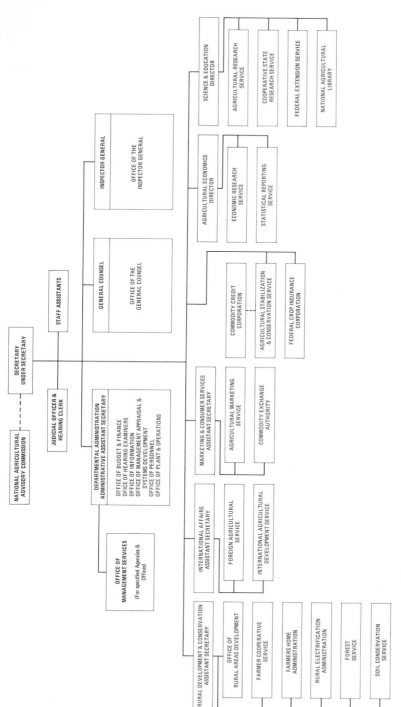

Fig. 12–1. Organization chart of the U. S. Department of Agriculture.

Because many of the forests lie in remote areas, it has been necessary to build access roads, telephone lines, trails and portages, bridges, and ranger stations in order to make available the greatest possible forest development and utility.

Generally speaking, the objectives of national forest management may be summarized as follows:

1. Sustained production of timber supplies for both local and national uses under scientific principles of applied silviculture, including reforestation, fire protection, and other management measures, and programs to make the forests serve as demonstration areas for applied forest management.
2. Management and protection of watersheds (a) to insure a stable flow of water for municipal and industrial use, power, and irrigation, (b) to reduce or prevent floods and siltation of rivers, and harbors, and (c) to maintain navigability of streams.
3. Continued production of palatable forage for big game and livestock through managed use of the range.
4. Preservation of the beauty and attractiveness of the forests and development of opportunities and facilities for recreation.
5. Management of wildlife habitats for the maximum production of wildlife (especially game and fish) consistent with the other resources in the forest.

In addition to these objectives for the national forests, the Forest Service carries on an active forest and range research program through the regional Forest Experiment Stations and research centers.

The headquarters of the Forest Service are maintained in Washington, D. C., under the direction of the chief forester and his staff of assistant chiefs. Their work is divided into six major units: Administrative Management, National Forest Administration, Lands, State and Private Forestry, Research, and Program Planning. The organization chart shown in Fig. 12–1 outlines the relationship of each of these divisions to the whole Service and to the other Bureaus in the U.S.D.A. The most important functions of the Washington office involve direction of policy, handling relations with Congress, supervising the work of the Regional Offices and the Experiment Stations, and correlating programs involving state cooperation.

In 1908 it was found that the work of the national forests required decentralization from Washington and that many of the local problems and much of the work could be better and more efficiently administered from the Regional Offices strategically located in the major forest regions. Since that time the work has been divided into nine field regions (Fig. 12–2).

Each national forest is operated through a forest supervisor's office located in a nearby town and is divided into a number of Ranger Districts, containing up to 100,000 acres each. The forest supervisor, who has general charge of all the forestry activity in his forest, is assisted by district forest rangers with direct on-the-ground responsibility.

As might be guessed, the district ranger is the key man in running his forest unit. He makes important decisions dealing with the sale of timber, layout of roads, management of grazing lands, supervision of the protection program, outdoor recreational uses, and the one thousand and one other important details which go with forest administration. The district ranger usually has an assistant and a number of other trained men, as well as a seasonal labor force for reforestation after logging, fire fighting, fence repairs, road building, campground maintenance, etc. To help him in his planning and in making his decisions, the district ranger is able to rely upon the staff specialists in the supervisor's and regional offices where engineering plans are drawn up, timber estimates compiled, timber sales announced, bids received on timber, equipment purchased, and accounts maintained.

The actual work in marking for a timber sale, surveying a road, and checking on logging progress, including scaling of timber, is frequently handled under the ranger's supervision by a forestry technician familiar with these activities. Many of these operations are becoming increasingly complex so that training in forestry is essential. Foresters often begin their life work in the Forest Service at this level, and their rise to positions of greater responsibility depends to a large extent upon their broadening their knowledge through additional training.

Soil Conservation Service. The "S.C.S.," established in the Department of Agriculture in 1935, maintains a small forestry program directly connected with its farm planning work on the approximately 2,700 Soil Conservation Districts through which it functions. Each district has a district conservationist who is assigned by the S.C.S. to develop farm plans for soil and water conservation. Although the major part of the district conservationist's work is in planning soil conservation measures on crop and pasture land, he includes recommendations for improvements

THE NATIONAL FOREST SYSTEM

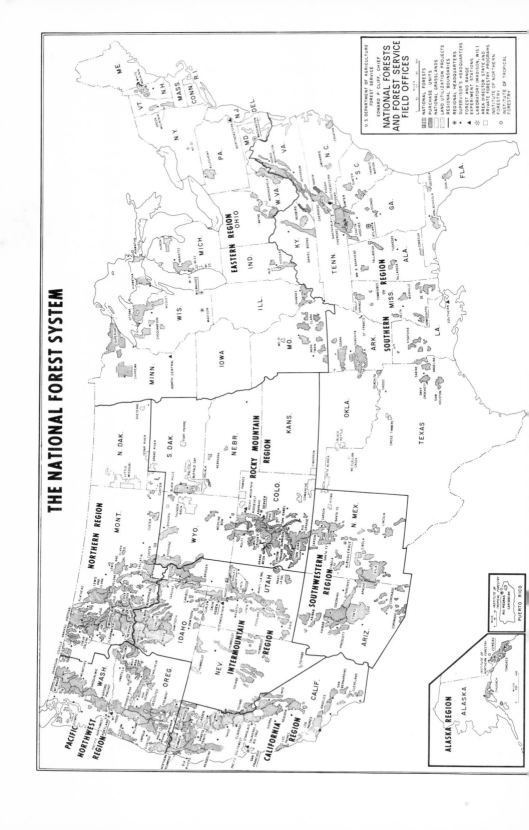

U.S. DEPARTMENT OF AGRICULTURE
FOREST SERVICE
EDWARD P. CLIFF, CHIEF

NATIONAL FORESTS AND FOREST SERVICE FIELD OFFICES

NATIONAL FORESTS
PURCHASE UNITS
NATIONAL GRASSLANDS
LAND UTILIZATION PROJECTS
REGIONAL BOUNDARIES
⦿ REGIONAL HEADQUARTERS
• SUPERVISOR'S HEADQUARTERS
▲ FOREST AND RANGE EXPERIMENT STATIONS
✳ FOREST PRODUCTS LABORATORY (MADISON, WIS.)
☐ AREA DIRECTOR STATE AND PRIVATE FORESTRY PROGRAMS
⦾ INSTITUTE OF NORTHERN FORESTRY
○ INSTITUTE OF TROPICAL FORESTRY

in woodland management as well. Some of the measures suggested for open land (especially steeper slopes) must include revegetation, and forest planting is often given high priority. Although technically trained men usually have been appointed to the district jobs, men with vocational agricultural experience are being increasingly called upon. Opportunities for forestry technicians are greater where forest areas are a dominant part of the district.

U. S. Department of the Interior

The Bureau of Land Management. This bureau is responsible for large areas of public lands—mainly in the Western states and Alaska. Although most of these lands are organized into grazing districts and contain little or no timber, there are several millions of acres of timberland in Oregon which are managed intensively for timber production. As Alaskan forests become more accessible, protection and management will be extended more intensely within them. Most of the forestry work of the B.L.M. is carried on by its Resources Management Division, which concerns itself with planning for timber sales, building of access roads, administration of fire protection programs, mapping and estimating forest areas preliminary to development of management plans, and many of the associated activities related to forest administration. One of the most important functions of the B.L.M. is to continue the basic land survey system originally begun by the General Land Office. Fig. 12–3 shows an organization chart of the U. S. Department of the Interior.

The Bureau of Indian Affairs. This bureau has long had charge of the management of forests on a number of Indian reservations. Recent "termination" legislation leaves the status of the reservation forestry programs in doubt on several reservations with large timber tracts.

The National Park Service. This service has charge of all National Parks, Monuments, and related historical sites included in the National Park System. The service carries on an active forestry program designed to protect the forests, but not to cut timber or harvest game from them, because undisturbed forests in our National Parks are an essential part of these outstanding natural scenic areas. Forestry is largely confined to protecting the forests

Fig. 12–2. Regional organization of the U. S. National Forest System.

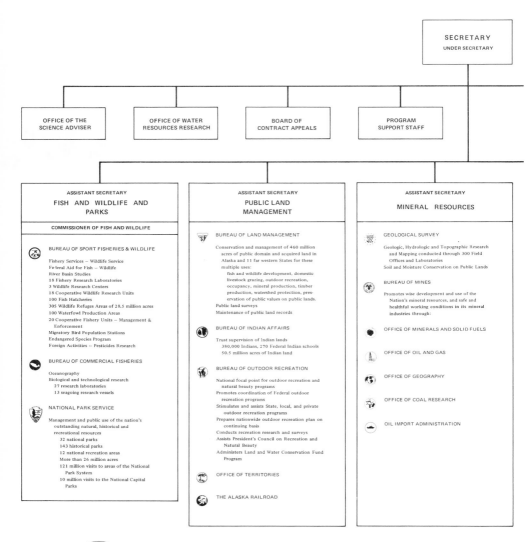

Fig. 12–3. Organization chart of

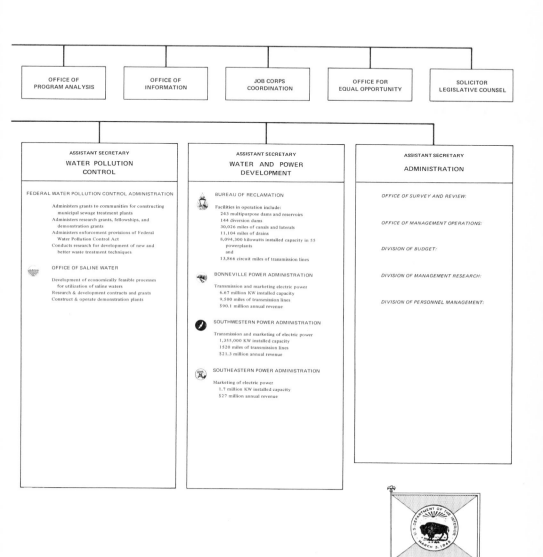

| OFFICE OF PROGRAM ANALYSIS | OFFICE OF INFORMATION | JOB CORPS COORDINATION | OFFICE FOR EQUAL OPPORTUNITY | SOLICITOR LEGISLATIVE COUNSEL |

ASSISTANT SECRETARY

WATER POLLUTION CONTROL

FEDERAL WATER POLLUTION CONTROL ADMINISTRATION

    Administers grants to communities for constructing municipal sewage treatment plants
    Administers research grants, fellowships, and demonstration grants
    Administers enforcement provisions of Federal Water Pollution Control Act
    Conducts research for development of new and better waste treatment techniques

OFFICE OF SALINE WATER

    Development of economically feasible processes for utilization of saline waters
    Research & development contracts and grants
    Construct & operate demonstration plants

ASSISTANT SECRETARY

WATER AND POWER DEVELOPMENT

BUREAU OF RECLAMATION

    Facilities in operation include:
      243 multipurpose dams and reservoirs
      144 diversion dams
      30,026 miles of canals and laterals
      11,104 miles of drains
      8,094,300 kilowatts installed capacity in 55 powerplants
      and
      13,866 circuit miles of transmission lines

BONNEVILLE POWER ADMINISTRATION

    Transmission and marketing electric power
      6.67 million KW installed capacity
      9,500 miles of transmission lines
      $90.1 million annual revenue

SOUTHWESTERN POWER ADMINISTRATION

    Transmission and marketing of electric power
      1,355,000 KW installed capacity
      1520 miles of transmission lines
      $21.3 million annual revenue

SOUTHEASTERN POWER ADMINISTRATION

    Marketing of electric power
      1.7 million KW installed capacity
      $27 million annual revenue

ASSISTANT SECRETARY

ADMINISTRATION

OFFICE OF SURVEY AND REVIEW:

OFFICE OF MANAGEMENT OPERATIONS:

DIVISION OF BUDGET:

DIVISION OF MANAGEMENT RESEARCH:

DIVISION OF PERSONNEL MANAGEMENT:

the U. S. Department of the Interior.

from fires, insects, and diseases, removal of dead and diseased trees, and some planting. Many of the National Parks also have specific tracts set aside in their natural state in order that scientists will have an undisturbed outdoor laboratory of plants and animals for research purposes. In these tracts, forest management stops short of any attempt at changing the primitive and undisturbed nature of the forest. Roads are limited to those necessary for proper access to major points of attraction, and campgrounds are placed only in designated places. Management of park areas must include much planning for recreational use as well as wildlife and fisheries habitat management. Basic training in forestry is of value in the handling of protection programs, but special consideration must be given to the recreational and wildlife aspects discussed previously.

The Fish and Wildlife Service. This service carries on some forestry activities on the National Wildlife Refuges for which it is responsible. Forestry is mostly incidental since most of these federal refuges are devoted primarily to waterfowl or the preservation of scarcer species of wildlife. Forests do occupy considerable land areas in the refuges and require proper management for their best development. Consequently, in making their management plans the refuge managers include provisions for forest protection, timber sales, reforestation, and improvement cuttings where needed. Timber sales are quite common. Generally the men in charge have sufficient background in forestry to handle such problems whenever they arise. Many forestry-trained men who start out in forestry are employed by the Fish and Wildlife Service working in wildlife management.

Forestry in Other Federal Agencies

In addition to the agencies named previously, several others carry on forestry programs or hire foresters in connection with their activities. The Tennessee Valley Authority has maintained quite an active forestry program throughout its whole area— largely devoted to assisting private owners to attain better management on their lands. The U. S. Army Engineers and defense agencies hire foresters to manage reservoir lands and military reservations. Other agencies employ forestry specialists in tax matters, for forest industry statistical and research studies, and for other similar activities.

STATE FORESTRY PROGRAMS

Most of the states with forested lands operate and maintain forestry divisions either within their conservation departments or as separate units. The responsibilities of these divisions are large and encompass a sizable group of programs, many of which were established with the encouragement of the federal government. While close cooperation with the federal forestry programs continues, the states administer their own with a large degree of flexibility. Most important is their forest fire protection system, but they also operate tree nurseries and distribute seedlings to private owners for forest planting, administer state forests and parks in ways not unlike those of the federal agencies, and provide technical woodland management assistance programs to private owners.

The organization of the state forestry divisions is usually divided along these major lines of responsibility, under the supervision of a state forester (Fig. 12–4). The state is divided into forestry districts for administration and protection purposes, with a system of forest fire towers and ranger stations equipped with fire-fighting tools and machinery. State forest land administration is handled by a forester-in-charge of one or more state forests, with duties and assisting personnel comparable to the federal forest rangers. Technical forest management assistance to private owners is carried out, under the Cooperative Private Forestry Assistance program, by service foresters located in smaller towns in the forested areas. Usually the tree nursery program includes one or more state-operated nurseries under the supervision of technically trained supervisors and a tree distribution system handled through the state forester's office.

The agricultural colleges' extension service in most states also employs extension foresters whose job it is to assist private owners through education and field demonstration in carrying out approved forestry techniques. Extension foresters also work through county agricultural agents in order to make their efforts most effective and to give them wider distribution. One important job which many extension foresters are doing is to assist owners with marketing and price information; another is to demonstrate new forestry techniques at group meetings.

Employment opportunities with the states are many and varied and include nearly all of the jobs described in Chapter 1. The entrance requirements are usually less complex than those for en-

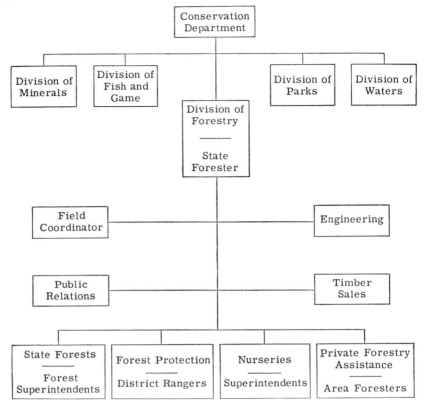

Fig. 12–4. Generalized organization chart of a typical state forestry division.

tering the federal services, and advancement opportunities for men with technical training develop quite rapidly. Most states have civil service or merit systems in their forestry and conservation programs, which reward men with ability through promotions. Many men who have started at the lower levels and who develop and broaden their knowledge through formal courses of self-study have reached important positions in state organizations. For example, if a man who is employed as a fire control assistant takes the trouble to inform himself on other branches of the forestry program and organization and learns to do such work as timber cruising and mapping, and if he masters the essentials of silviculture, he will find that he can qualify for openings in the other activities of the division beyond those of his limited fire-control experience.

INDUSTRIAL FORESTRY PROGRAMS

Private companies which need wood as a raw material for their plants conduct large-scale forestry programs. On the industrial forests and larger tree farms, regular forestry organizations with a full-time forestry staff carry out many of the activities of the public agencies heretofore described. Their major forestry work, of course, centers around timber inventories, mapping, stand improvement and planting, and supervising the logging operations on their forests. Road maintenance is important to assure access to all parts of the timberland. Although the state forest fire protection system is usually relied upon to protect private forests from fire, some companies have supplementary facilities to take care of emergency situations. One activity which industrial foresters have found to be of increasing importance has been insect and disease control to suppress outbreaks of forest-destroying infestations. Public agencies usually take the leadership, but close cooperation with private owners is essential to assure prompt action and to coordinate the control effort. In addition, many private companies are furnishing technical forestry advice and assistance to individual forest owners, including farmers, in their wood-buying areas.

Employment opportunities on large private forests for trained men have been increasing by leaps and bounds, and salaries compare well or better with those of other forestry organizations. Basic training is essential to the man who wants to rise above the skilled labor group to a variety of types of jobs within the organization. Most of the private forestry jobs are on the more than 30,000 industrial tree farms sponsored by the American Forest Products Industries, Inc.

FORESTRY FACILITIES AVAILABLE FOR SMALL PRIVATE FOREST LANDS

Because most owners of small tracts of forest land do not have enough timber to warrant hiring full-time foresters, forestry programs have been developed to assist them in undertaking sound management practices. They need forestry advice and service at nearly every stage: planting, stand improvement, marking mature timber for harvesting, marketing standing timber or cut products, and mapping and estimating timber volumes. To take care of this need, both private and public facilities are available.

Private forestry assistance programs include the services available through private consulting foresters and those services which are furnished by the foresters of the larger forest industries and their trade associations in many parts of the country. Consultants are more often employed by owners who have several hundred or more acres of woodland and who are anxious to apply forestry measures which will yield good returns for the cost of the services. Mention has already been made of the services which industry foresters will give to landowners located within the areas served by the mills. Owners are not ordinarily required to market their products through the company performing the service but usually it is more convenient to do so. In addition, a number of services are available locally through some of the industry-sponsored or other groups, including Trees for Tomorrow at Merrill, Wisconsin; the Southern Pulpwood Conservation Association and Forest Farmers Cooperative at Atlanta, Georgia; and the Industrial Forestry Association in Portland, Oregon. The American Forest Products Industries, Inc., in Washington, D. C., acts informally as a coordinating group and is available to tell forest owners where to look for advice. The AFPI is the sponsor of the national Tree Farm movement, which includes more than 30,000 forest properties embracing over 70,000,000 acres of private forest land under management.

A number of publicly sponsored forestry assistance programs have grown up through the years. These are set forth in Fig. 12–5. Probably the most widespread is the Private Forest Management Assistance program, a joint federal-state effort. Area cooperative foresters, called "service foresters," "farm foresters," "county foresters," or "local foresters," who work under the state forester and serve a group of counties, are available in most forested states. Although their work is not restricted to small owners, much of their effort is devoted to helping such owners by making preliminary examinations of their lands and by giving advice and assistance in measuring and marketing the tree crop. On larger holdings this work is frequently followed up by private consulting or industrial foresters. Also available to private owners are the services of the extension forester who, as we have seen, coordinates the forestry advisory work of the county agricultural agents.

Fig. 12-5. Forestry programs to assist private owners.

Program or Facility:	Publicly Sponsored*						Privately Sponsored	
	Nursery Stock for Tree Planting	State-Federal Cooperative Management Assistance	Soil Conservation Districts	Agricultural Conservation Program	Cooperative Insect and Disease-Control Programs	Extension Foresters	Forest Industry Sponsored Programs**	Consulting Foresters
Type of ownership serviced:	Public and private	Farmers and other individual landowners	All landowners in district	Farmers and small forest owners	All landowners	All landowners	Farmers and forest landowners	All landowners
Purpose:	Production and distribution of tree planting stock for forests and windbreaks, Christmas tree stock	Provide technical service to smaller landowners and wood processors	Land use planning service to farmers and other landowners	Direct payment to small forest owners for part of cost of tree planting, stand improvement, etc.	Provide for control measures against outbreaks of insects and diseases	Assist county agents and local forestry groups to disseminate latest forestry techniques	Provide technical service to landowners in cruising, marking, planting, marketing, etc.	Provide technical service to all landowners on all phases of forestry
Cost of payment:	Usually at cost	Small per-acre fee or free for service	Service usually available at no cost	Payment rates based on cost of practice	On cost-sharing or other basis	No cost to owners	Usually at no cost	Service charges on fee basis
To obtain further information write:	State Forester in your state capital	State Forester or U.S. Forest Service, Washington, D.C.	Soil Conservation Service in your county seat	Department of Agriculture ACP Committee in your county seat	State Forester in state capital (see Appendix E)	Extension Forester at the Agricultural College in your state	American Forest Products Industries, Washington, D.C.	Society of American Foresters, Washington, D.C.

* Includes Tree Farm and Tree Farm Family programs, Trees for Tomorrow program in Wisconsin, and programs of local forest industries.

** In addition the Farmers Home Administration and the Federal Land Banks make credit available to forest owners for both long and short term loans.

Extension foresters have taken the lead in bringing new forestry methods to landowners through group meetings, and they have provided invaluable market and price information. In order to encourage private owners to carry out sound forestry measures, the Agricultural Conservation Program provides funds for cost sharing in timber stand improvement and tree-planting projects. Tree planting is encouraged under the Soil Bank Act. Insect and disease control measures are also available cooperatively to private owners under programs supervised by the state forester's office.

Fig. 12–5 sets forth in summary form the programs available to assist private forest owners and the means of finding out about them. Vocationally trained forest managers are finding opportunities opening up in both private and public programs as assistants to the technical foresters in charge. Appendix E lists forestry organizations employing technically trained men.

RESEARCH—THE SCIENTIFIC RIGHT ARM OF FORESTRY

Americans have become accustomed to the many new products which scientists have developed for our use. In fact, too many people think of science as a device to develop new gadgets or chemicals. Actually, scientific effort is a system of disciplined thought which brings to bear all the knowledge developed on the problem at hand in order to learn more about it. Scientists obtain new knowledge by controlled experiments in which they test out new ideas. Sometimes new inventions come from applied science; sometimes new knowledge is gained which is basic before any concrete results may be foreseen. Sometimes no answer comes forth after much scientific effort, except to learn what the limitations might be. But this basic science often leads to and underlies the discovery of new scientific truths.

Much that is new in forestry has developed from scientific effort: new chemicals for controlling brush and insects, new methods for estimating and mapping timber, new types of logging machinery, mechanical equipment for fighting forest fires, and many other things. We also owe to science much of the knowledge we have for managing each type of timber. New methods are continually being developed which are more efficient than the old methods, so we must always keep an open mind—read, study, observe, and learn.

Most of the new developments in timber growing come from the research of forest experiment stations of the U. S. Forest Service and from university and state research. The McIntyre-Stennis

Act passed by Congress in the early 1960's has provided federal assistance to state university research and has proven to be a strong stimulus. Research in the development of new wood products and better methods in processing all products has been widespread. In addition to the Forest Products Laboratory at Madison, Wisconsin, the industry-sponsored Timber Engineering Company, the Institute of Paper Chemistry, and a number of universities have made important contributions in the wood-utilization field. Several universities and many companies support research laboratories or sponsor special research projects done by others.

Research as an Element in Future Forestry Progress*

The complex nature of producing, protecting, and utilizing the nation's basic forest resources—timber, soil and water, forage, wildlife and fish habitats, and recreation—emphasizes the need for a strong supporting research program in the years ahead. The steady and rapid upswing in the need for resources and services from the forests and the growing pressures and conflicts in use cannot be met and solved without reliable information produced by systematic study. The current and anticipated changes in forest resource use are very great, as the following brief summarization shows:

The estimated 350 million people in the United States in the year 2000 will need at least twice as much timber as is now being produced.

Forest fires, insects, diseases, and other destructive agents continue to take a heavy toll of forest growth. They constitute a serious drain on timber resources and growth potential. Newly discovered destructive diseases and insect pests are a serious threat to expanding tree-planting activities and intensified forest management programs.

Forest recreational use is climbing rapidly. The estimated 400 million annual visits on publicly owned forests represents only part of the current use on all forest lands, expected conservatively to increase fourfold by the year 2000.

The country's 940 million acres of grazed range, more than one-fourth forested and one-half intermingled with forests, support about one-half of our beef cattle and more than three-fourths of our sheep for at least 6 months of the year. Many of these grazing lands are vital watershed areas as well.

* Summarized from U. S. Department of Agriculture, *A National Forestry Research Program*, Miscellaneous Publication 965 (Washington: U. S. Government Printing Office, 1964).

Forests and related rangelands provide the main habitat for 10 million big-game animals and countless other forms of wildlife. Thousands of miles of forest streams provide habitat for fish. Today a hunter or fisherman lives in every third home and the numbers are increasing and adding to the demands for increased fish and wildlife resources.

The needs for water will increase from the present use of 270 billion gallons per day to 600 billion gallons by the year 1980. Since more than half of the nation's streamflow originates on forest lands, the future protection and management of these watersheds to maintain and increase good quality water supplies is an absolute necessity.

The expanding needs of the nation's future economy can best be met with a rich and abundant natural resources base. Wood, the most versatile of raw materials, occupies a key place in providing the needed structural materials, fiber, extractives, and chemicals. But improved and more efficient utilization of forest products must be achieved in the face of general lowering of quality and size of timber trees and stiffer competition from substitute materials.

Needs for all forest and range resources are mounting rapidly. These pressures against the forest resource base give sharp emphasis to conflicts in use that are occurring now and could greatly increase in the future. They stress the need for harmonious management of forest and range lands to get maximum benefits under the principles of multiple use.

FOREST AND RANGE MANAGEMENT RESEARCH PROGRAMS

The basic renewable natural resources of the forest and ranges upon which the nation will rely to an increasing extent in the years to come are timber, soil and water, forage, wildlife and fish habitats, and recreation. Their greatly intensified development is necessary during the next few years to meet both near and long-term objectives. This will require a substantial step-up in the research to support and guide the accelerated resource production and management programs.

Timber

The overriding objectives of timber management research will be to provide the improved forest trees and the intensive cultural practices needed to double the nation's production of wood and related tree products by the year 2000. There are more than 130 commercially important forest tree species in the United States, each differing in its quality and product value and each varying in the requirements for crop production. Natural forests, moreover, are usually made up of mixtures of species and have strong responses to and interactions with environmental changes.

Accomplishment of timber management research objectives will require increased emphasis on the fundamentals of genetics, growth, and other vital life processes of the tree itself, areas of study that have heretofore been largely neglected. Also required will be expanded efforts to provide answers to many practical operating problems to increase the efficiency of establishing, growing, and harvesting of timber on a sustained-yield basis under a wide variety of conditions.

The research proposed, emphasizing both basic and applied aspects, will:

1. Accelerate, through work in forest genetics, the production of trees superior to present ones—in growth rate, wood quality, resistance to insects and diseases, and other special qualities for use in planting programs on public and private forest lands.
2. Develop new cultural practices to increase the production of high-quality seed through establishment and management of seed orchards; better methods of harvesting, storing, and processing seed; and more efficient and faster planting practices, including direct seeding with aircraft. It must intensify plantation-management research.
3. Find cheaper and more effective methods for converting brush-fields and other low-value vegetation on potential timber sites to profitable timber stands.
4. Improve the agricultural techniques for stand culture, such as weeding to control composition, thinning to regulate spacing and growth rate, pruning to improve quality, and other practices to increase the health, vigor, and quality of the forest. It must especially emphasize methods suitable for use by the owners of small forest properties.
5. Perfect methods for correcting soil deficiencies or improving the productive capacity of forest soils through use of soil fertilizers and other measures such as silvicultural control to favor soil-improving tree species that promote the decomposition of forest humus.
6. Find ways to control animal damage to tree crops, including

loss of seed and newly planted seedlings to birds and rodents, and loss of older trees to porcupines, bears, and browsing animals.

7. Develop better timber harvesting systems to maintain productive amounts of growing timber in logged areas for sustained yield and to insure natural regeneration of preferred timber species.

8. Improve volume and yield tables, rotation age data, and other information for regulating timber growing-stock densities in managed forests, including methods to estimate growth rate, yield, allowable cut, and quality of forests as affected by environment and silvicultural treatment.

Forest Soil and Water

The basis for effective and efficient watershed management practices is an understanding of the fundamental relationships involving soil, climate, vegetation, and water. These factors and their interactions are varied and complex over the wide span of forest and related range lands. A more complete understanding of them is required to speed the development of applicable techniques and measures to insure good protection and management of the vital watersheds of the National Forests and National Grasslands and other forest and range lands.

The research proposed will include:

1. Studying soil erosion processes as related to chemical, physical, and biotic characteristics of soils, and developing effective and efficient measures to stabilize eroding slopes.

2. Developing better information and guides for logging and road location, construction, and maintenance under various soil and topographic conditions so as to prevent accelerated erosion and sedimentation.

3. Studying snow deposition, melt, evaporation, and metamorphism as related to possible alterations of forest types and timber harvest patterns so as to increase water yields or prolong stemflow into the summer.

4. For wetland forest areas, developing methods for control of water to increase forest regeneration and growth, giving attention to the basic hydrologic relations involved.

5. Improving the use of forest soil surveys in land management planning and action programs.

Wildlife and Fish Habitats

The use of the wildlife and fish resources of the nation is being continually increased by a growing army of hunters and fishermen. Serious conflicts have developed between wildlife habitat needs on one side and augmented requirements for production of water, timber, and forage for livestock on the other. The research planned will determine the food and cover requirements of various wildlife species. It will point out the way forest and related range lands could be managed and improved to better meet the increased requirements for forest resources while supporting maximum game and fish populations.

The proposed research will:

1. Determine the wildlife populations that can be supported by the various vegetation types; develop practices that improve wildlife distribution and allow more uniform and efficient utilization of available forage and cover.
2. Develop methods for improving depleted and naturally unproductive big-game habitats by seeding and planting browse, controlling undesirable vegetation, manipulating desirable plant cover, or other measures to alter or regulate the environment.
3. Work out ways to improve wildlife habitat through modified timber cutting and stand improvement practices so that wildlife production will be encouraged, while watershed values are maintained or enhanced.
4. Devise techniques of seeding and planting to create improved habitat for small upland game in forest openings and permanently cleared powerline and pipeline rights-of-way, particularly in the eastern forests.
5. Accelerate work on problems of improving game fish habitat and food supplies by regulating shade and water temperatures through management of streamside vegetation, by stabilization of channels and other measures.

Forest Recreation

Research on forest recreation problems is basic to the development of sound administrative policies and the formulation of programs to meet skyrocketing future recreational needs on public forests and private forest lands. The research planned gives emphasis to National Forest problems, but the problems of other forests will not be neglected. Hence, research results are expected to have broad application to both public and private forest lands.

Examples of the research needs are:

1. Determining the most efficient physical layouts for forest campgrounds and other recreational installations to provide for optimum use and recreational enjoyment with minimum adverse effects on the forest environment.
2. Determining ways of administering forest recreation business efficiently and at minimum cost. This will include the development, maintenance, and operation of recreation areas and the use of self-help devices and other procedures for reducing litter cleanup and similar maintenance costs on mass recreation areas.
3. Developing guides for measuring recreational carrying capacity of various forest types, based on water, soil, and vegetation conditions and users' sense of satisfaction.
4. Obtaining information needed to plan and administer the special use of wild-land resources as wilderness, including data on the use wilderness areas receive; what kind and how much, when it occurs, and how it is distributed. Defining the key features of wilderness environment as a basis of inventory, evaluation, and allocation of resources as wilderness.
5. Determining how timber harvesting can be modified to embrace forest recreation, with particular attention to road, stream, trail, and lakeside zones, and commercial stands of old-growth timber.
6. Developing biologically sound measures to rehabilitate recreational areas depleted by overuse.

FOREST PROTECTION RESEARCH

Some of the possibilities of greatest gains in extending the supply of forest resources and maintaining forests and ranges at highly productive levels lie in prevention and control of fire, insects, and disease. Acceptable progress will require strong fundamental research programs to establish the basis for new methods of attack. Destructive forces such as fire, insects, and diseases do not halt at property lines and hence are of direct concern to all types of forest-land owners.

Forest Fire

Abolition of forest fires as an obstacle to profitable long-term investment in intensive forestry is a major objective for organized research. For a number of years 90 per cent of the costs and damages suffered from fires has resulted from less than 5 per cent of the total number of fires. Yet we lack the knowledge that will enable the fire-control specialist to identify the potential runaway fire early in its life. Since the heaviest losses occur from unpredictable and erratic fire behavior, scientists must look deeply into the fundamentals of the combustion process, as influenced by an ever-changing environment, for an understanding of runaway fires, their prevention and control. Moreover, federal, state, and local fire-control agencies have many problems in preventing and suppressing fires. These deal with improving aerial fire attack, more effective planning for use of forces and facilities, and techniques and programs for reducing numbers of man-caused fires.

The forest fire research proposed will:

1. For each important forest region, develop improved methods of measuring and rating fluctuating forest fire danger through studies of microclimate and the integration of these systems into a national fire danger rating procedure.
2. Improved fire control systems and organization through operations research techniques, leading to more efficient, faster, and safer fire suppression.
3. Develop new and more effective systems of aerial fire control, including the improvement of chemicals to retard and extinguish fires and devise better methods of application.
4. Expand knowledge relating to the prevention of man-caused fires and effective methods of minimizing careless, thoughtless, or malicious fire-starting activities of man.
5. Intensify basic research on atmospheric factors leading to the formation of fire-starting lightning storms, and develop methods for reducing the lightning potential by cloud seeding or other means.
6. Improve the techniques for using fire effectively and safely as a silvicultural or a hazard-reduction device to eliminate unwanted vegetation, litter, or accumulations of logging slash.

Forest Insects

Although provisional measures of direct chemical control are available for suppressing outbreaks of many forest insects, the greatest promise for the future lies in breakthroughs in preventive control through the use of biological control factors or in improved forest management measures. Accelerated research on the use of insect enemies, or on utilization of radiation techniques to control insect reproduction cycles, offers great promise. Many practical questions also need continuing research attention to provide for modern solutions to special insect problems. Of particular concern are problems that arise from sudden buildups in endemic populations of pests in areas where forest management is most advanced and where investments are highest. In such instances, strong programs of basic research on insect life histories, their biology and physiology, and relations of insect populations to environments are extremely important to future control.

The balanced program of proposed investigation will embrace studies illustrated by the following examples:

1. Research on parasites, predators, and diseases of insects that damage forests and ranges and develop techniques to control new epidemics.
2. Intensified research on factors responsible for insect outbreaks and development of silvicultural practices designed to prevent outbreaks.
3. Research to develop safer and more effective and economical chemicals for direct control of Dutch elm disease.
4. Increased understanding of insects that damage wood by boring into the trunks of living trees or attack and destroy wood products used in structures or for other purposes; and development of improved methods for preventing or controlling damage caused by these insects.
5. Accelerated research on the physiology of the most destructive forest insects with emphasis on nutrition, genetics, and the development of sterilization techniques.
6. Expansion of knowledge concerning prevention or control of destructive populations of forest insects, through acceleration of fundamental studies of insect habits and behavior and of environmental factors affecting insect abundance.

Forest Diseases

Before effective measures can be devised to substantially reduce the annual loss of billions of board feet of sawtimber from diseases, the nature and extent of this damage needs much more intensive study. Of special concern are the mounting problems caused by the introduction of new diseases or the sudden flare-up of previously innocuous ones that are favored by more intensive management practices, such as one-species plantation culture, thinning, and pruning. These problems are costly to cope with and they cannot be quickly solved without more basic information on the identity and life processes of pathogens, which can be obtained only through study of their taxonomy, genetics, physiology, and ecology. Similarly, there is need for a great deal more knowledge of the toxic principles associated with the damage caused by noninfectious diseases due, for example, to air pollution, severe weather, or unfavorable soil conditions. Control measures utilizing direct chemical or biological or indirect silvicultural approaches must be developed. Once control measures are applied, continuing study is needed to evaluate their effectiveness under a variety of conditions and to better adapt and adjust them to meet many different situations.

1. Create an understanding of relationships between tree roots and microorganisms in various soils to develop preventive and control methods for *annosus* root rot of southern pines and *poria* root rot of Douglas fir.
2. Select and breed trees genetically resistant to epidemic diseases such as fusiform rust and little-leaf of southern pines, blister rust of white pines, dwarf mistletoes on western conifers, and heart rots of all important species.
3. Determine the physiological and biochemical action of systemic antibiotic compounds for the direct control of forest diseases such as the rusts and dwarf mistletoes of conifers, stem cankers of hardwood, and oak wilt.
4. Determine the toxic components in noxious industrial fumes and how they interfere with normal tree growth and health.

FOREST PRODUCTS AND ENGINEERING RESEARCH

A strong program of basic and applied research on forest products utilization problems is vital to achievement of the nation's future timber production and utilization objectives for three main reasons: (1) ways must be found to remove and utilize at reasonable cost large volumes of poor-quality timber that now occupy extensive and valuable growing space; (2) logging and mill residues and bark and wood extractives, now wasted or little used, must be used more extensively to increase processing efficiency and the income from forest products; and (3) ways must be found to realize the full potential of wood as a versatile raw material base for industries that will expand markets for timber and create industrial employment opportunities, especially in rural areas. Much valuable research has been done in forest products to expand the basis for increased utilization. However, many important problems need more intensive study. Research to utilize wood in unmodified forms through better engineering design and fabrication techniques will contribute to increased utility. Basic studies of how wood substance may be modified and converted into new or improved fiber and chemical products hold great promise.

The engineering aspects of establishing forests, tending them, and harvesting crops systematically and with the benefits of mechanization have received far too little research effort up to the present. Future forest management efforts must be well engineered and appropriately mechanized to keep costs at acceptably low levels.

FOREST RESOURCE ECONOMICS AND MARKETING RESEARCH

At every step in the complex process of producing, protecting, and utilizing forest resources, the landowner or manager must consider the costs and economic advantages of alternate methods of organizing and operating his resource program. Administrators of public forests must develop economically sound management policies. They must have a sound basis for selecting alternative combinations of resource uses that are necessarily based on sound biological principles but also on favorable economic returns. Industrial foresters must base their recommendations and practices on cost and return determinations within the framework of company policies and objectives. The 4½ million farmers, businessmen, professional people, and other occupational groups who own in small parcels 53 per cent of the nation's commercial forest land make decisions on timber growing that are influenced to a large degree by economic considerations. Thus, a comprehensive program of forest resource data collection and analysis and of research on the economics of production, harvesting, and the processing and marketing of forest products occupies a key place in future forest development.

Forest Economics

Research in forest economics will have as one of its major objectives the determination of the costs and returns that may be expected from timber growing and harvesting activities. Another aim will be to develop concepts and principles for economic evaluation of combinations of forest land uses and guides for decisions on coordinated management of timber production, grazing, recreation, wildlife, and water uses. The problems of the small owner will receive special emphasis.

Projects that illustrate the research needs are:

1. Determining the opportunities for profitable timber growing for different combinations of site, forest type, class of ownership, and market location, and the potential returns from investments in planting, thinning, pruning, or other cultural measures.

2. Developing procedures and guides for evaluation of multiple uses of forest lands for timber, water, recreation, forage, and wildlife and fish habitats, to be aimed especially at optimum use and management of National Forests and other public forest lands.

3. Evaluating opportunities and methods for profitable combination of timber growing, recreation, and other uses of small forest ownerships.

4. Providing criteria for evaluating relative benefits from capital investments in forest development and road construction in the National Forests and private holdings, and for investment of private capital in industrial facilities for timber production.

5. Evaluating forestry programs for small ownerships aimed at improving forestry practices on the major part of the nation's forest land that is in such holdings, including pilot area studies of owner associations and other devices for stimulating timber production.

6. Developing and evaluating more efficient arrangements for harvesting and marketing timber crops produced on small ownerships. These embrace various forms of leases, management and marketing cooperatives, price and market reports, and promising modifications of marketing practices, which will be pilot tested.

7. Determining possibilities for increasing efficiency in the processing and marketing of lumber and other wood products, with the aim of reducing costs and improving the competitive position of timber products.

8. Evaluating potential markets for wood products and opportunities for new or expanded forest industries, particularly in areas needing economic development and relief from chronic underemployment.

QUESTIONS

1. What is the largest federal forestry agency and in which department is it located?

2. Give the names of three other federal agencies employing forestry-trained men.

3. Name at least two important forestry activities of state forestry agencies.

4. Give two important duties of forestry-trained men on private company forestry operations.

5. Name two programs where a private owner of a small tract of forest land can get technical assistance.

6. What does research contribute to the practice of forestry?

7. Give the name and address of the state forestry agency in your state.

8. Name two industry-sponsored forestry associations.

9. Name the principal centers engaged in forestry research.

10. In your own words describe the purpose of scientific research.

11. Why is forest economics research needed for small private forestry operations?

EXERCISES

1. Obtain the name of your state forester and the nearest local forester employed by the state.

2. List the local conservation agencies operating in your area and the names and titles of the men in charge of each.

3. Find out how many tree farms are in your county.

4. Find out how many private owners are using technical or other assistance programs.

5. Visit the nearest forestry research activity in your area and describe two research projects in process, including the problem to be solved.

6. Describe two proposed research studies and tell how they will contribute to the solution of forestry problems.

APPENDIXES

A

Forestry Terminology

All definitions, except those marked with an asterisk (*), are cited in part or entirely from *Forestry Terminology*, published by the Society of American Foresters in 1958.

Access Road. A road built into isolated stands of commercial timber so they can be reached by loggers, fire fighters, and others.

*Acre.** A unit of land measurement, 43,560 square feet, 10 square chains, or a square 208.7 feet on the side.

Age, Rotation. The age at which the stand is considered ready for harvesting under the adopted plan of management.

*Alidade.** An instrument used in fire towers to locate forest fires. The alidade is equipped with sights for determining direction of fire.

All-aged. Applied to a stand in which, theoretically, trees of all ages up to and including those of the felling age are found. See also **Even-aged** and **Uneven-aged.**

Allowable Cut. The volume of timber which may be cut from a forest under optimum sustained-yield management.

Annual Ring. A ring of wood put on each year by a growing tree; that is, the line indicating the growth for the period of one year. From the annual rings the age of the tree may be determined.

Aphid. A plant louse, a very small insect that lives on plants.

Arboriculture. The science and art of growing trees, especially as ornamental or shade trees.

Aspect. The direction toward which a slope faces; exposure.

Back Fire. A fire intentionally set along the inner edge of a control line located ahead of an advancing fire. The back fire is set against the fire to be fought, so that when the two fires meet, both go out.

Bacteria. Very tiny living plants, some of which cause diseases, and others of which are useful.

Barber Chair. In logger's slang, a stump on which is left standing a slab that splintered off the tree as it fell. Generally it indicates careless felling.

°**Bearing (of a line).** The direction or course of a line in relation to the cardinal points of the compass.

°**B.F.** The abbreviation for "board feet" (also **B.M.**, board measure).

Blaze. A mark made on the trunk of a standing tree by painting or chipping off a spot of bark with an ax. It is used to indicate a trail, boundary, location for a road, trees to be cut, and so on.

B.M. Abbreviation for "board measure" meaning board foot or feet.

Bole. The stem or trunk of a tree, usually the lower, useable or merchantable portion of the tree trunk.

Bolts. Small logs or sections of larger logs that have been split. A bolt is usually less than 4½ feet long.

Broadleaf. A tree with two cotyledons, or seed leaves; it usually is deciduous, that is, it sheds all its leaves annually. The broadleaved trees, such as maple and oak, have relatively broad, flat leaves, as contrasted with the conifers, such as pines, which have narrow leaves, or needles.

Buck. As used in forestry: To saw felled trees into logs or bolts.

Burl. A hard, woody growth on a tree trunk or on roots, more or less rounded in form. It is usually the result of entwined growth of a cluster of buds. In lumber, a burl produces a distorted and unusual (but often attractive) grain.

Burning, Prescribed. Burning carried out under the direct supervision of crews especially trained in the methods of when, where, and how fire can be used beneficially to improve timber management.

Butt. Base of tree or lower end of log.

Caliper (or calipers), tree. An instrument used to measure diameters of trees or logs. It consists of a graduated rule with two arms, one fixed at right angles to one end of the rule, the other sliding parallel to the fixed arm.

Cambium. A laterally disposed sheath of generative tissues usually found between the xylem and phloem. It gives rise to secondary xylem (wood) and phloem, a part of the inner bark.

Capacity, Grazing. In range management, the ability of a range unit, exclusive of severe drought years, to give adequate support to a constant number of livestock for a stated period each year without deteriorating because of this or other proper land use; expressed in number of livestock per acre of given kinds, or in number of acres per specified animals.

Catface. A scar on the surface of a log, generally elliptical in shape, resulting from wounds which have not healed over; also a fire scar at the base of a tree.

°**Cells.** All plant life is made up of living cells which are microscopic units containing protoplasmic substances and a nucleus and separated by cell walls consisting of cellulose.

°**Cellulose.** A fibrous substance made up of carbohydrates (carbon, hydrogen, and oxygen) which forms the cell walls of plants. Common examples of cellulose are cotton fibers and paper made up of tiny matted wood fibers.

Check. A lengthwise separation of the wood, which usually extends across the rings of annual growth, commonly resulting from stresses set up in wood during seasoning.

°Chlorophyll. The green coloring matter in plants necessary for photosynthesis.

Class, Age. One of the intervals into which the range of ages of vegetation is divided for classification and use.

Clear Cutting. A method of cutting that removes all merchantable trees on the area in one cut.

Climax. A plant community that does not change unless there is a change in conditions, e.g., from climate, logging, or fire. It is the culminating stage in natural plant succession. The plants in a climax community are favored by the environment which they themselves create, and so are in balance with it.

Closed Crown. A full, close, forest canopy which excludes sunlight.

Conifer. A tree belonging to the order Coniferae, usually evergreen, with cones and needle-shaped leaves, and producing wood known commercially as softwood.

Conk. A definite, individual, woody, spore-bearing fruiting body of a wood-destroying fungus, which projects beyond the bark.

Contour Planting. Planting so that the rows run around the hill or slope on the same level, rather than up and down.

°Cord. A volume measure of stacked wood. A standard cord is 4 x 4 x 8 ft. or 128 cu. ft. of space. A long cord (unit) contains 160 cu. ft. of space and is 4 x 5 x 8 ft. Since round wood cannot be stacked to give solid volume, actual wood volume varies between 70 and 90 cu. ft. per cord.

Corduroy Road. A road built of logs or poles laid side by side across the roadway, usually in low or swampy places.

Core. A slender cylinder of wood taken from a tree by an increment borer. Growth rings are counted on such cores to determine rate of tree growth.

Cotyledon. One of the first leaves of the embryo plant in a seed. In corn and bean seeds the cotyledons are thickened with a store of food for the young plant.

°Crop Trees. Trees which are designated to make up the final or rotation timber crop.

Crosshaul. A method of loading log-transportation vehicles. One end of a line is passed over the load, around the log to be loaded, and made fast to the load. Power applied to the other end of the line imparts a rolling motion to the log.

Crown. The upper part of a tree, including the branches with their foliage.

Crown Fire. A forest fire which extends to and sweeps along in the tops and branches of trees.

Cruise. A survey of forest lands to locate and estimate volumes and grades of standing timber; also, the estimate obtained in such a survey. (Scaling is the measurement of the volumes of individual logs after the trees have been felled.)

Cull. A tree or log of merchantable size rendered unmerchantable because of poor form, limbyness, rot, or other defects.

Cut. The yield, during a specified period, of products that are cut, as of grain, timber, or, in sawmilling, lumber.

Cutting, Improvement. A cutting made in a stand past the sapling stage for the purpose of improving its composition and character by removing trees of less desirable species, form, and condition in the main crown canopy.

Cycle, Cutting. The planned interval between major felling operation in the same stand.

D.B.H. Diameter (of a tree) at breast height, or 4½ ft. above the ground.

*°***Deciduous.** A term applied to trees which lose their leaves in the fall.

Deck, Log. A pile of logs or a rollway.

Defect. Any irregularity or imperfection in a tree, log, piece product, or lumber that reduces the volume of sound wood or lowers its durability, strength, or utility value.

*°***Defoliation.** Loss of a tree's leaves by insects, disease, or other causes.

Dendrometer. An instrument for measuring tree growth.

Density, Crown. The compactness of the crown cover of the forest, dependent upon (a) the distance apart and (b) the compactness of the individual crowns. A loose term combining the meanings of crown closure and shade density.

Dibble. A tool used in planting tree seedlings.

Dominant Trees. Those in the forest that are tallest, largest, and most valuable.

Drive. Logs or timbers that are being floated on a stream from the forest to a mill or shipping point.

Ecology. The science which deals with the relation of plants and animals to their environment and to the site factors that operate in controlling their distribution and growth.

Entomology, Forest. The science that deals with insects and their relation to forests and forest products.

Erosion. The mechanical moving of soil (1) by water; (2) by wind.

Even-aged. A term applied to a stand in which relatively small age differences exist between individual trees. The maximum difference in age permitted in an even-aged stand is usually 10 to 20 years, although where the stand will not be harvested until it is 100 to 200 years old, larger differences, up to 25 per cent of the rotation age, may be allowed.

*°***Exotic.** Not native; foreign. Of trees and plants, those introduced from other climates or countries.

Fire, Surface. A fire which runs over the forest floor and burns only the·surface litter, the loose debris, and the smaller vegetation. Ground fire also is used.

Firebreak. An existing barrier, or one constructed before a fire occurs, from which all or most of the inflammable materials have been removed; designed to stop or check creeping or running but not spotting fires, or to serve as a line from which to work and facilitate the movement of men and equipment in fire suppression.

Forest Floor. The covering of the mineral soil of a forest—humus, duff, and litter under forest growth.

Forestry, Multiple Use. The practice of forestry which combines two or more objectives, such as production of wood or wood-derivative products, forage and browse for domestic livestock, proper environmental conditions for wildlife, landscape effects, protection against floods and erosion, recreation, production and protection of water supplies, and national defense.

****Fungus.** A plant without chlorophyll which derives its nourishment from the organic matter of other plants.

Girdle. To encircle the stem of a living tree with cuts that completely sever bark and cambium, and often are carried well into the outer sapwood, for the purpose of killing the tree by preventing the passage of nutrients or by admitting toxic materials.

Go-devil. A small, short sled (scoot) without a tongue, used in skidding logs.

Ground Fire. A forest fire which consumes humus and duff beneath the surface.

Ground Water. Water that stands or flows beneath the ground surface in soil or rock material which is thoroughly saturated. The upper surface of this saturated zone is called the water table.

Habitat. The unit area of environment, practically synonymous with site; the kind of place in which the plant or animal lives.

Hardwood. Generally, one of the botanical group of trees that have broad leaves, in contrast to the needle-bearing conifers; also wood produced by broadleaved trees, regardless of texture or density.

Heartwood. The inner core of a woody stem, wholly composed of nonliving cells and usually differentiated from the outer enveloping layer (sapwood) by its darker color.

Heeled In. Trees or plants covered with moist earth in a shallow trench or ditch.

High-grading. The removal from the stand of only the best trees.

Hot-logging. A logging operation in which logs go from the stump to the mill without pause.

Humidity, Relative. The ratio of actual mass of water vapor per unit of volume to mass of water vapor that would saturate that volume at the same temperature and pressure, or roughly the per cent saturation of the space.

Humus. The plant and animal residues of the soil, litter excluded, which are undergoing decomposition.

Hybrid. The offspring resulting from mating two plants or animals that differ in one or more hereditary factors. This is the narrowest—the geneticist's—use of the term. A hybrid is more commonly understood to be the plant resulting from crossing two plants that are so distantly related as to belong to different races, varieties, species, or even genera.

Incendiarism. Malicious setting of fires.

Increment Borer. An instrument for measuring the growth of trees.

Indigenous. Native to the locality.

Integrated Logging. A method of logging designed to make the best use of all timber products. It removes in one cutting all timber that should be cut, and distributes the various timber products to the industries that can use them to best advantage.

Intolerance. The incapacity of a tree to develop and grow in the shade of and in competition with other trees.

Kiln-dry. The seasoning of lumber in a kiln.

Litter. The uppermost layer of the organic debris composed of freshly fallen or slightly decomposed organic materials. Commonly designated by the letter L.

Log. To cut and remove logs from an area.

Log Rule. (1) A table indicating the amount of lumber which can be sawed from logs of given sizes. (2) A log-scaling stick.

Log Scale. A scaling stick for measuring the contents of logs in terms of board feet.

Logger. (1) A man who is engaged in logging operations. (2) Locally, a man who hauls logs to landings and skidways.

Lookout. A station or post used primarily in the detection of fires. A permanent lookout is generally equipped with a lookout tower or structure.

Lumber Jack. One who works on logging operations; colloquial for logger.

Marking, Timber. Selecting and indicating, usually by blaze or paint spot, trees to be cut or retained in a cutting operation; spotting.

Maturity. For a given species or stand, the approximate age beyond which growth declines or decay begins to increase at a rate likely to assume economic importance.

M.B.F. Thousand board feet.

M.B.M. Thousand (feet) board measure.

Mensuration, Forest. A science dealing with the measurement of volume, growth, and development of individual trees and stands, and the determination of various products obtainable from them.

Merchantable. Trees or stands of a size and quality suitable for marketing and utilization. They may or may not be so located as to be accessible for logging. Also, a specific grade of southern yellow pine timbers.

Nitrate. A type of compound that contains nitrogen. Nitrates are one kind of mineral found in the soil and required by plants.

Node. A place on the stem where a leaf or bud grows; a joint in a stem.

Normal Forest. One in which growing stock is so distributed by size and age classes as to provide a sustained yield of nearly equal annual volumes through growth.

Normal Growing Stock. The maximum volume which any given site is capable of maintaining in relation to economic conditions and the desires of the operator.

Notch. To cut a notch in a tree before sawing to prevent splitting and binding and to control the direction of fall.

Old Growth. Timber stands in which no cutting has been done. Synonyms: first-growth timber, virgin timber.

Over-grazing. Grazing so heavy as to impair future forage production and cause range deterioration through consequential damage to plants or soil or to both.

Overrun. The excess of the amount of lumber actually sawed from logs over the estimated volume or log scale, usually expressed in per cent of log scale.

Overstory. Upper crown canopy of a forest.

Parasite. A plant or animal that lives in or on the body of another living thing and takes its food from that living thing.

Pathology, Forest. The science which deals with diseases of forest trees.

Peavey. A stout wooden lever for rolling logs. A curvy metal hook is hinged to the lower part of the handle, and the tip is armed with a sharp steel spike.

Peeler. (1) Usually one who removes bark from timber cut in the spring months when bark slips. (2) A log used in the manufacture of rotary-cut veneer.

Petiole. A leafstalk; the slender stalk by which the blade of a leaf is attached to the stem.

Pistil. The female part of the flower which receives the pollen.

Plan, Management. A written plan for the operation of a forest property, using forestry principles. It usually records data and prescribes measures designed to provide optimum use of all forest resources.

Pollen. The fertilizing dustlike powder produced by stamens; functionally the same as the male sperm in animal reproduction.

Precipitation. Deposits of atmospheric moisture in liquid or solid form, including rain, snow, hail, dew, or frost.

Preservative. A chemical substance which, when suitably applied to wood, makes it resistant to attack by fungi, insects, or marine borers.

Preserve. In wildlife management, a game shooting area on which game species are propagated, released, or otherwise maintained.

Pruning. The removal of live or dead branches from standing trees. This may be done artificially or naturally. Natural pruning results from such causes as decay, snow, ice, deficiency of light, etc.

Public Domain. Territory over which a commonwealth has dominion or control; used in connection with the land owned by the federal government.

Pulpwood. Wood cut or prepared primarily for manufacture into wood pulp, for subsequent manufacture into paper, fiber, board, or other products, depending largely on the species cut and the pulping process.

Range. Land not under cultivation which produces forage suitable for grazing by livestock; includes forest land producing forage.

Ranger. An administrative officer in charge of a unit of forest land, usually a subdivision of a public forest or park. Various classifications are recognized, as forest ranger, district ranger, park ranger, and county ranger.

Reforestation. The natural or artificial restocking of an area with forest trees; most commonly used in reference to the latter.

Regeneration. See **Reproduction, natural.**

Release Cutting. A cutting of larger individual trees that are over-topping young trees, for the purpose of freeing the young trees to permit them to make good growth.

Reproduction. The process by which a forest or range is renewed, including (1) **artificial**: renewal by direct seeding or planting (reforestation); and (2) **natural**: renewal by self-sown seeds, sprouts, rhizomes, etc. (regeneration). Also seedlings or saplings of any origin (young growth), the result of reproduction.

Reseeding, Range. Sowing of seed on range lands to restore or increase forage production.

Resistance. The ability of a plant to develop and function normally despite adverse environmental conditions or the attacks of disease or insects.

Restocking. Applied to an area on which the forest is being re-established by natural means.

Ring, Annual. The growth layer of one year, as viewed on the cross-section of a stem, branch, or root.

Root Hairs. Tiny feed roots which absorb water and plant food.

Rosin. A hard, brittle, natural resin obtained from the oleoresin exudate of certain trees. Rosin is a particular kind of resin. Rosin is obtained either from gum that exudes from the living pine tree or from wood by extraction. Wood rosin and gum rosin are kinds of resin.

Rot, Heart. A decay characteristically confined to the heartwood; it usually originates in the living tree.

Runoff, Surface. The rate at which water is discharged from a drainage area, usually expressed in cubic feet per square mile of drainage area.

Sapling. A young tree less than 4 in. d.b.h. The minimum size of saplings is usually, though not invariably, placed at 2 in. d.b.h.

Saprophyte. A plant that gets its food from plants or animals that have died.

°Sapwood. The light-colored wood which appears on a cross-section of wood. The sapwood is composed of living cells and serves to conduct water and minerals to the crown.

Saw Timber. Timber stands in which trees of sawlog size make up most of the volume.

Scale. The estimated sound contents in terms of a given log rule or a log or group of logs; to estimate the sound contents of a log or group of logs.

Scarify. To tear up earth by disking or dragging to prepare for seeding.

Schoolmarm. A term used by loggers to describe a tree forked above the first log.

Season, Fire. The period or periods of the year during which fires are likely to occur, spread, and to do sufficient damage or otherwise warrant organized fire control.

Second-growth. Timber growth which comes up after removal of the old stand by cutting, fire, or other cause. Typical second-growth conditions may come about in a forest that is untouched so far as lumbering is concerned.

°Section. A unit of land measurement, 640 acres or 6,400 square chains, 1 mile or 80 chains square; 1/36 of a township.

Seedling. A tree grown from seed. The term is restricted to trees smaller than saplings.

Seed Tree. A tree that produces seed; usually trees reserved in a cutting operation to supply seed.

Selective Logging or Cutting. The removal of selected mature, large, or diseased trees as single, scattered trees or in small groups of trees. Young trees start in the openings thus made; the result of this type of cutting is an uneven-aged forest.

Shake. A lengthwise separation of wood which usually occurs between and parallel to the growth layers.

Shelterbelt. A wind barrier of living trees and shrubs maintained for the purpose of protecting farm fields. As applied to individual farmsteads, termed windbreak; also called belt.

Silvics. The life history and general characteristics of forest trees and stands, with particular reference to environmental factors.

Silviculture. The art of producing and tending a forest; the application of the knowledge of silvics in the treatment of a forest; the theory and practice of controlling forest establishment, composition, and growth.

Site. An area, considered as to its ecological factors with reference to capacity to produce forests or other vegetation: the combination of biotic, climatic, and soil condition of an area.

Skid. To pull logs from the stump to the skidway, landing, or mill.

Skidway. Two skids laid parallel at right angles to a road, usually raised above the ground at the end nearest the road. As they are brought from the stump, logs are usually piled upon a skidway for loading upon sleds, wagons, or cars.

Slash. Branches, bark, tops, chunks, cull logs, uprooted stumps, and broken or uprooted trees left on the ground after logging; also, large accumulation of debris after wind or fire.

Smokechaser. A member of a fire-fighting crew.

Snag. A standing, dead tree from which the leaves and most of the branches have fallen, or a standing section of the stem of a tree broken off at a height of 20 ft. or more. If less than 20 ft. high, it is properly termed a stub.

Softwood. One of the botanical group of trees that generally have needle or scalelike leaves—the conifers; also, the wood produced by such trees, regardless of texture or density.

Species (of trees). Subordinate to a genus; trees having common characteristics. In common language, a kind of variety such as sugar maple, white pine.

Springwood. The less dense, larger-celled, first-formed part of a growth layer.

Spud. A hand tool used in stripping bark from felled trees.

Stand. An aggregation of trees or other growth occupying a specific area and sufficiently uniform in composition (species), age, arrangement, and conditions as to be distinguishable from the forest or other growth on adjoining areas.

Stand, Mixed. A stand in which less than 75 per cent of the trees in the main crown canopy are of a single species.

Stand, Pure. A stand in which at least 75 per cent of the trees in the main crown canopy are of a single species.

Stock, Growing. The sum (in number and volume) of all the trees in a forest.

Strip Survey. Estimating timber by strips running through the stand.

Succession. The progressive development of the vegetation toward its highest ecological expression, the climax. The replacement of one plant community by another.

Summerwood. The denser, smaller-celled, later-formed part of a growth layer.

Survey, Forest. An inventory of forest land to determine area, condition, timber volume, and species for specific purposes such as timber purchase, forest management, or as a basis for forest policies and programs.

Table, Volume. A table showing the average contents of trees by diameter and merchantable length, in a specified unit of volume.

*****Technician, Forestry.** One who is familiar with the principal field activities connected with the practice of forestry. Usually trained in vocational, technical, or ranger school as distinguished from professional forestry course.

Thinning. Cutting in an immature stand to increase its rate of growth, to foster quality growth, to improve composition, to promote sanitation, to aid in litter decomposition, to obtain greater total yield, and to recover and use material that would be lost otherwise.

Tolerant. Ability of tree to grow in shade of other trees.

*****Tote Road.** A term used for smaller logging roads in some parts of the country.

Towerman. A lookout man stationed at a tower.

Trainer. A tree intermediate in size which shades lower branches of adjacent larger trees.

Transpiration. The process by which water moves up through the living plant and vapor leaves the plant and enters the atmosphere.

Transplant. To replant a nursery seedling in another part of the nursery for further development.

Tree, Weed. A tree of a species with relatively little or no value.

Tree, Wolf. A tree occupying more space than its silvicultural value warrants, curtailing better neighbors. A term usually applied to broad-crowned, short-stemmed trees.

T.S.I. Timber stand improvement—usually applied to intermediate cutting.

Type, Forest. A descriptive term used to group stands of similar character as regards composition and development due to certain ecological factors, by which they may be differentiated from other groups of stands.

Understory. That portion of the trees in a forest stand below the overstory.

Uneven-aged. A term applied to a stand in which there are considerable differences in age of trees and in which three or more age classes are represented. See also **All-aged.**

Utilization, Forest. That branch of forestry concerned with the operation of harvesting and marketing the forest crop and other resources of the forest.

*****Watershed.** A drainage area separated from other watersheds by divides; an area of land from which the runoff drains into a given stream.

Wedge. In logging, to drive a wedge into the saw-cut to prevent the saw from binding and to direct the fall of the tree.

Widow-maker. Logger's term to describe a tree cut off at the stump but hung up in tops of adjacent trees which keep it from falling.

Windbreak. A wind barrier of living trees and shrubs maintained for the purpose of protecting the farm home, other buildings, garden, orchard, or feedlots.

Wind-firm. Able to withstand heavy wind.

Year, Seed. A year in which a given species produces (over a considerable area) a seed crop greatly in excess of the normal. Applied usually to trees of irregular or infrequent seed production.

Yield, Sustained. As applied to a policy, method, or plan of forest management the term implies continuous production, with the aim of achieving, at the earliest practicable time, an approximate balance between net growth and harvest, either by annual or somewhat longer periods.

B

Characteristics of Important Commercial Timber Species

The purpose of this Appendix is not to supply detailed tree identification information concerning all commercial species for use in the field. Rather, its purpose is to acquaint the student with the scientific names and a few essential characteristics of important forest trees, and their principal uses. Tree identification manuals, which are available at low cost, do not usually give all of this information. The student is urged to obtain one for field use, however. Previously, the forest regions in which these species are naturally found have been described and the species listed.

None of the exotic (or nonnative) tree species which have been planted in the United States are listed here. Only a very few have developed to the extent that they may be a factor in the production of forest crops; the principal species are Norway spruce (*Picea excelsa*), Scotch pine (*Pinus sylvestris*), and European larch (*Larix europa*), all from northern Europe and planted in our northern states. Most other exotics are ornamentals only.

The descriptive information is set forth in the following order: common name, scientific name (genus and species), size of tree, principal uses and products, and description of needles, leaves, fruit, and other pertinent information.

320

IMPORTANT EASTERN FOREST TREES*

Common and Scientific Name	Size[1]	Uses[2]	Characteristics[3]
Eastern Conifers			
Eastern white pine (*Pinus strobus*)	L	1, 2	Fine timber tree; leaves in clusters of 5, 3 to 5 in. long.
Jack pine (*Pinus banksiana*)	S	1, 2, 3	Common on sandy soil; leaves in clusters of 2, ¾ to 1¼ in. long.
Red pine (*Pinus resinosa*)	M-L	1, 2, 3, 4, 8	Leaves in clusters of 2, 5 to 6 in. long.
Loblolly pine (*Pinus taeda*)	L	1, 2, 3, 4	Leaves in clusters of 3, 6 to 9 in. long. Cone 2 to 3 in. in diameter.
Shortleaf pine (*Pinus echinata*)	L	1, 2, 3, 4	Leaves in clusters of 2 and sometimes 3, 3 to 5 in. long. Cone small, 1 to 2 in. in diameter.
Virginia pine (Scrub pine) (*Pinus virginiana*)	S		Leaves in clusters of 2, 1½ to 3 in. long.
Slash pine (*Pinus caribaea*)	L	1, 2, 3, 4	Leaves in clusters of 2, sometimes 3, 8 to 12 in. long. Important turpentine tree.
Longleaf pine (*Pinus palustris*)	L	1, 2, 3, 4	Leaves in clusters of 3, 8 to 18 in. long. Important turpentine tree.
Tamarack or Eastern Larch (*Larix laricina*)	S-M	1, 2, 3, 4	Leaves needle-shaped, ¾ to 1¼ in. long, in dense, brushlike clusters; falling off in winter. A swamp tree.
White spruce (*Picea glauca*)	M-L	1, 2, 8	Leaves ⅓ to ¾ in. long, arranged singly around the smooth twigs; whitish.
Black spruce (*Picea mariana*)	S	2, 8	Similar to white spruce, but twigs are minutely hairy; cones strongly attached. A swamp tree.
Red spruce (*Picea rubra*)	M-L	1, 2, 8	Similar to black spruce, but cones begin to fall when ripe.
Eastern hemlock (*Tsuga canadensis*)	L	1, 2	Leaves ⅓ to ⅔ in. long, attached by tiny leafstalks; cones ½ to ¾ in. long.
Bald cypress (*Taxodium distichum*)	L	1	Leaves ½ to ¾ in. long, falling off in winter; cones ball-like. A swamp tree.
Balsam fir (*Abies balsamea*)	S	2, 8	Leaves ½ to 1¼ in. long; cones upright, falling to pieces when ripe.

* Mainly eastern half of the United States, east of the Great Plains.
[1] Size: L, large; M, medium; S, small.
[2] Uses: 1, lumber; 2, pulpwood; 3, poles and posts; 4, piling; 5, railroad ties; 6, tool handles; 7, specialty; 8, Christmas trees; 9, veneer.
[3] Characteristics. Most fruits ripen in fall unless otherwise noted.

Important Eastern Forest Trees* *(Continued)*

Common and Scientific Name	Size[1]	Uses[2]	Characteristics[3]
Northern white cedar (*Thuja occidentalis*)	M	3	Leaves scalelike; cones ⅓ to ½ in. long, bent backward on twigs, which are flat.
Atlantic white cedar (*Chamaecyparis thyoides*)	M	3	Cones ball-like; leaves somewhat resembling arborvitae.
Eastern red cedar (*Juniperus virginiana*)	M	1, 3	Leaves scalelike, those on young shoots and seedlings awl-shaped and spreading; young cones changed into a firm berry.

Broadleaved Hardwoods

Common and Scientific Name	Size[1]	Uses[2]	Characteristics[3]
Sweet gum (*Liquidambar styraciflua*)	L	1, 5, 9	Leaves star-shaped; fruit a bur-like ball suspended by a long stalk.
American Sycamore; plane (*Platanus occidentalis*)	L	1, 5	Leaves broad and coarsely toothed; base of leafstalk inclosing a winter bud in peculiar manner; fruit a hard-surfaced, long-stalked ball.
White oak (*Quercus alba*)	L	1, 5, 7, 9	Leaves deeply lobed, not bristle-tipped; acorns ripening in one season.
Bur oak (*Quercus macrocarpa*)	L	1, 5, 7, 9	A white oak with fringe-edged acorn and larger leaves more deeply lobed.
Chestnut oak (*Quercus prinus*)	L		A white oak with leaves resembling those of the chestnut, and with long, large, shallow-cupped acorns.
Northern red oak (*Quercus borealis* var. *maxima*)	L	1, 5, 9	Leaves deeply cut, with bristle-tipped points. The acorns, ripening in 2 seasons, are large, with very shallow cups.
Black oak (*Quercus velutina*)	L	1, 5	An oak with thicker, large glossy leaves which are more or less minutely woolly beneath; acorns with small cups, as deep or deeper than wide.
Pin oak (*Quercus palustris*)	L	1, 5	A red oak with smaller leaves and smaller and shallower cupped striped acorns.
Southern red oak (*Quercus rubra*)	L	1, 5, 9	A red oak with leaves very deeply cut, the upper central portion being very narrow and sometimes slightly curved, and with dense, tawny-yellow wool beneath.

IMPORTANT EASTERN FOREST TREES* *(Continued)*

Common and Scientific Name	Size[1]	Uses[2]	Characteristics[3]
Live oak *(Quercus virginiana)*	M-L	1	An evergreen oak with narrow, smooth-bordered leaves which are turned under on the edge, pale woolly beneath and glossy above; small, pointed acorns with long stalks.
American basswood; American linden *(Tilia americana)*	L	1, 9	Leaves smooth, broadly heart-shaped with finely toothed edge; fruit a cluster of little woody balls suspended from the middle of a long narrow leaflike bract.
American (white) elm *(Ulmus americana)*	L	1, 5	Leaves sharply toothed; fruit flat, papery, about ½ in. long, fringed with tiny hairs.
Slippery (red) elm *(Ulmus rubra)*	M-L	1, 5	Long leaves, very rough on the upper side; inner bark is slippery when chewed, and the flat fruits have a smooth edge.
Rock elm *(Ulmus thomasii)*	M	1, 5	Differing from other elms in having fruit minutely hairy all over, and twigs with conspicuous, corky ridges.
American beech *(Fagus grandifolia)*	L	1, 5	Leaves with saw-toothed edge; fruit a light brown spine-covered bur containing a 3-cornered brown nut.
Eastern cottonwood *(Populus deltoides)*	L	1, 2	Leaves triangular, long-pointed, toothed, smooth, with flattened leafstalk.
Quaking aspen *(Populus tremuloides)*	S	1, 2	Leaves broad, finely toothed, leafstalks flat, longer than blades.
Bigtooth aspen *(Populus grandidentata)*	S	1, 2	Leaves broad, coarsely toothed, with flattened leafstalks.
Paper birch *(Betula papyrifera)*	M	1, 2, 5, 9	Leaves broad at base, finely toothed, fruit a papery cone which falls apart when ripe; white bark peeling off in thin sheets.
Yellow birch *(Betula lutea)*	L	1, 5, 9	Bark yellow-gray; tiny scales of the cones minutely hairy along edges.
Black cherry *(Prunus serotina)*	M	1, 5, 9	Fruit resembles common choke-cherry, but smaller and thin-fleshed.
Yellow poplar; tulip tree *(Liriodendron tulipifera)*	L	1, 2, 9	Leaves large, blunt or with deep notch at end; flowers large yellow, tulip-like; fruit a woody, upright cone.

Iᴍᴘᴏʀᴛᴀɴᴛ Eᴀsᴛᴇʀɴ Fᴏʀᴇsᴛ Tʀᴇᴇs* *(Continued)*

Common and Scientific Name	Size[1]	Uses[2]	Characteristics[3]
Black tupelo (or gum) (*Nyssa sylvatica*)	M	1, 5	Large tree; leaves oval with smooth edge. Fruit an elongated black berry with seed but little flattened and scarcely ridged.
Sugar maple (*Acer saccharum*)	M-L	1, 5, 9	Leaves 3- to 5-lobed with large rounded teeth; fruit a pair of keys ripening in early autumn. Yields maple sugar.
Red maple (*Acer rubrum*)	M-L	1, 5, 9	Leaves 3- to 5-lobed, finely toothed; reddish fruit ripening in spring or early summer. Yields maple sugar.
Boxelder (*Acer negundo*, including 6 varietal forms)	M	1, 5	Leaves compound, the leaflets toothed; fruit ripening in early summer and remaining on trees during winter.
Black locust (*Robinia pseudoacacia*)	S	3	Leaves compound, leaflets with smooth margins; fruit a pod 3 to 4 in. long. Trees with pairs of short thorns at base of leaves and twigs.
Bitternut hickory (*Hicoria cordiformis*)	M	1, 5, 6	Nut broader than long, without angles, very thin-shelled; bitter kernel, husk thin.
Shagbark hickory (*Carya ovata*)	M	1, 5, 6	Buds with many scales (all of the preceding hickories have buds with few scales); bark loosening from trees in shaggy strips.
Mockernut hickory (*Carya alba*, known also as bigbud or white hickory)	M	1, 5, 6	Leaves large, hairy; buds large, budscales many; bark closely furrowed, not separating from the trunk. Nut with thick husk, large, angled, thick-shelled.
Black walnut (*Juglans nigra*)	M	1, 9	Leaves compound with toothed edges; spherical fruit growing singly or in pairs; bark brown, furrowed.
Butternut (*Juglans cinerea*)	M	1	Leaves compound, with toothed edges; fruit in clusters of 3 to 5, pointed and elongated, with viscid hairs when young. Velvety cushion just above leaf-scar; bark gray and smooth on young trees.
White ash (*Fraxinus americana*)	M-L	1, 5, 6, 9	Smooth twigs, opposite; leaves compound, leaflets toothed or wavy on the margins and paler beneath; seed with a

IMPORTANT EASTERN FOREST TREES* *(Continued)*

Common and Scientific Name	Size[1]	Uses[2]	Characteristics[3]
			plump, well-rounded body and a wing extending almost entirely from the end and borne in dense clusters. High-ground tree.
Green ash *(Fraxinus pennsylvanica* var. *lanceolata)*	M	1, 5, 6	Like the preceding, except twigs are smooth, leaflets sharply toothed; body of seed and pointed wing very narrow. Bottomland tree.
Black ash *(Fraxinus nigra)*	M	1, 5	Leaflets stemless, finely toothed, 7 to 11; seeds with a flat, wide wing, which extends conspicuously down the sides of the seed body and is blunt. Swamp tree.

IMPORTANT WESTERN FOREST TREES*

Common and Scientific Name	Size[1]	Uses[2]	Characteristics[3]
Conifers			
Western white pine *(Pinus monticola)*	L	1	Needles 5 in a cluster, blue green, 2 to 4 in. long. Cone slender, 5 to 12 in. long.
Sugar pine *(Pinus lambertiana)*	L	1	Needles 5 in a cluster, 3 to 4 in. long. Important timber tree; largest of the pines.
Ponderosa pine *(Pinus ponderosa)*	L	1	Needles 3 or 2 in a cluster, stout, 4 to 7 in. long. Cones short-stalked, 3 to 6 in. long, with prickles.
Lodgepole pine *(Pinus contorta)*	L	1, 2, 5	Needles 2 in a cluster, stout, yellow green, 1 to 3 in. long. Cones up to 2 in. long, staying closed on tree many years.
Western larch *(Larix occidentalis)*	L	1	Needles many in a cluster, about 1 in. long, shedding in fall. Cones upright, 1 to 1½ in. long.
Western hemlock *(Tsuga heterophylla)*	L	1, 2	Needles ¼ to ¾ in. long, flat, shiny. Cone 1 in. long. Important timber tree.
Engelmann spruce *(Picea engelmannii)*	L	1, 2, 9	Needles 4-angled, ⅝ to 1⅛ in. long. Cones 1½ to 2½ in. long.
Blue spruce *(Picea pungens)*	S-M	2, 7	Needles 4-angled, ¾ to 1⅛ in. long, blue green. Cones 2½ to 4 in. long.

* Mainly Rocky Mountains, Black Hills, and Pacific Coast States, west of the Great Plains States.

IMPORTANT WESTERN FOREST TREES* *(Continued)*

Common and Scientific Name	Size[1]	Uses[2]	Characteristics[3]
Sitka spruce *(Picea sitchensis)*	L	1, 2, 9	Needles flat, ⅝ to 1 in. long, dark green. Cones 2 to 3½ in. long, with long, stiff scales, rounded and irregularly toothed. Used as lumber for many purposes, and as pulpwood.
Douglas fir *(Pseudotsuga taxifolia)*	L	1, 2, 8, 9	Needles flat, ¾ to 1¼ in. long, dark green. Cones 2 to 4 in. long, with long, 3-toothed bracts extending between scales. Pointed buds.
Grand fir *(Abies grandis)*	M-L	1, 2, 8	Needles flat, 1 to 2 in. long, dark green above, silvery white beneath. Cones upright, 2 to 4 in. long, green.
Noble fir *(Abies procera)*	M	1, 2, 8	Needles of lower branches flat, and of top branches 4-angled, 1 to 1½ in. long, blue green. Cones upright, 4 to 6 in. long, with long bracts covering the scales.
Redwood *(Sequoia sempervirens)*	L	1, 3, 5, 7	Leaves both scalelike and needlelike, unequal in length, ¼ to ¾ in. long, spreading in 2 rows. Cones ¾ to 1 in. long. Tree up to 370 ft. tall and 25 ft. in diameter. Used for heavy construction, planing-mill products, tanks.
Giant sequoia *(Sequoia gigantea)*	L	1, 3	Leaves scalelike, ⅛ to ¼ in. long. Cones 1¾ to 2¾ in. long. Tree up to 320 ft. tall and 35 ft. in diameter at swollen base. Largest trees preserved in national parks and national forests.
Western red cedar *(Thuja plicata)*	L	1, 3, 7	Leaves scalelike, 1/16 to ⅛ in. long, dark green. Cones ½ in. long.
Port Orford cedar *(Chamaecyparis lawsoniana)*	L	1, 3, 7	Leaves 1/16 to ¼ in. long. Cones about ⅜ in. in diameter. Bark thick.

C

Forest Management Plans
for Small Properties

I. SAMPLE OF FOREST MANAGEMENT PLAN

Case History of a Southern Pine Tree Farmer*

Robert Bryant, an independent oil operator, purchased minerals, royalty, and leases all over his state during the 1930's and 1940's and, when the price appeared to be cheap, bought the surface also. In this manner, he acquired in 1939 a tract of 2,130 acres 120 miles southeast of his headquarters. At the time of the purchase, he gave only minor consideration to its operation as a tree farm. Rentals from mineral leases produced an adequate return on his investment; ad valorem taxes were low; most merchantable timber had recently been removed. By 1952, however, all of these conditions have changed, and sound money management makes it necessary to explore other possibilities. What steps does he take:

Step 1: Choose Forestry Adviser

Unfamiliar with the services available to tree farmers, Bryant calls on the state forestry department and receives a list of private consulting foresters. Interviews with three consultants who furnish references provide a basis for Bryant to choose the man whom he feels most qualified for the job. Agreement is then reached on the services and rates which is to be stated in a letter by Bryant.

Step 2: Make a Tree Farm Inventory

The forester recommends a 10 per cent inventory, describes what data will be gathered, and quotes a fee on a per-acre basis. Owner ac-

* Adapted from James M. Vardaman, *Tree Farm Business Management*. Copyright © ; 1965, The Ronald Press Company, New York.

cepts arrangement after being assured of a planning conference after report is submitted. The forester, ten days later, submits his report as follows:

HOWARD, STEPHENS AND DOUGLAS
Consulting Foresters
COURT SQUARE SOUTH BUILDING
ANYTOWN, STATE

September 30, 1967

Mr. Robert Bryant
P. O. Box 187
Anytown, State

Dear Mr. Bryant:

During the last ten days, we have completed a tree farm inventory of your property described as SW/4, W/2, NW/4, Section 26; Entire less NWNW, Section 27; S/2 NE/4, SE/4, Section 28; E/2, Section 33; W/2, NE/4, E/2 SE/4, Section 34; W/2 NW/4, W/2 NENW, SWSW, Section 35, all in Township 5 North, Range 10 West, and NWNW less West 10 acres, Section 2, Township 4 North, Range 10 West, containing a total area of 2,130 acres. Our report is presented below and on the attached map.

Specifications and Sampling Procedure

We tallied as sawtimber all pine trees 9.0″ and up DBH and all hardwood trees 11.0″ and up DBH and as pulpwood all trees over 5.0″ DBH but smaller than sawtimber. We divided the trees into 2″ DBH classes and estimated volumes as to the following top diameters inside bark: pine sawtimber 7″, hardwood sawtimber 9″, pulpwood 4″. Pulpwood volumes include standing trees only; we made no estimate of pulpwood volume in tops of sawtimber trees. We tallied all pine species as pine, all gums as gum, all oaks as oak, and yellow poplar as poplar.

Sawtimber inventory is based on a 10% strip sample; we passed twice through each forty-acre block and, on each pass, tallied the sawtimber trees on a strip 66 feet wide. Pulpwood inventory is based on a 5% strip sample; we tallied trees of this size on one-half of this strip for sawtimber. Number of pine trees in the 4″ DBH class were tallied on four ¼-acre plots per forty-acre block (a 2.5% plot sample). Growth data were obtained by taking an increment core from the tree nearest the center of each plot on which 4″ trees were tallied.

Timber Inventory

Our estimate of the total number and volume of trees by DBH class, species, and product is as follows:

DBH	Pine		Gum		Oak		Poplar	
	No. of Trees	Volume	No. of Trees	Volume	No. of Trees	Volume	No. of Trees	Volume
	Pulpwood							
4	57,260							
6	31,180	1,091						
8	27,340	2,051						
		3,142						
	Sawtimber							
10	12,790	314,300						
12	5,390	264,700	240	8,500	130	4,200	60	2,300
14	1,370	138,500	150	10,600	120	6,800	50	3,700
16	680	107,000	40	4,000	70	5,900	20	2,700
18	380	86,300					10	2,200
20	30	7,800						
	136,420	918,600	430	23,100	320	16,900	140	10,900

Pulpwood volumes are given in unpeeled units of 168 cubic feet each, and sawtimber volumes are given in board feet, Doyle scale. 4" trees are listed under pulpwood although they are below merchantable size. Hardwood trees occur on the tract only in scattered strips of pine-hardwood type (see map); therefore, we do not believe we took a sufficient sample of them to produce a reliable estimate. Because of their small volume and low values, this is not a serious error.

Trees smaller than the 4" DBH class are present in considerable numbers under stands of larger trees; most of them became established at the same time as the larger trees and are small now because they are overcrowded or overtopped. They will not make a significant contribution to future growth. Your problem is either too many trees per acre or none at all. Average volume per acre is low because trees are small and because many acres are idle or used for other purposes. We divided the tract arbitrarily into seven blocks during inventory, and volumes for each block are given on sheets following the map.

Scattered all over the tract are patches of old pine stumps suitable for distillate wood. We think their volume is between 500 and 1,000 tons; they are concentrated enough to be merchantable.

Forest Types

The map shows the location of the two main forest types on your tract. One is pine and is almost a pure stand of longleaf pine. The other is pine-hardwood made up of 50% pine and 50% hardwood. In this type the pine species is loblolly, and the hardwood species groups are those shown under timber inventory.

Growth Study

In calculating timber growth on your property, we ignored the hardwood component; it contains only about 5% of the volume and less of the value. We estimate annual growth of pine to be 81,000 board feet of sawtimber and 100 units of pulpwood, and we believe you can remove this volume each year without dipping into timber capital.

Growth rates vary widely by DBH classes; 12" trees grow better than 8%, 20" trees less than 3.5%. There is also a great difference within DBH classes depending upon condition of individual trees. Well-spaced, vigorous trees grow rapidly; suppressed trees grow hardly at all.

Soil Analysis

We did not make a thorough study of the soils, but information available from the U.S. Soil Conservation Service indicates that the site index for your pine areas is 75 and that for the pine-hardwood areas is 90. This is a very general statement, but indicates that you have no serious problems here and will do for the time being. At present, your major concern is making the best possible use of existing stands, and measurements of growth in the field will provide all necessary guides. We recommend more thorough study of your soils when markets and financial resources make possible more intensive forest management.

Markets and Market Prices

Markets for all forest products are excellent. Within thirty miles of the tract, there are ten sawmills, seven pulpwood dealers, and three pole buyers, and competition among them is spirited. We estimate stumpage values for pine pulpwood to be $8.00 per unit and for sawtimber per MBF to be as follows: pine $40.00, gum and oak $20.00, and poplar $30.00. Stumpage value of distillate wood is $2.00 per ton. There is an insignificant volume of hardwood pulpwood—so small that we did not include it in the inventory—which has a market value of $1.00 per unit and can be expected to double or triple within the next ten years. Unfortunately, it can never contribute substantially to income.

Fire

Except for pine-hardwood areas too wet to burn, the entire tract burned over this past winter, and there are signs that this is a common occurrence. Since almost every tree is a longleaf pine, there is little loss from death of merchantable trees. On the other hand, there is a definite growth loss each year because many trees are defoliated by fire, and constant burning prohibits establishment of young pines in many areas that are now idle. These idle acres, inherently productive, are scattered all over the tract in irregular strips and patches which show on aerial photographs but are much too complicated to show on the map. We believe they can be made productive quickly and cheaply by planting, but no planting should be done until the fire problem is solved. The fires appear to be of incendiary origin to provide early spring grazing for numerous cattle in the area, and although your county is under the state fire control program, several determined firebugs completely overpower all fire suppression organizations. This is a major problem; we estimate your timbered land is at least 30% idle because of fire.

Development Work

Planting is needed on about 600 acres, but should not be undertaken until you can control fire. No TSI work is needed now or in the near future; constant burning has eliminated all pine reproduction and almost all hardwood from pine areas. Thinning is desirable on 480 acres as shown on the map. We estimate that a thinning from them will produce about two units of pulpwood per acre now.

Trespass

All merchantable timber has been removed within the last year from about 35 acres in the southwest corner of SWSE, Section 33. This appears to be trespass; we found no evidence of an established boundary line either south or west of cut area. Mr. Rice, mentioned below, knew nothing about cutting.

Adverse Possession and Other Use

The gravel pit in NESW, Section 26, occupies five acres, is abandoned, and is being recaptured by pine seedlings.

The pasture north of Highway 42 occupies forty acres, is heavily grazed, but receives no cultivation. These conditions also apply to the fifteen-acre pasture on east side of NESE, Section 34.

The cultivated fields in southeast portion of tract occupy eighty acres and have been prepared for planting this year. The two barns are in use. All four houses on the tract are occupied, and Julius Rice, General Delivery, Anytown, lives in the one in southeast corner of SESE, Section 34. Mr. Rice told us that he leases the pastures, fields, and houses from you and sub-leases some facilities to others. He said that all fences shown are yours and necessary for his operations; if not, they may be evidence of adverse possession.

Rights of Way

The map shows rights of way we found and measured on the ground. The largest is that of ABC Power Company; it is 100 feet wide, about 8,000 feet long, and contains 18.6 acres. The DEF Pipeline Company ROW is 25 feet wide, about 3,000 feet long, and contains 1.7 acres; there is also a telephone or telegraph line down its center. There are three ROW's of the local electric power association; they are 20 feet wide, a total of 16,830 feet long, and contain 7.7 acres. The ROW for State Highway 42 is 60 feet wide, about 10,560 feet long, and contains 14.5 acres. The only other road ROW's that reduce timber-growing area are those in the extreme southeastern portion and a short stretch just south of the highway; they are 30 feet wide, about 4,500 feet long, and contain 3.1 acres. The total area used for all ROW's is 45.6 acres; there may be additional areas affected if any power-line ROW agreement permits cutting of danger trees.

Boundary Lines

Some boundary lines are established by fences shown on map; these fences appear to be accepted by adjoining owners. In the northern portion, you have at least one mile of common boundary line with XYZ Paper Company; these two strips of line are painted white and maintained by the company. Although we investigated at several points, we found no evidence of established lines on the west side of the land in Sections 28 and 33 or the south side of the land in Sections 33 and 34; this situation may have led to the cutting, and we believe these must be surveyed.

Please call on us if we can give you any further information or assistance. After you have a chance to study these data, we will be happy to help you plan and execute those programs you select.

Respectfully submitted,

Howard, Stephens and Douglass

Calvin R. Douglass

Timber Volumes by Arbitrary Blocks

	Pine		Gum		Oak		Poplar	
DBH	No. of Trees	Volume	No. of Trees	Volume	No. of Trees	Volume	No. of Trees	Volume

Block 1: W/2 NW/4, Section 26 and NE/4, E/2 NW/4, Section 27
320 Acres

Pulpwood

4	10,240							
6	5,560	195						
8	4,240	318						
		513						

Sawtimber

10	1,580	39,200						
12	990	49,300	30	1,100				
14	270	27,500	20	1,600				
16	240	37,800	20	2,000				
18	110	25,300						
	23,230	179,100	70	4,700				

	Pine		Gum		Oak		Poplar	
DBH	No. of Trees	Volume	No. of Trees	Volume	No. of Trees	Volume	No. of Trees	Volume

BLOCK 2: E/2, Section 33
320 Acres

Pulpwood

DBH	No. of Trees	Volume	No. of Trees	Volume	No. of Trees	Volume	No. of Trees	Volume
4	10,020							
6	5,560	195						
8	3,100	233						
		428						

Sawtimber

DBH	No. of Trees	Volume	No. of Trees	Volume	No. of Trees	Volume	No. of Trees	Volume
10	1,070	25,600						
12	680	33,900	60	2,000	30	900		
14	260	27,600	20	1,000	20	1,000	30	2,400
16	130	24,800	10	800	20	2,000		
18	130	30,300						
	20,950	142,200	90	3,800	70	3,900	30	2,400

BLOCK 3: SE/4, E/2 SW/4, Section 27
240 Acres

Pulpwood

DBH	No. of Trees	Volume	No. of Trees	Volume	No. of Trees	Volume	No. of Trees	Volume
4	5,940							
6	3,220	113						
8	3,800	285						
		398						

Sawtimber

DBH	No. of Trees	Volume	No. of Trees	Volume	No. of Trees	Volume	No. of Trees	Volume
10	1,680	39,300						
12	660	31,100	10	300	10	300	10	300
14	50	5,400			10	500	10	500
16	20	2,800						
18	10	2,500						
	15,380	81,100	10	300	20	800	20	800

BLOCK 4: W/2, Section 34
320 Acres

Pulpwood

DBH	No. of Trees	Volume	No. of Trees	Volume	No. of Trees	Volume	No. of Trees	Volume
4	14,260							
6	7,740	270						
8	6,480	485						
		755						

Sawtimber

DBH	No. of Trees	Volume	No. of Trees	Volume	No. of Trees	Volume	No. of Trees	Volume
10	2,320	54,300						
12	430	20,200	20	900				
14	50	4,900	10	800				
16								
18	10	2,500						
	31,290	81,900	30	1,700				

DBH	Pine No. of Trees	Volume	Gum No. of Trees	Volume	Oak No. of Trees	Volume	Poplar No. of Trees	Volume
	Pine		*Gum*		*Oak*		*Poplar*	

BLOCK 5: NE/4, E/2 SE/4, Section 34: SWSW, Section 35; NWNW less West 10 Acres, Section 2
310 Acres

Pulpwood

DBH	Pine No. of Trees	Volume	Gum No. of Trees	Volume	Oak No. of Trees	Volume	Poplar No. of Trees	Volume
4	3,440							
6	1,860	65						
8	2,600	195						
		261						

Sawtimber

DBH	Pine No. of Trees	Volume	Gum No. of Trees	Volume	Oak No. of Trees	Volume	Poplar No. of Trees	Volume
10	1,340	32,300						
12	540	26,900	120	4,200	80	2,700	40	1,600
14	280	27,900	100	7,200	70	4,000		
16	140	22,800	10	1,200	50	3,900	10	1,500
18	60	15,300					10	2,200
	10,260	125,200	230	12,600	200	10,600	60	5,300

BLOCK 6: SW/4, Section 26; W/2 NW/4, W/2 NWNE, Section 35
260 Acres

Pulpwood

DBH	Pine No. of Trees	Volume	Gum No. of Trees	Volume	Oak No. of Trees	Volume	Poplar No. of Trees	Volume
4	3,840							
6	2,080	72						
8	2,200	166						
		238						

Sawtimber

DBH	Pine No. of Trees	Volume	Gum No. of Trees	Volume	Oak No. of Trees	Volume	Poplar No. of Trees	Volume
10	1,920	48,800						
12	990	49,600					10	400
14	280	28,600			10	500		
16	80	8,800					10	1,200
18	50	9,200						
20	20	5,200						
	11,460	150,200			10	500	20	1,600

BLOCK 7: SWNW, W/2 SW/4, Section 27; SE/4, S/2 NE/4, Section 28
360 Acres

Pulpwood

DBH	Pine No. of Trees	Volume	Gum No. of Trees	Volume	Oak No. of Trees	Volume	Poplar No. of Trees	Volume
4	9,520							
6	5,160	181						
8	4,920	368						
		549						

Sawtimber

DBH	Pine No. of Trees	Volume	Gum No. of Trees	Volume	Oak No. of Trees	Volume	Poplar No. of Trees	Volume
10	2,880	74,800						
12	1,100	53,700			10	300		
14	180	16,600			10	800	10	800
16	70	10,000						
18	10	1,200						
20	10	2,600						
	23,850	158,900			20	1,100	10	800

Bryant now has the information he needs to evaluate his asset and plan for the future. Of course, every property is different and so is every owner, but this gives you an illustration of what a tree farm inventory should contain. You probably have some data on your property, but they may be incomplete or out-of-date. You should resist the temptation to economize by using such data; even under optimum conditions, you must make many assumptions and plans about the future, and plans based on a shaky foundation lead to trouble. Although economy is fundamental in tree farming, false economy in inventory may prevent sound decisions and doom the enterprise to failure.

Step 3: Make Financial Forecast

Bryant and his forester now sit down with paper and pencil to see what returns can be had, now and later, from operation of the property as a tree farm, and to determine whether the money that can be realized from its sale could be better used in some other way.

First, they look at income. Annual growth is 81 MBF of sawtimber and 100 units of pulpwood, which, at the values in the report, can be sold for $4,040. The forester states that he will mark the trees for cutting, sell them, and supervise logging operations for a fee of 10 per cent ($404), leaving a net of $3,636. Rental from the lease to Mr. Rice is $160 per year, bringing total income to $3,796.

The forester estimates that the tract, without minerals, can be sold for $40 per acre ($85,200). If the value is $85,200, an income of $3,320 produces an annual return of 3.9 per cent. Bryant thinks that land prices will rise steadily, and this consideration makes him content with a 3.9 per cent return for the present.

There are two possibilities for increased income. Rice pays $160 per year for the use of four houses, 137 acres of cultivable land, and 240 acres of fenced woods pasture; this seems a low price and may be increased. Substantial increases in timber growth will be possible when elimination of uncontrolled fire permits intensive forest management; the forester states that the tree farm is capable of producing a net annual timber harvest of over $10,000. Therefore, Bryant has a fair return and good prospects. Without them, he would sell the tract at this point; with them, he proceeds to the next step.

Step 4: Choose and Implement Forest-Management Plan

The inventory provides the basic data for the management plan which provides specific recommendations by the forester for the owner. Four steps are suggested:

1. Sale of all old pine stumps suitable for distillate wood
2. Sale of all sawtimber growing at a compound rate of less than 5 per cent, and of other sawtimber trees that are diseased, crooked, or otherwise defective (The forester states, and the inventory indicates, that

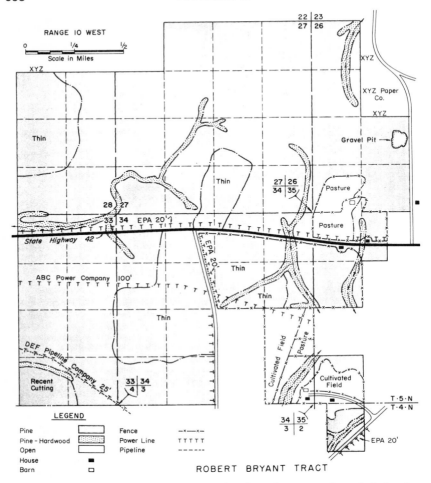

ROBERT BRYANT TRACT

this timber is located in the pine-hardwood areas and at their borders and that the sale will produce about $7,500.)

3. Sale of all pulpwood that should be removed from the thinning areas, which will produce about $7,700 and must be coordinated with saw-timber sales to prevent disputes between loggers

4. A survey of 2¾ miles of unestablished boundary line on the south and west sides of the tract, at an estimated cost of $200.00

Step 5: Choose Tax and Accounting Adviser

Because depletion allowances under the federal tax law, basic allocations of expenditures (are they current production costs or capital investments?), and many other fiscal decisions determine profit or loss, sound and experienced professional advice is needed both in establishing an accounting system and in reporting income and expenses to the Internal Revenue Service.

Step 6: Choose a Lawyer

A good attorney in a local community familiar with the land and trusted by the owner will assure proper handling of many legal matters —title clearance, easements, contract arrangements, and even special tax situations involving legal tax law interpretation. Choice of an attorney with experience in land, forestry, and tax affairs will be more than rewarding in money saved.

Step 7: Executing the Plan

A series of actions will be taken to carry out the management plan and to provide for other land use and legal problems. These may include:

a. Surveying the boundaries of the property and locating all corners. To do this the owner will wish to hire a registered surveyor, particularly if any lines or corners are in dispute with other owners.

b. Set up a system of forest operations records. By using transparent "overlays" (one for each year), the owner can trace the main features of the base map on the overlay and show all developments for the year on a single map. Thus he would show any new road built, where tree planting took place, power lines constructed, or any other project.

c. Establish a forest operation accounting system. If the forest tract is large, the owner will need to have the services of a professional accountant. Smaller tract owners can refer to Chapter 7 of this book where accounting suggestions are set forth. Receipts and expenses should be entered systematically right from the beginning.

d. Provide a schedule for regular timber sales of merchantable forest products. The searching out of markets is a final step for the owner— either local forest products industries or buyers for more distant lumber, veneer, and pulp concerns. If equipped with a logging crew and time for supervision, the owner may wish to carry his own logging operations and sell cut products—sawlogs, veneer logs, and pulpwood. This procedure enables him to gain a profit from the logging operation. An alternative—if time for supervision is lacking—is to sell the stumpage to a timber buyer. In each case the owner will wish to sign a contract as set forth in Appendix D. Seeking price and cost quotations from independent sources (market and price reports) is essential to profitable operations.

e. Handle other demands and uses for the land including grazing, recreation, rights-of-way for power and other easement uses. Agricultural uses may be possible on better soils and should be handled under supplemental landlord-tenant agreements. These are usually available at the state agricultural college. Opportunities for leasing hunting, fishing, or other recreational uses can often increase revenue where sportsmen interest is shown in game and fish resources. Power company lines, or gas and oil pipelines, may be registered under easement arrangements. These should be worked out by the lawyer for the owner with the corporation requesting the easement.

II. SAMPLE OF DETAILED FOREST MANAGEMENT PLAN

For Property Which Has Been Managed for Several Decades

Wolf Springs Forest
Minong, Wisconsin

Location and Area. 280 acres, comprising seven 40-acre tracts described as follows: N½-SE¼, S½-NE¼, W½-NW¼, and NW-NW, of Section 9, T 42N R 11W, located in the northeastern part of Washburn County, Wisconsin. (See forest type, Fig. 6–5, and aerial photo maps, also Figs. 6–6 and 7–3, which apply to this property.)

Land and Timber

Total land area	280 acres
Forest land	190 acres
Unproductive swamp	38 acres
Water area (3 ponds, 2 lakes, springs, and stream)	40 acres
Open upland (plowable fields and pastures)	12 acres

Distribution of Forest Cover Types

Norway (red) and white pine type (upland)	60 acres
Balsam fir, spruce, tamarack, and cedar (swamp)	35 acres
Pine and spruce plantations (upland)	32 acres
Mixed pine and balsam fir reproduction under aspen (upland)	40 acres
Nonforested, brush, plantable upland	23 acres

History of the Tract. The property was originally acquired by James Wolfe, who settled on it in 1889, and worked with the logging crew that cut off the pine timber the same winter. By protecting the area from fire, a dense volunteer stand of pine developed, which was allowed to grow untouched until the present owner acquired the property in 1936. In the spring of 1931 a light ground fire passed through the area. The fire scarred larger trees and killed seedlings and saplings in the open areas. The tract has been managed since 1936.

Forest growing stock has been inventoried at regular intervals; sample plots for growth studies established; thinnings, release cuttings, pruning of crop trees, and application of shelterwood and selection methods in timber harvesting (a total volume of 63.2 m.b.f. and 380 cords plus 1,500 cedar posts and 300 cedar poles have been removed during the management period); 20 acres of forest plantation established; 40 acres in white pine reproduction with blister rust protection.

Physical Features

12 flowing cold water springs near headwaters

3 trout ponds (stocked with brook, rainbow, and brown trout)

2 artificial lakes (constructed in 1955 and 1959), planted to wild rice in the first experimental effort to grow this as a commercial crop; waterfowl nesting area in upper end and on two artificial islands; muskrat, mink, otter, and beaver use whole area; bait minnow production under lease

⅓ mile of deep trout stream (stocked with brook and brown trout above lake)

Small tree and wildlife shrub nursery

Wildlife Habitat. Excellent waterfowl nesting and resting habitat at upper end of new lake and on islands; ruffed grouse on logging roads; sharptail grouse use open fields and food patches; deer "yard up" in cedar swamps; woodcock along swamp borders; brook, rainbow, and brown trout stocked in ponds, stream, and lake; game food shrubs have been established near wildlife nesting and concentration areas.

Buildings and Equipment

Main lodge with capacity for 8 adults

1 guest cabin with facilities for 3

1 machine shed and tool shop

1 livestock pole barn

1 lodge and 2 bunk houses for boys' camp

Forest Management Record. COMPARTMENT I: NE PINE BLOCK—10 ACRES. This stand is composed of well-stocked white and Norway pine about 80 years of age averaging 8 to 14 in. d.b.h. The site index varies from medium to good.

Management History. Thinned in 1938, 1941, 1952, and 1956–57; volume removed 59.3 cords of pine pulpwood. Crop trees pruned in 1939–41 and 1946–47. Area protected from blister rust by pulling *Ribes* in 1935 (by C.C.C. workers), in 1943, 1954, and again in 1966 (also applies to Compartments II, IV, and VII). Five sample plots for growth measurements established.

Future Plans. One more pre-harvest thinning planned about 1970. Harvest cuttings following 3-Cut Shelterwood System with very light first cut to reduce invasion by hazel brush to start in 1980.

Present Volume: 151 m.b.f. plus 111 cords pulpwood (next measurement in m.b.f. and cords)

Growth Rate: 1.1 cords per acre per year

COMPARTMENT II: SOUTH SIDE PINE BLOCK—13.1 ACRES. Medium to well-stocked second-growth Norway and white pine ranging in age from 10 to 80 years, with aspen and balsam fir (removed in 1946–48); average of main stand 10-16 in. in diameter, variably composed of pulpwood and sawtimber. Reproduction in understory largely balsam fir and white pine supplemented with planted Norway (red) pine and white spruce in 1941 and 1947. Site index varies from medium to good. Brush killer (2,4,5-T) used to reduce invasion of hazel and ironwood following logging. Good site.

Management History. Release cutting of mature aspen over pine and balsam fir in 1940 removed 28.4 cords of excelsior bolts; light harvest cutting and thinning in 1946 and 1947 removed remaining aspen, all poorly formed sawtimber, and pulpwood-sized trees; salvage cutting of windthrown trees in 1949. Pruning of selected crop trees in 1941 and 1947. Total cut between 1946 and 1950, 42.2 m.b.f. pine and 47.4 cords of pine, 67.6 cords of aspen, and 33.5 cords of white birch. One 2½-acre plantation of Norway (red) pine established in 1939.

Future Plans. One more thinning scheduled for 1970. Harvest cuttings to follow individual tree selection, group selection, and shelterwood to fit each portion of area will begin about 1977. Additional brush killing as needed.

Present Volume: 242 m.b.f. and 78 cords of pine, 36 cords of balsam fir

Growth Rate: 210 b.f. per acre per year plus 0.2 cord

COMPARTMENT III: SW LINE FENCE—PINE BLOCK—3.8 ACRES. Medium stocked Norway pine sawtimber 70 to 80 years old averaging 14 to 18 in. d.b.h. and three 16 ft. logs per tree. Understory of white pine and underplanted (1940) Norway and Scotch pine in heavy brush. Good site.

Management History. Salvage of windthrow in 1949 removed 3 m.b.f. pine.

Future Plans. Further underplanting after brush killing in 1958–59. Harvest cutting began 1962 under 3-cut shelterwood system.

Present Volume: 16 m.b.f. plus 8 cords
Growth Rate: 359 b.f. per acre per year
Estimated Allowable Cut: Harvest of entire merchantable volume in 1968–70 period

COMPARTMENT IV: WEST SWAMP CONIFER BLOCK—31.1 ACRES. Mixture of balsam fir, black spruce, tamarack, white cedar, and some white spruce (edges), with scattered black ash and yellow birch. All age and size well-stocked stand until cutting in 1945–47 and windstorm of 1949. Sizes ranged from 2 to 8 in. d.b.h., with merchantable pulpwood, cedar pole, and post material predominating. Fairly well drained and good site.

Management History. Undisturbed until partial logging in 1946–47, which was followed by a good stocking of seedling conifers and a heavier salvage cutting of windthrown timber in 1949. Heavy timber removal 1946–49:

30 cords spruce

85 cords balsam

15 cords tamarack

230 cedar poles

1200 posts

No cutting since. No additional cultural or other work performed. Reproduction of spruce, balsam, and black ash developing well, but cedar and yellow birch being overbrowsed by deer. Some spots with too much alder or raspberry for satisfactory tree growth.

Future Plans. No silvicultural work planned except some thinning of merchantable material in remaining balsam thickets, about 1970.

Present Volume: About 235 cords of scattered and young merchantable material

Growth Rate: Estimated at 0.3 cord per acre per year

COMPARTMENT V: POND SWAMP CONIFER BLOCK—6.1 ACRES. Balsam fir, cedar, with some spruce, white birch, and aspen lying along and around upper trout pond and spring and within Compartment I. All ages and sizes up to 12 in.

Management History. Logging in upper ends of swamp in 1946–47 removed 28 cords (balsam, spruce), scattered posts, and a few poles. Salvage cutting in beaver flowage area in 1948. Black spruce planted in a few open spots, 1954.

Future Plans. No cultural work except salvage of such windthrow as may develop from time to time. Harvest cuttings on south and west edges planned in near future will require cable skidding because of springy ground.

Present Volume: Scattered—about 75 cords

Growth Rate: No record

COMPARTMENT VI: WEST SIDE, OPEN UPLAND—128.9 ACRES. Located on west side of Compartment I, Sprague Lake, and Wolf Creek. Contains three plantations (A) white spruce, (B) mixed jack and Norway pine, and (C) Norway pine. Balance of areas understocked, with poor aspen and scattered pine and balsam fir reproduction. No merchantable volume.

Management History. Plantations (A) established in 1939, (C) in 1940, and (B) in 1961. Access road built in 1955 and 1957.

Future Plans. Continue planting pine and spruce in open spots.

Prune plantations in 1970; harvest Christmas trees in 1969. No merchantable volumes for growth estimate or other estimate until 1970.

COMPARTMENT VII: NORTH SIDE, ASPEN-PINE UNDERSTORY BLOCK— 82 ACRES. Scattered aspen which sprouted after 1931 ground fire, badly damaged by June, 1946, hailstorms, serves as overstory for white pine reproduction up to 12 ft. in height. Two hay fields totaling 7 acres (bordered with wildlife food shrubs) and about 8 acres of nonproductive swamp.

Management History. Four plantations established in following years: (A) 1946, (B) 1951, (C) 1952, (D) 1954–55. *Ribes* eradication in 1954–55 and 1966; no thinning or stand improvement to date. White pine weevil control—intensive—1960, annual maintenance thereafter.

Future Plans. Thinnings will be needed in plantation during next decade; release of white pine saplings under aspen during same period, after trees reach 15 or more ft. and danger of weevil damage to tips has largely passed. Continue plantings and underplantings in open areas. Continue *Ribes* eradication again in 1976 and white pine weevil control by pruning.

General Forest Management Considerations

Utilization and Marketing. Timber stand improvement cuttings and thinnings for pulpwood to coincide with fall demand for pine, balsam, and cedar boughs. Cut pulpwood from tops of sawlog trees when making harvest cuttings. Hire logging done by contract or piece cutters and sell cut products in order to make operating profit (rather than sell timber as stumpage). Keep list of buyers in files, and limit cutting to periods of best prices.

Fire Protection. Located 6½ miles from State Ranger Station at Minong and on accessible road. Fire on the property can be easily detected by state tower and controlled by state equipment. Road on east side, access roads to all parts of interior, and streams, ponds, lake, and swamps lend property facilities for fire protection not common to most areas. Essential fire equipment maintained: back and power pumps, hand tools, tractor, and plow.

Insects and Disease. White pine blister rust control has been undertaken by *Ribes* elimination in 1935, 1943, 1954, and in 1966. Should be done again at 10-year intervals or if outbreak develops. Control white pine weevil by pruning tips of white pine reproduction until 15 ft. in height. Observe for other insects, especially in Norway pine. Report to state forester and obtain control information if needed.

Agriculture. Twelve acres of open lands to be maintained for pasture or hay for beef cattle and saddle horses. Estimate carrying capacity of range, 10 to 12 head (if supplementary winter hay is purchased) without damage to forest reproduction. Watercress beds established and planted at springs. Small acreage of blueberry land burned over at intervals to maintain new canes.

Wildlife. The following measures have been undertaken to improve wildlife habitat: seeding of woods roads to white clover for ruffed grouse feed; annual planting of buckwheat-sunflower food patches for sharptail grouse; establishment of variety of berry-bearing shrubs for wildlife food to persist above snow height; placing of houses for wood ducks along lake shore; establishment of two islands in lake for waterfowl resting and nesting. Other measures include maintenance of small openings and edges; application of new techniques as they develop. Harvest furbearers.

Fisheries. Spring at upper end of first pond has been dammed with rock masonry to aerate water; trout-rearing pens established below springs for raising fingerling rainbow and brook trout to release at catchable size in 3 trout ponds; bundles of brush, log rafts, log and rock deflectors established at effective spots in 3 trout ponds; Sprague Lake planted to brown and rainbow trout and bait minnows; regular harvest of bait minnows. Dredging of trout ponds and stream at inlet of Sprague Lake to increase depth and capacity for trout completed in 1967.

Recreational Development. Rental of guest cottage to trout fishermen to continue as in past; new camping area developed on north side of Sprague Lake for tent campers at fee; sanitation and water facilities installed in 1957. Trout fishing permitted at special rates for club groups.

Amendments. The basic plan can be revised as needs develop. Revisions and new technical developments should be incorporated on Compartment Operations Record Map (see Fig. 7–3), as should a running record of various technical applications, management, and operating results.

Records. Current cash records will be kept in the Timbermen's Operating Account book and job records (as suggested in Chapter 7).

Wolf Springs Forest has been licensed by the state of Wisconsin as a Private Fish Hatchery and as a Tree Nursery, and certified as a Tree Farm by the American Forest Products Industries. If game birds or fur bearers are to be raised and sold as a crop, it will be necessary to obtain Game and Fur Farm license from the state. The property is also operated in cooperation with the Washburn County Soil Conservation District and with the Agricultural Conservation Program of the U. S. Department of Agriculture.

D

Timber Sale and Operating Agreement Forms

Three suggested forms for use by forest owners are presented to help in firming up the terms of marketing and operating arrangements. Modifications may be necessary to fit the requirements of individual situations but if they are of significant proportion the assistance of a lawyer is suggested. These forms include (1) *Timber Sale Contract* (for selling standing trees of determined volume at stated price per unit of stumpage), (2) *Forest Landowner-Logging Operator Contract* (for hiring of logging contractor), and (3) *Forest Products Sale Agreement* (for selling of cut forest products to wood-using industry or buyer).

SAMPLE TIMBER SALE CONTRACT

CONTRACT entered into this _____ day of _____ 19____, by and between _____ of _____ (state), hereinafter called the Seller, and _____ of _____, hereinafter called the Purchaser,

WITNESSETH:

I. The Seller agrees to sell and the Purchaser agrees to buy for the total sum of _____ dollars ($_____) under the conditions set forth in this contract all of the live standing timber marked or designated upon an area of approximately _____ acres, situated in the_____ of Section _____, Twp. _____, R. _____, _____ County, (state) on land owned and recorded in the name of _____ _____.

The Purchaser further agrees to pay to the Seller as an initial payment

344

under this contract the sum of _____
dollars ($_____), receipt of which is hereby acknowledged, and a
final payment in the sum of _____
dollars ($_____), prior to any cutting or removal of timber under
this contract.

II. The Seller further agrees to mark and dispose of the timber conveyed
in this contract in strict accordance with the following conditions:

(a) All trees to be included in this sale will be marked with a distinctive
mark on the bole and stump of each tree.

(b) No trees under _____ inches in diameter at a point 4½ feet from
the ground will be marked for cutting.

(c) No concurrent contract or subcontract involving the area or period
covered in this contract has been or will be entered into by the Seller
without the written consent of the Purchaser.

(d) The Purchaser and his employees shall have access to the area at all
reasonable times and seasons for the purpose of carrying out the
terms of this contract, and he shall maintain roads in serviceable condition during the contract period and restore them for use at end of
contract.

(e) Unless otherwise specified, all material contained in the marked or
designated trees is included in this sale.

III. The Purchaser further agrees to cut and remove all of the timber
conveyed in this contract in strict accordance with the following conditions:

(a) Unless an extension of time is agreed upon in writing between the
Seller and Purchaser, all timber shall be paid for, cut, and removed
on or before and none after the _____ day of _____,
19____, and any material not so removed shall revert to the Seller.

(b) Timber shall be scaled by the _____
rule and measured at _____
by the _____.

(c) To furnish the Seller a statement of actual scaled volume removed,
each _____ such statement to be
furnished on or before _____ in which
such removal takes place and if requested, duplicate copies of scaling
records.

(d) Unmarked trees and young timber shall be protected against un-
necessary injury from felling and logging operations. If, however,
unmarked trees are cut, damages shall be paid the Seller at the rate
of $_____ per tree plus $_____ per M. bd. ft. for _____
and $_____ per M. bd. ft. for all other species, and in the event that
any such trees are cut, said trees shall remain upon the premises and
shall be the property of the Seller.

(e) Necessary logging roads shall be cleared by the Purchaser only after
their locations have been definitely agreed upon with the Seller or
his representative and any trees to be removed in the clearing operations shall first be marked by the Seller. The Purchaser and his em-

ployees have right of ingress and egress during the life of this agreement.

(f) During the life of this contract and on the area covered, care shall be exercised by the Purchaser and his employees against the starting and spread of fire, and they shall do all in their power to prevent and control fires.

(g) Any liability for damage, destruction, or restoration of private or public improvements or personal damages occasioned by or in the exercise of this contract shall be the sole responsibility of the Purchaser, and the Purchaser shall save harmless the Seller on account of such damages.

IV. The Seller and Purchaser mutually agree as follows:

(a) All modifications of the contract will be reduced to writing, dated, signed, and witnessed and attached to this contract.

(b) The total volume conveyed is _____, composed of the following species:

_____, _____,

_____, _____, _____.

(c) In case of dispute over the terms of this contract, final decision shall rest with a reputable person to be mutually agreed upon by the parties to this contract. If the parties hereto do not agree upon a third party within 10 days following the initiation of the dispute, or in the case of further disagreement, then within 15 days from the initiation of the dispute, it shall be submitted to a Board of Arbitration of three persons, one to be selected by each party to this contract and the third to be selected by the other two. The Board shall decide the dispute within 5 days after the matter has been referred to it.

In the event that damages are awarded to the Seller by the Board of Arbitration and are not paid on the date that the award is made, then all operations of the Purchaser shall immediately cease, and if the award is not paid or satisfied within 30 days after the date of award, the Seller may take immediate possession of the premises upon which the timber is located, shall retain as liquidated damages all money paid by the Purchaser, and the title to all timber shall revert to and become the property of the Seller.

In Witness Whereof, the parties hereto have set their hands and seals this _____ day of _____, 19____.

WITNESSES:

SIGNED:

_____   _____, Purchaser

(For the Purchaser)

_____   _____, Seller

(For the Seller)

FOREST LANDOWNER-LOGGING OPERATOR CONTRACT

This CONTRACT made and entered into this _____ day of _____, 19____, by and between _____ _____ of _____ (state), owner of timber to be cut hereinafter referred to as the Owner, and _____ of _____, hereinafter referred to as the Operator.

WITNESSETH:

Whereas, the Owner owns standing timber located in_____ _____ and whereas, the Operator desires to contract with the Owner to _____ _____ and _____ for the requirements of the Owner, now, therefore, it is agreed between the parties,

I. The Operator agrees that he will _____ _____ and _____ all the marked or designated timber, standing and being on the _____ _____ owned by the Owner, situated in _____ _____.

II. The Owner agrees to pay for the _____ _____ and _____ of said timber the sum of _____ per _____ as measured by the _____ rule by _____ at the _____. Payment for these services shall be made to the Operator on _____

III. The Operator agrees to use proper precautions to avoid damage to fences and other property of the Owner; and agrees to indemnify the Owner against any and all damage and injury to any person or persons, including employees of the Operator caused or arising out of said operation.

IV. The Operator further agrees that the work will be done in a workmanlike manner and completed on or before _____.

V. The Operator agrees to comply with all federal and state laws or regulations controlling his operations, including state forest practice laws governing leaving of seed trees. The Operator agrees to indemnify and hold harmless the Owner from any and all claims or demands which may be made against him by reason of the Operator's operation or violation by the Operator of any laws or regulations governing said operation.

VI. It is mutually understood by the parties hereto that the Operator is not an employee of the Owner, but that he is an independent contractor; also, that if the Operator subcontracts any portion of the operation, the

Operator as primary contractor shall be responsible for all acts by sub-contractor.

VII. It is agreed between the Owner and Operator that the payment of _____ per _____ of timber cut as hereinbefore specified shall include full payment for the use of any and all equipment used in connection with the operation.

VIII. It is agreed that the Owner may terminate the cutting at any time by providing the Operator with written notice of date of termination at least _____ in advance of date of termination and by paying in full as above specified for all material _____ _____ and _____ by the Operator.

In Witness Whereof, the parties have hereunto set their hands the day and the year first above written.

WITNESSES: SIGNED:

_____   _____, Operator

(For the Operator)

_____   _____, Owner

(For the Owner)

FOREST PRODUCTS SALE AGREEMENT

[For selling forest products cut by owner to industry or other buyer]

This contract made and entered into this ____ day of _____, 19____, by and between _____ of _____ (state), hereinafter called the seller, and _____ of _____, hereinafter called the Purchaser.

WITNESSETH:

The Seller agrees to deliver to the Purchaser at _____ _____ the products listed below, estimated to be about _____ more or less on or before _____.

The Purchaser agrees to purchase said products at the prices listed below as measured by _____ at _____ _____ by _____, products subject to specifications of the Purchaser.

Product

———————	@ ———————	per	———————
———————	@ ———————	per	———————
———————	@ ———————	per	———————
———————	@ ———————	per	———————

It is mutually agreed that payment for said products will be made —————
————————————————————————————————————.

In Witness Whereof, the parties have hereunto set their hands on the day and year first above written.

WITNESSES: SIGNED:

———————————————   ———————————————, Purchaser

(For the Purchaser)

———————————————   ———————————————, Seller

(For the Seller)

E

Principal Federal, State, and Private Forestry Organizations

Federal

Bureau of Indian Affairs, U. S. Department of the Interior, Washington, D. C. 20240

Bureau of Land Management, U. S. Department of the Interior, Washington, D. C. 20240

Farmers Home Administration, U. S. Department of Agriculture, Washington, D. C. 20250

Forest Service, U. S. Department of Agriculture, Washington, D. C. 20250

National Park Service, U. S. Department of the Interior, Washington, D. C. 20240

Soil Conservation Service, U. S. Department of Agriculture, Washington, D. C. 20250

State Agencies

Alabama: Division of Forestry, State Department of Conservation, Montgomery 36104

Alaska: State Forester, Department of Natural Resources, Division of Lands, 344 6th Avenue, Anchorage 99501

Arkansas: Arkansas Forestry Commission, Little Rock 72203

California: Division of Forestry, Department of Conservation, Resources Bldg., Sacramento 95814

Colorado: Colorado State Forest Service, Colorado State University, Fort Collins 80521

Connecticut: Forestry Division, State Park and Forest Commission, Hartford 06115

Delaware: State Forestry Department, State House, Dover 19901

Florida: Florida Forest Service, Tallahassee 32304

Georgia: Georgia Forestry Commission, Macon 31202

Hawaii: Division of Forestry, Department of Land and Natural Resources, Honolulu 96813

Idaho: State Forestry Department, State Capitol Bldg., Boise 83701

Illinois: State Forester, Department of Conservation, State Office Bldg., Springfield 62706

Indiana: Division of Forestry, State Department of Conservation, Indianapolis 46204

Iowa: Division of Lands and Waters, Iowa Conservation Commission, Des Moines 51101

Kansas: Forestry, Fish and Game Commission, Box F, Pratt 67124

Kentucky: Division of Forestry, Department of Natural Resources, Frankfort 40601

Louisiana: Louisiana Forestry Commision, Baton Rouge 70804

Maine: Maine Forest Service, Augusta 04330

Maryland: Department of Forests and Parks, State Office Building, Annapolis 21401

Massachusetts: Division of Forests and Parks, State Department of Natural Resources, Boston 02108

Michigan: Division of Forestry, State Department of Conservation, Lansing 48926

Minnesota: Division of Forestry, State Department of Conservation, State Office Bldg., St. Paul 55101

Mississippi: Mississippi Forestry Commission, Jackson 39201

Missouri: Forestry Division, State Conservation Commission, Jefferson City 65102

Montana: Office of State Forester, 2705 Spurgin Road, Missoula 59801

Nebraska: Game, Forestation and Park Commission, State Capitol Bldg., Lincoln 68509

Nevada: Division of Forestry, Department of Conservation and Natural Resources, State Office Bldg., Carson City 89701

New Hampshire: Department of Resources and Economic Development, 318 State Office Bldg., Concord 03301

New Jersey: Bureau of Forestry, Department of Conservation and Economic Development, Trenton 08625

New Mexico: Department of State Forestry, Box 2167, Santa Fe 87501

New York: Division of Lands and Forests, New York State Conservation Department, Albany 12226

North Carolina: Forestry Division, State Department of Conservation and Development, Raleigh 27602

North Dakota: State School of Forestry, Bottineau 58318

Ohio: Division of Forestry and Reclamation, State Department of Natural Resources, Columbus 43215

Oklahoma: Oklahoma Planning and Resources Board, State Capitol, Oklahoma City 73105

Oregon: Department of Forestry, Salem 97301

Pennsylvania: Pennsylvania Department of Forests and Waters, State Capitol, Harrisburg 17120

Rhode Island: Division of Forests, State Department of Agriculture and Conservation, Providence 02903

South Carolina: State Commission of Forestry, Columbia 29202

South Dakota: State Forester, State Department of Game, Fish and Parks, Pierre 57501

Tennessee: Division of Forestry, State Department of Conservation, Cordell Hull Bldg., Nashville 37220

Texas: Texas Forest Service, Texas A & M University, College Station 77841

Utah: State Forester, State Board of Forestry and Fire Control, Capitol Bldg., Salt Lake City 84115

Vermont: Director of Forests, Vermont Forest Service, Department of Forests and Parks, Montpelier 05602

Virginia: Virginia Division of Forestry, State Department of Conservation and Economic Development, Box 3347, Richmond 22903

Washington: Division of Forestry, Department of Natural Resources, Public Land-Social Security Bldg., State Capitol, Olympia 98501

West Virginia: State Forester, Department of Natural Resources, State Office Bldg. No. 3, Charleston 25305

Wisconsin: Division of Conservation, Wisconsin Department of Natural Resources, State Office Bldg., Madison 53702

Wyoming: State Forester, State Forestry Division, Capitol Bldg., Cheyenne 82001

Private Industry

The following associations can furnish the names of private forestry organizations:

American Forest Products Industries, Inc., Washington, D. C. 20036

American Forestry Association, Washington, D. C. 20006

American Pulpwood Association, New York, N. Y. 10016

Forest Farmers Association, Atlanta, Georgia 30309

National Forest Production Association, Washington, D. C. 20036

Southern Pulpwood Conservation Association, Atlanta, Georgia 30309

F

Bibliography

The following is not meant to be an inclusive bibliography, although it includes most of the books and publications which have been reviewed by the author in preparing the manuscript. Many of these are suggested for additional reading by the student.

General References

Callison, C. H. (ed.). *America's Natural Resources*. New York: The Ronald Press Co., 1967.

Clepper, H. *Careers in Conservation*. New York: The Ronald Press Co., 1965.

Clepper, H., and Arthur B. Meyer. *American Forestry: Six Decades of Growth*. Washington, D. C. Society of American Foresters, 1960.

Clepper, H., and Arthur B. Meyer. *The World of the Forest*. Boston: D. C. Heath and Co., 1966.

Forbes, Reginald D., and Arthur B. Meyer (eds.). *Forestry Handbook*. New York: The Ronald Press Co., 1955.

Forest Farmers Association. *Forest Farmers Manual*. Atlanta, Ga. (published annually).

Mobley, M. D., and R. N. Hoskins. *Forestry in the South*. Atlanta, Ga.: Turner E. Smith & Co., 1956.

Moon, Franklin, and Nelson C. Brown. *Elements of Forestry*. 3rd ed. New York: John Wiley & Sons, Inc., 1937.

Society of American Foresters. *Forestry Terminology*. Washington, D. C., 1958.

U. S. Department of Agriculture, *Trees* (Yearbook, 1949). Separate No. 2156. Washington, D. C.: U. S. Government Printing Office, 1949.

Weaver, H. E. and David A. Anderson. *Manual of Southern Forestry*. Danville, Ill.: Interstate Printers, 1954.

Chapter 1

Allen, S. W. *An Introduction to Forestry*. 2nd ed. New York: McGraw-Hill Book Co., Inc., 1950.

Clepper, H. E. *Origins of American Conservation*. New York: The Ronald Press Co., 1966.

Forest Service, U.S.D.A. *Careers in Forestry*. Miscellaneous Publication 249 revised. Washington, D. C.: U. S. Government Printing Office, 1965.

Forest Service, U.S.D.A. *In Your Service—The Work of Uncle Sam's Forest Rangers*. Agriculture Information Bulletin No. 136. Washington, D.C.: U. S. Government Printing Office, 1955.

Greely, W. B. *Forests and Men*. New York: Doubleday & Co., 1951.

McCulloch, Walter F. *The Foresters on the Job*. Corvallis, Ore.: Oregon State College Cooperative Association, 1950.

Meyer, Arthur B. *Forestry as a Profession*. Washington, D. C.: Society of American Foresters, 1956.

Shirley, Hardy S. *Forestry and Its Career Opportunities*. 2nd ed. New York: McGraw-Hill Book Co., Inc., 1964.

Chapter 2

Dana, Samuel T. *Forest and Range Policy*. New York: McGraw-Hill Book Co., Inc., 1959.

Forest Service, U.S.D.A. *Highlights in the History of Forest Conservation*. Agriculture Information Bulletin No. 83. Washington, D. C.: U. S. Government Printing Office, 1952.

Forest Service, U.S.D.A. *Timber Resources for America's Future*. Washington, D. C.: U. S. Government Printing Office, 1958.

Forest Service, U.S.D.A. *Timber Trends in the United States*. Forest Resource Report No. 17. Washington, D. C.: U. S. Government Printing Office, 1965.

Ise, John. *United States Forest Policy*. New Haven: Yale University Press, 1920.

Chapter 3

Collingwood, Harris, and Warren D. Brush. *Knowing Your Trees*. Rev. ed. Washington, D. C.: The American Forestry Association, 1955.

Fowells, H. A. (ed.). *Silvics of Forest Trees*. Agricultural Handbook No. 271. Washington, D. C.: U. S. Government Printing Office, 1965.

Fuller, H. J. and O. Tippo. *College Botany*. New York: Henry Holt & Co., Inc. 1950.

Harlow, W. M. and E. S. Harrar. *Textbook of Dendrology*. 4th ed. New York: McGraw-Hill Book Co., Inc., 1958.

Little, Elbert L., Jr. "To Know the Trees" in *Trees* (U.S.D.A. Yearbook, 1949). Separate No. 2156. Washington, D. C.: U. S. Government Printing Office, 1949.

Spurr, S. H. *Forest Ecology*. New York: The Ronald Press Co., 1964.

Chapter 4

Graham, E. H. *Natural Principles of Land Use*. New York: Oxford University Press, 1944.

Lutz, H. J., and R. F. Chandler, Jr. *Forest Soils*. New York: John Wiley & Sons, Inc., 1946.

Society of American Foresters. *Forest Cover Types of North America*. Washington, D. C., 1954.

Toumey, J. W., and C. F. Korstian. *Foundations of Silviculture upon an Ecological Basis*. 2nd ed. New York: John Wiley & Sons, Inc., 1947.

U. S. Department of Agriculture. *Forest Trees and Forest Regions of the United States*. U.S.D.A. Miscellaneous Publication No. 217. Washington, D. C.: U. S. Government Printing Office, 1939.

Wilde, S. A. *Forest Soils*. New York: The Ronald Press Co., 1958.

Chapter 5

Baker, F. S. *Principles of Silviculture*. New York: McGraw-Hill Book Co., Inc., 1950.

Barrett, John W. *Regional Silviculture of the United States*. New York: The Ronald Press Co., 1962.

Bruckhart, John R. "Taming a Wild Forest," in *Trees* (U.S.D.A. Yearbook, 1949). Separate No. 2156. Washington, D. C.: U. S. Government Printing Office, 1949.

Forest Service, U.S.D.A. *Managing the Small Forest*. Farmers Bulletin No. 1989. Washington, D. C.: U. S. Government Printing Office, 1962.

Hawley, R. C., and D. M. Smith. *The Practice of Silviculture*. 6th ed. New York: John Wiley & Sons, Inc., 1954.

Koroleff, A., and J. P. Fitzwater. *Managing Small Woodlands*. Washington, D. C.: The American Forestry Association, 1947.

Chapter 6

Breed, C. B., and G. L. Hosmer. *Principles and Practices of Surveying*. 8th ed. New York: John Wiley & Sons, Inc., 1945.

Bruce and Schumacher. *Forest Mensuration*. 3rd ed. New York: McGraw-Hill Book Co., Inc., 1950.

Bureau of Land Management, U.S.D.I. *Surveying our Public Lands*. Washington, D. C., 1960.

Chapman, H. H., and W. H. Meyer. *Forest Mensuration*. New York: McGraw-Hill Book Co., Inc., 1949.

Demoisy, Ralph G. *Forest Surveying*. Corvallis, Ore.: Oregon State College Cooperative Association, 1949.

Forest Service, U.S.D.A. *The Service Forester's Tool Kit*. Region 9, Milwaukee, Wisc., 1957.

Husch, Bertram. *Forest Mensuration and Statistics*. New York: The Ronald Press Co., 1963.

Küchler, A. W. *Vegetation Mapping*. New York: The Ronald Press Co., 1967.

Kulow, D. L. *Elementary Point Sampling*. Circular 116. W. Va. Agricultural Experiment Station, Morgantown, W. Va.

Soil Conservation Service, U.S.D.A. *Forestry Handbook*. 5th ed. Agriculture

Handbook No. 13. Washington, D. C.: U. S. Government Printing Office, 1950.

Spurr, Stephen H. *Forest Inventory.* New York: The Ronald Press Co., 1952.

Spurr, Stephen H. *Photogrammetry and Photo-Interpretation.* 2nd ed. New York: The Ronald Press Co., 1960.

Chapter 7

Matthews, Donald M. *Management of American Forests.* New York: McGraw-Hill Book Co., Inc., 1935.

Meyer, H. A., A. B. Recknagel, D. D. Stevenson, and Ronald A. Bartoo. *Forest Management.* 2nd ed. New York: The Ronald Press Co., 1961.

Vardaman, James M. *Tree Farm Business Management.* New York: The Ronald Press Co., 1965.

Chapter 8

Brown, Nelson C. *Logging.* New York: John Wiley & Sons, Inc., 1949.

Forbes, Reginald D., and Arthur B. Meyer (eds.). *Forestry Handbook.* New York: The Ronald Press Co., 1956.

Forest Service, U.S.D.A. *Logging Farm Wood Crops.* Farmers Bulletin No. 2090. Washington, D. C.: U. S. Government Printing Office, 1955.

Forest Service, U.S.D.A. *Measuring and Marketing Farm Timber.* Farm Bulletin No. 1210. Washington, D. C.: U. S. Government Printing Office (out of print).

Myers, J. Walter, Jr. (ed.). *Forest Farmers Manual.* Atlanta, Ga.: Forest Farmers Association Cooperative (annual issue).

Wackerman, A. E. *Harvesting Timber Crops.* New York: McGraw-Hill Book Co., Inc., 1949.

Chapter 9

Baxter, D. V. *Pathology in Forest Practice.* 2nd ed. New York: John Wiley & Sons, Inc., 1952.

Craighead, F. C. *Insect Enemies of Eastern Forests.* U.S.D.A. Miscellaneous Publications 657. Washington, D. C.: U. S. Government Printing Office, 1950.

Davis, Kenneth. *Forest Fire.* New York: McGraw-Hill Book Co., Inc., 1959.

Forest Service, U.S.D.A. *Fire Control Equipment Handbook.* Washington, D. C.: U. S. Government Printing Office, 1946.

Forest Service, U.S.D.A. *Protecting the Forests from Fire.* Agricultural Information Bulletin No. 130. Washington, D.C.: U. S. Government Printing Office, 1954.

Graham, S. A. *Forest Entomology.* 4th ed. New York: McGraw-Hill Book Co., Inc., 1965.

U. S. Department of Agriculture. *Control of White Pine Blister Rust.* Washington, D. C.: U. S. Government Printing Office, 1950.

U. S. Department of Agriculture. *Reducing Losses from Tree Diseases.* Washington, D. C.: U. S. Government Printing Office, 1942.

Chapter 10

American Forest Products Industries. *The Story of Lumber and Allied Products.* Washington, D. C., 1957.

American Forest Products Industries. *The Story of Pulp and Paper.* Washington, D. C., 1957.

Brown, Nelson C. *Forest Products.* New York: John Wiley & Sons, Inc., 1950.

Forest Service, U.S.D.A. *Making Paper from Trees.* Washington, D. C.: U. S. Government Printing Office, 1955.

National Lumber Manufacturers Association. *Lumber from Forest to You.* Washington, D. C., 1957.

Panshin, Harrar, Bethel, and Baker. *Forest Products.* New York: McGraw-Hill Book Co., Inc., 1950.

Chapter 11

Clawson, Marion. *The Western Livestock Industry.* New York: McGraw-Hill Book Co., Inc., 1950.

Colman, E. A. *Vegetation and Watershed Management.* New York: The Ronald Press Co., 1953.

Forest Service, U.S.D.A. *Know Your Watersheds.* Washington, D.C.: U. S. Government Printing Office, n.d.

Gabrielson, Ira N. *Wildlife Management.* New York: The Macmillan Co., 1951.

Humphrey, R. R. *Range Ecology.* New York: The Ronald Press Co., 1962.

Kittridge, Joseph. *Forest Influences.* New York: McGraw-Hill Book Co., Inc., 1943.

Outdoor Recreation Resources Review Commission. *Outdoor Recreation for America* (Summary Report and 28 special studies). Washington, D. C.: U. S. Government Printing Office, 1962.

Stoddart, L. A., and A. D. Smith. *Range Management.* New York: McGraw-Hill Book Co., Inc., 1943.

Trippensee, R. E. *Wildlife Management.* New York: McGraw-Hill Book Co., Inc., 1948.

Chapter 12

Clawson, Marion, and Burnell, Held. *The Federal Lands, Their Use and Management.* Baltimore, Md.: Johns Hopkins Press, 1957.

Index